21ST CENTURY R

WISE PUBLICATIONS
LONDON / NEW YORK / PARIS / SYDNEY / COPENHAGEN / BERLIN / MADRID / TOKYO

EXCLUSIVE DISTRIBUTORS:
MUSIC SALES LIMITED
8/9 FRITH STREET, LONDON W1D 3JB,
ENGLAND.
MUSIC SALES PTY LIMITED
120 ROTHSCHILD AVENUE, ROSEBERY,
NSW 2018, AUSTRALIA.

ORDER NO. AM976096
ISBN 0-7119-9773-X

COMPILED BY NICK CRISPIN.
MUSIC ARRANGED BY JAMES DEAN.
MUSIC PROCESSED BY ANDREW SHIELS.

COVER DESIGN BY FRESH LEMON.
PRINTED IN MALTA BY
INTERPRINT LIMITED.

BOHEMIAN LIKE YOU

WORDS & MUSIC BY COURTNEY TAYLOR-TAYLOR

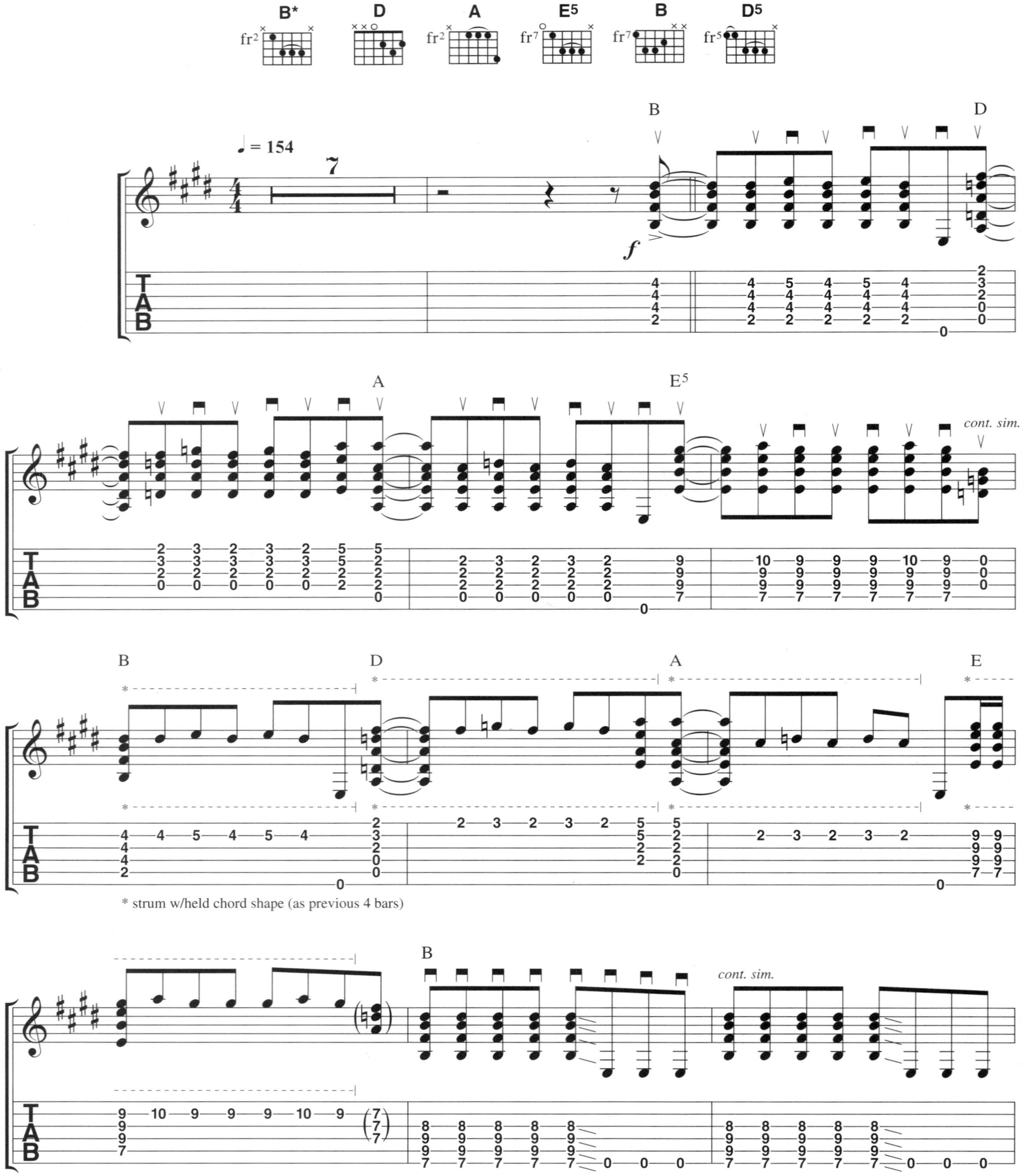

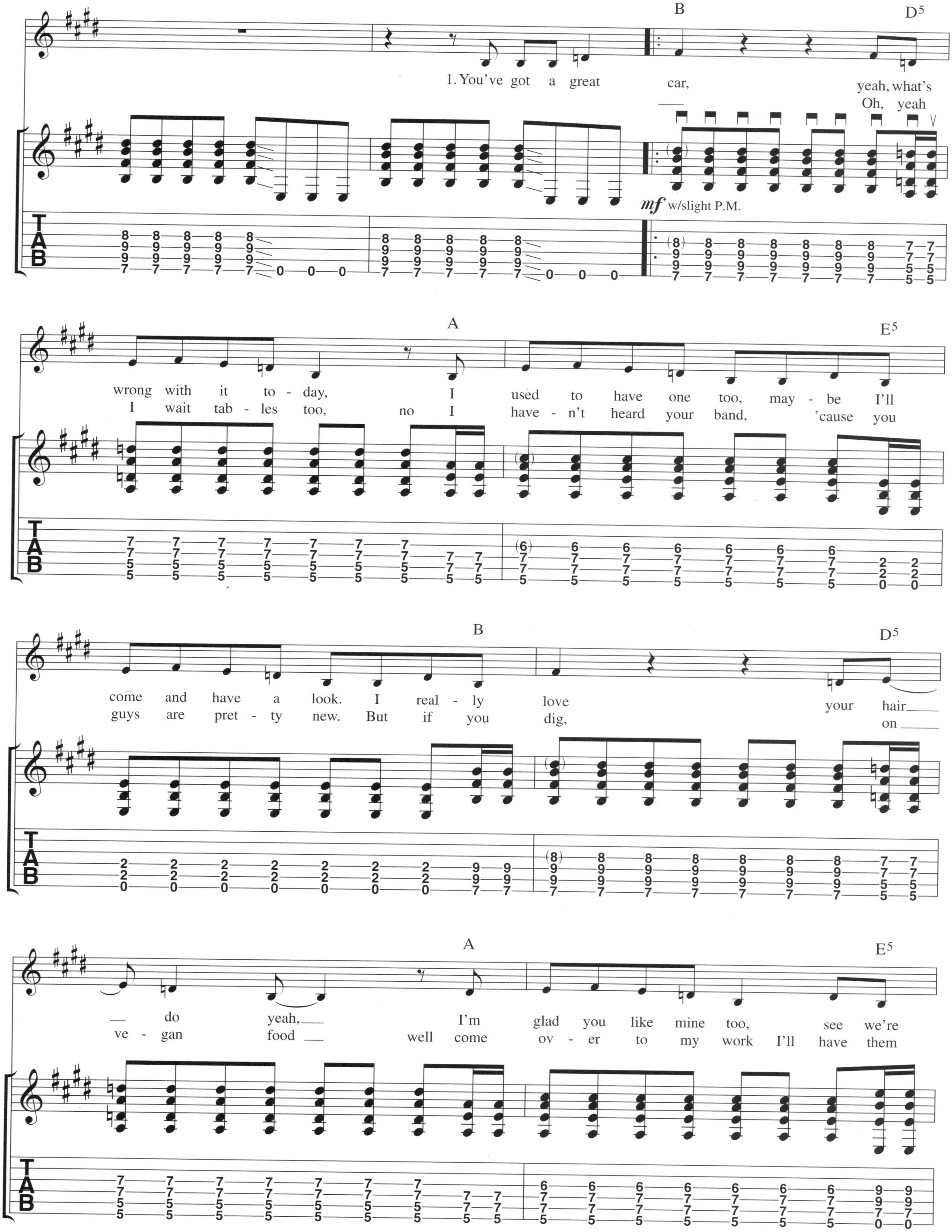
B
D5
1. You've got a great car, yeah, what's
Oh, yeah
mf w/slight P.M.
A
E5
wrong with it to - day, I used to have one too, may - be I'll
I wait tab - les too, no I have - n't heard your band, 'cause you
B
D5
come and have a look. I real - ly love your hair
guys are pret - ty new. But if you dig, on
A
E5
do yeah, I'm glad you like mine too, see we're
ve - gan food well come ov - er to my work I'll have them

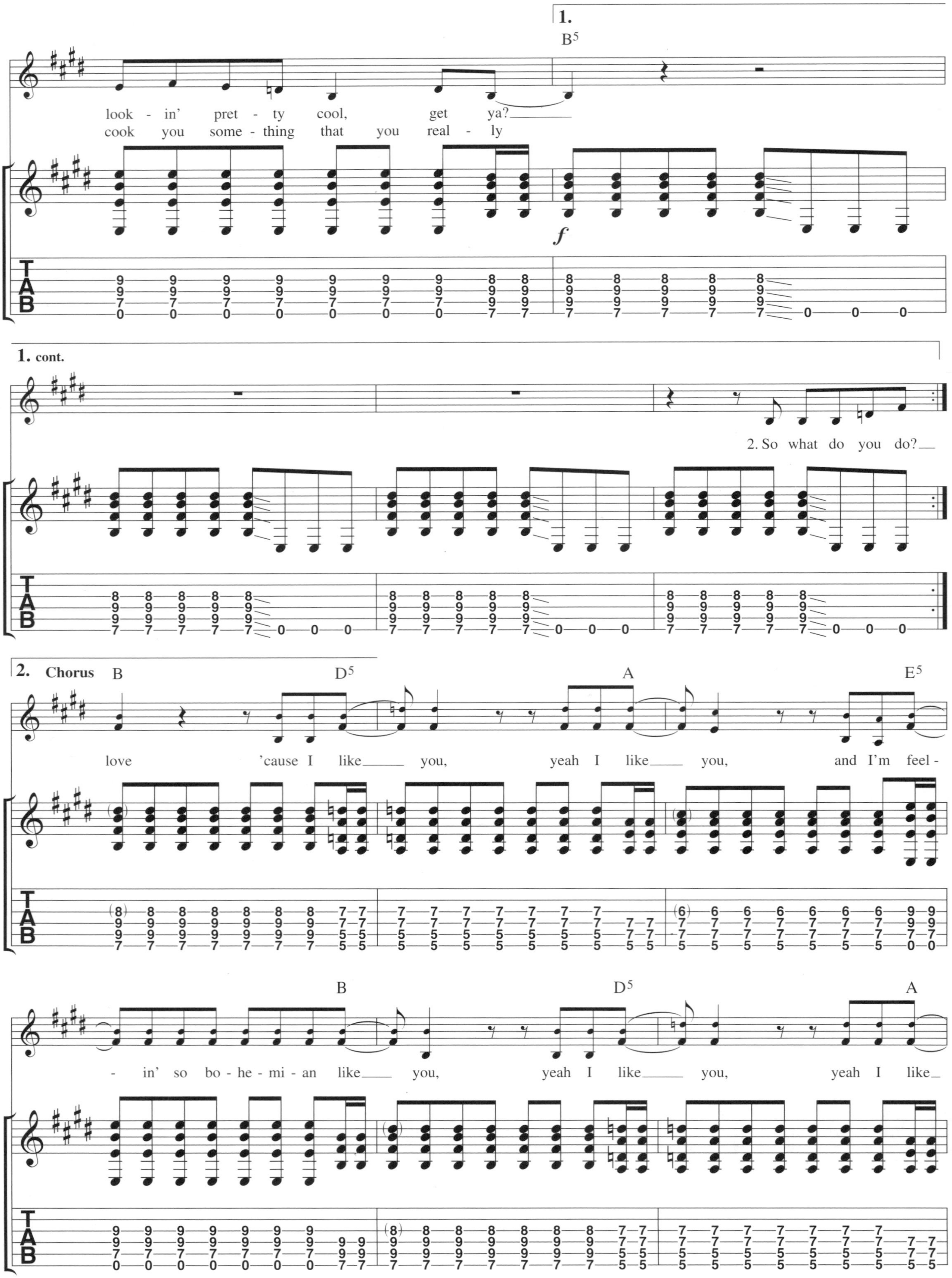
1.
B5
look - in' pret - ty cool, get ya?
cook you some - thing that you real - ly
f
TAB
1. cont.
2. So what do you do?
2. Chorus
B D5 A E5
love 'cause I like you, yeah I like you, and I'm feel -
B D5 A
- in' so bo - he - mi - an like you, yeah I like you, yeah I like

E5
8va
B
D5
you, and I feel whoa-ho. Woo!
* strum w/held chord shape as previously
A
E
Ooh oo ooh.
cont. sim.
Ooh ooh ooh.
B
D
A
E
Ooh ooh ooh.
B
Ooh ooh ooh.

Verse
(B5)
(Wait) 3. Who's that guy just
mp optional . . . .
(D5) (A5) (E5)
hang-in' at your pad? He's look-in' kind-a bummed, yeah you broke up, that's too bad. I guess it's
(B5) (D5) (A5)
fair if he al-ways pays the rent and he does-n't get bent a-'bout
Chorus
(E5) B5 D5 A5
sleep-in' on the couch when I'm there. 'Cause I like you, yeah I like
f

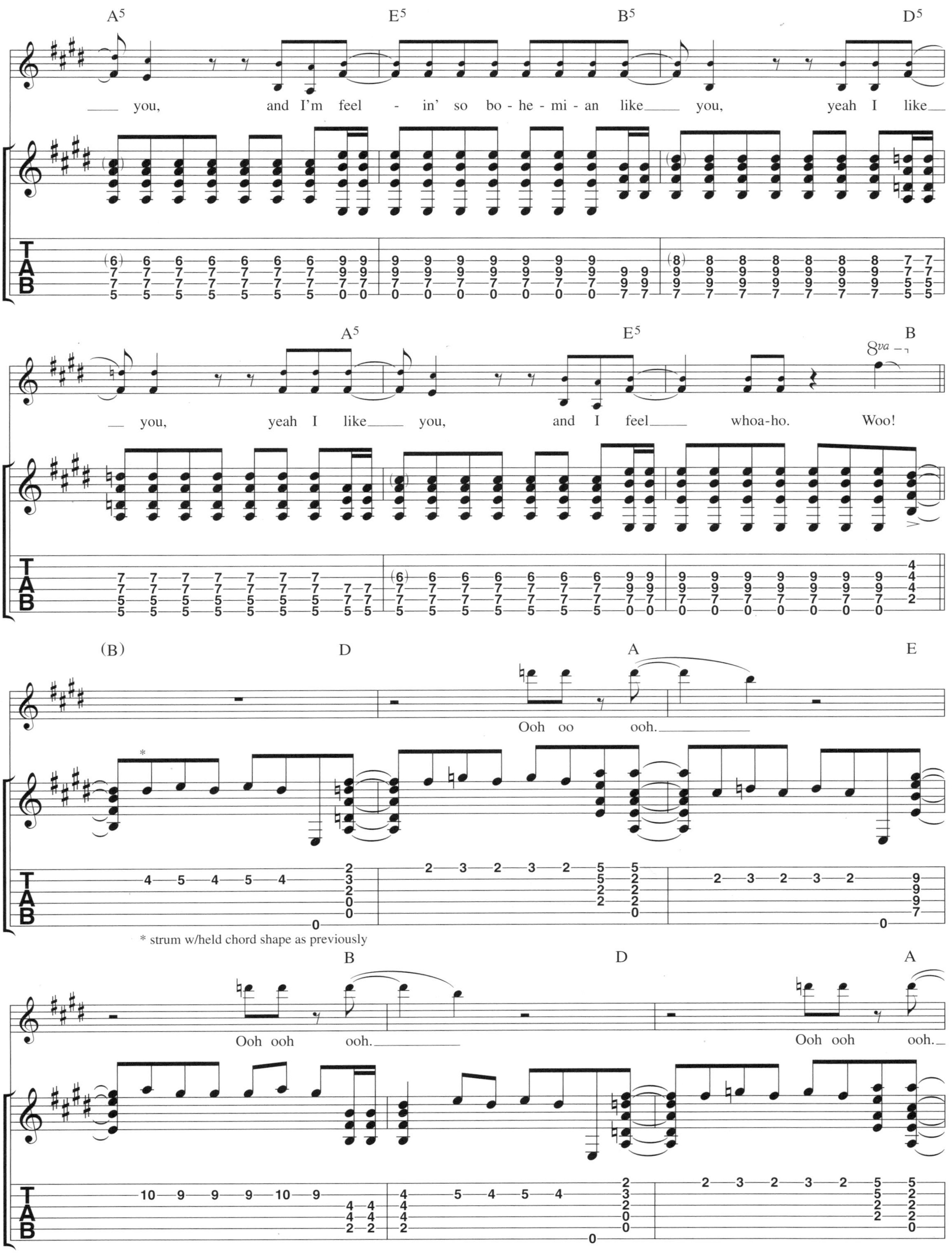
A5 E5 B5 D5
you, and I'm feel - in' so bo-he-mi-an like you, yeah I like
A5 E5 B 8va
you, yeah I like you, and I feel whoa-ho. Woo!
(B) D A E
Ooh oo ooh.
* strum w/held chord shape as previously
B D A
Ooh ooh ooh. Ooh ooh ooh.

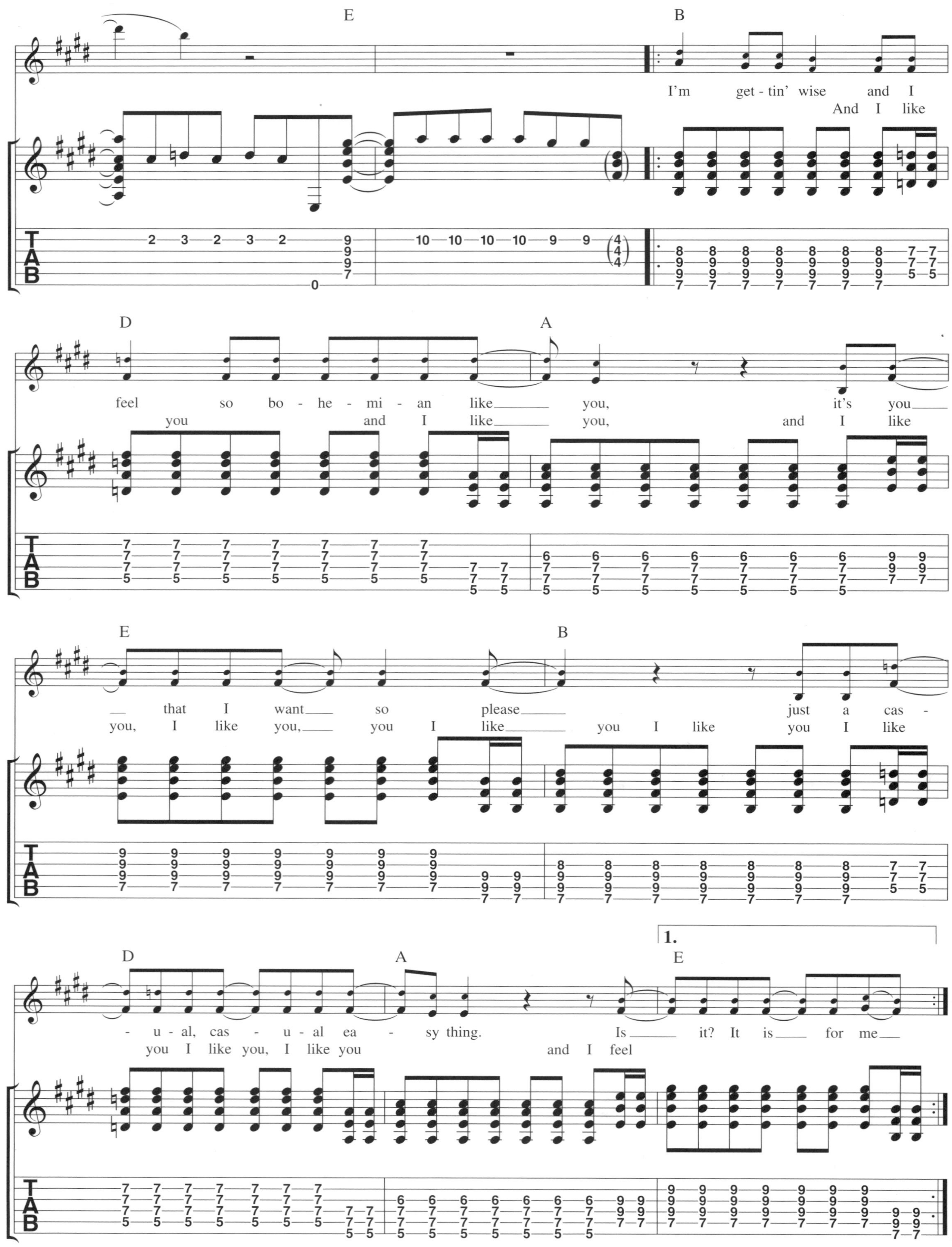
E
B
I'm get - tin' wise and I
And I like
D
A
feel so bo - he - mi - an like you, it's you
you and I like you, and I like
E
B
that I want so please just a cas -
you, I like you, you I like you I like you I like
1.
D
A
E
- u - al, cas - u - al ea - sy thing. Is it? It is for me
you I like you, I like you and I feel
TAB

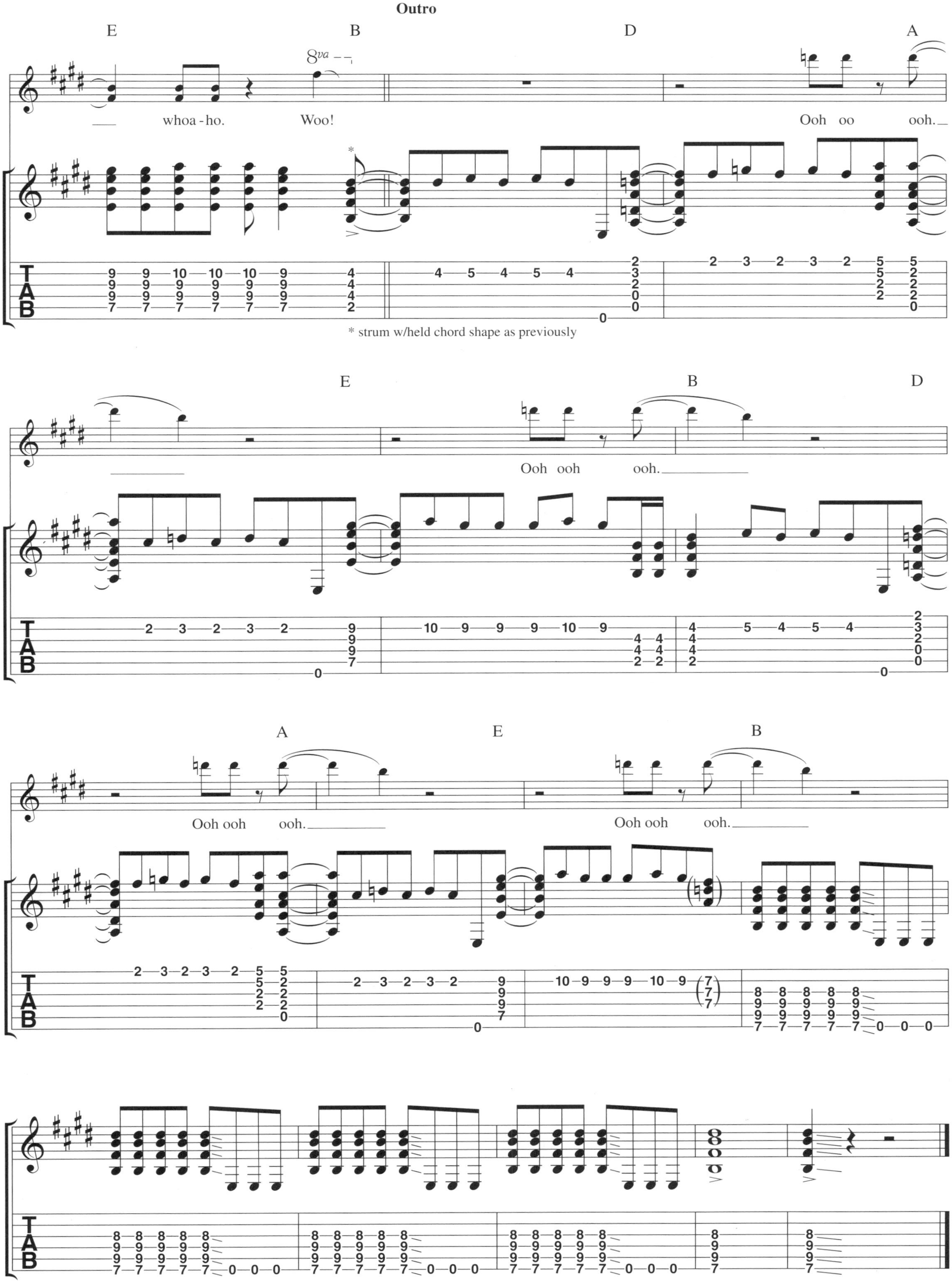
Outro
E
B
8va
D
A
whoa - ho.
Woo!
Ooh oo ooh.
* strum w/held chord shape as previously
E
B
D
Ooh ooh ooh.
A
E
B
Ooh ooh ooh.
Ooh ooh ooh.
T
A
B

Come Back Around

WORDS & MUSIC BY GRANT NICHOLAS

Gtrs. 1+2:
Drop D tuning

⑥ = D ③ = G
⑤ = A ② = B
④ = D ① = E

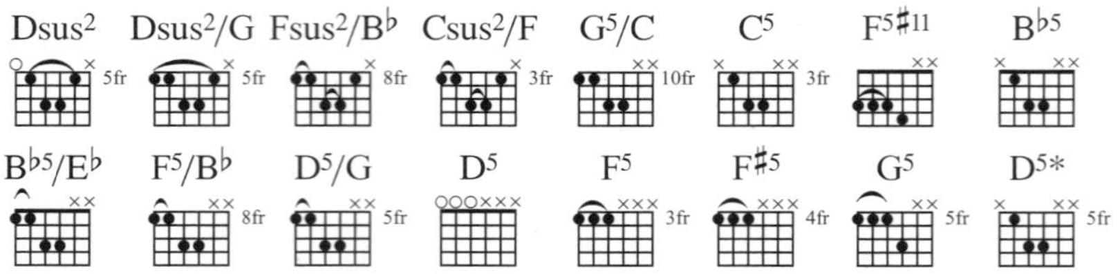

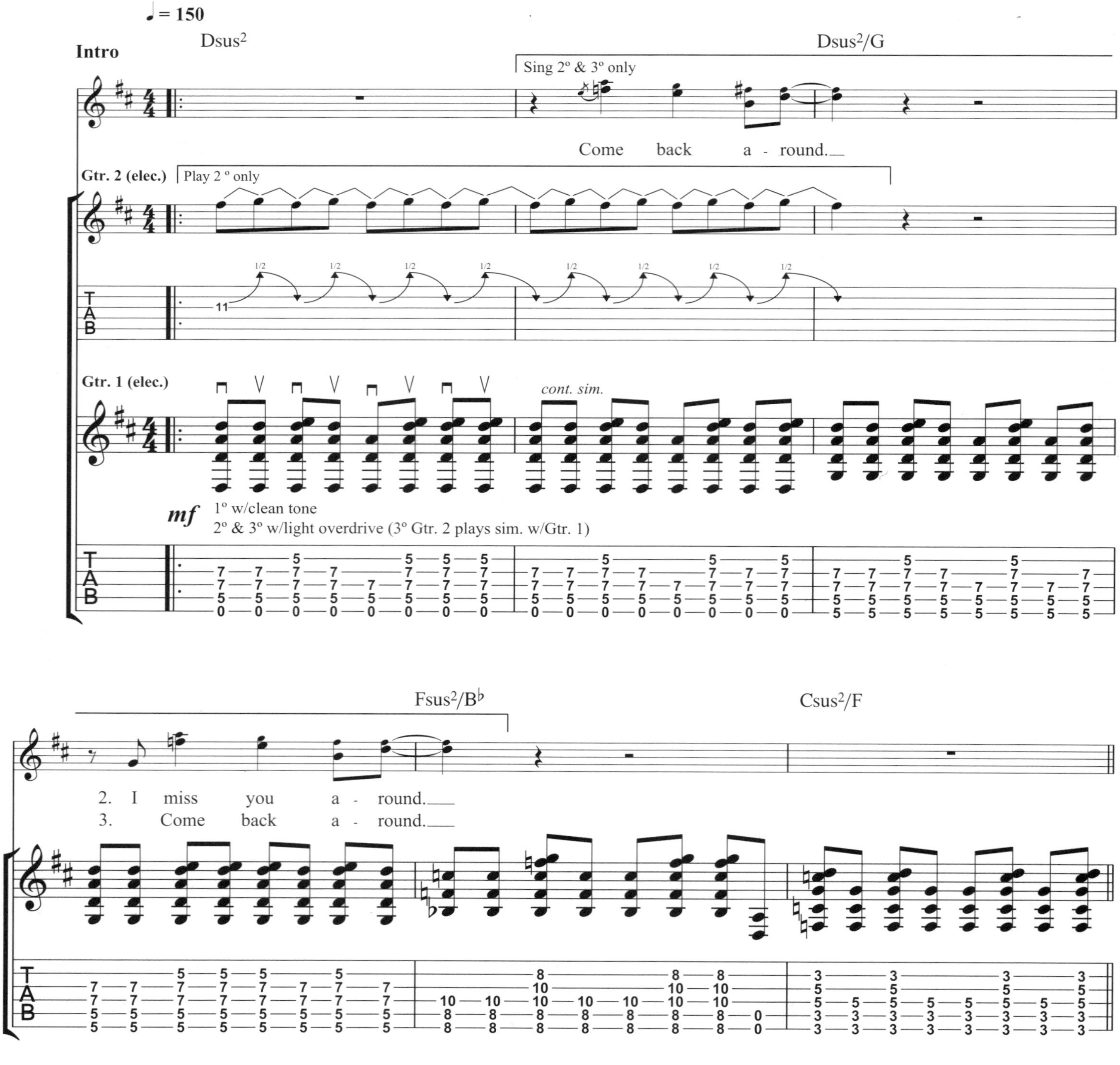

Verse

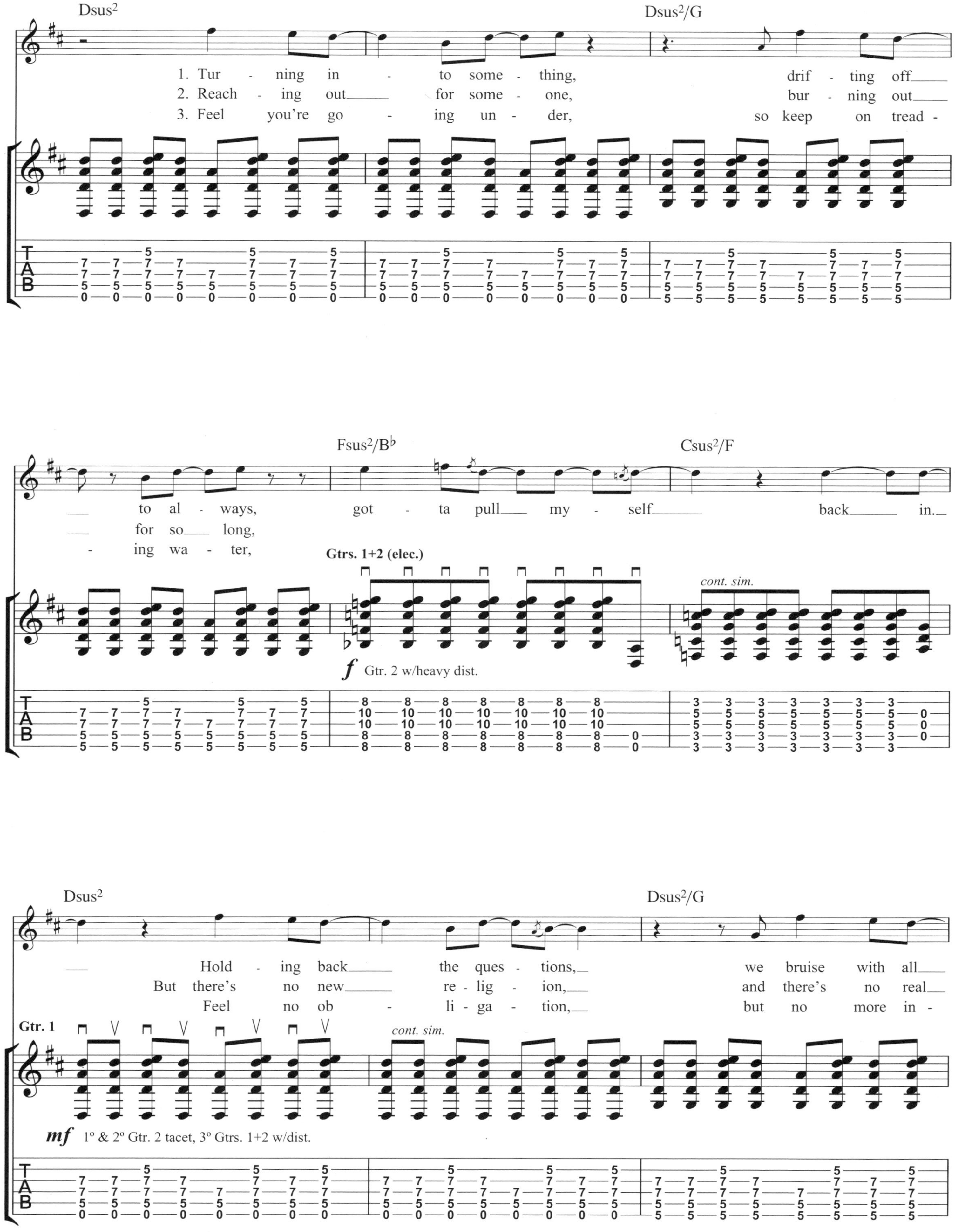
Dsus2
Dsus2/G
1. Turning into something, drifting off
2. Reaching out for someone, burning out
3. Feel you're going under, so keep on tread-
to always, gotta pull myself back in.
for so long,
ing water,
Fsus2/B♭
Csus2/F
Gtrs. 1+2 (elec.)
cont. sim.
f Gtr. 2 w/heavy dist.
Dsus2
Dsus2/G
Holding back the questions, we bruise with all
But there's no new religion, and there's no real
Feel no obligation, but no more in-
Gtr. 1
cont. sim.
mf 1º & 2º Gtr. 2 tacet, 3º Gtrs. 1+2 w/dist.
T
A
B

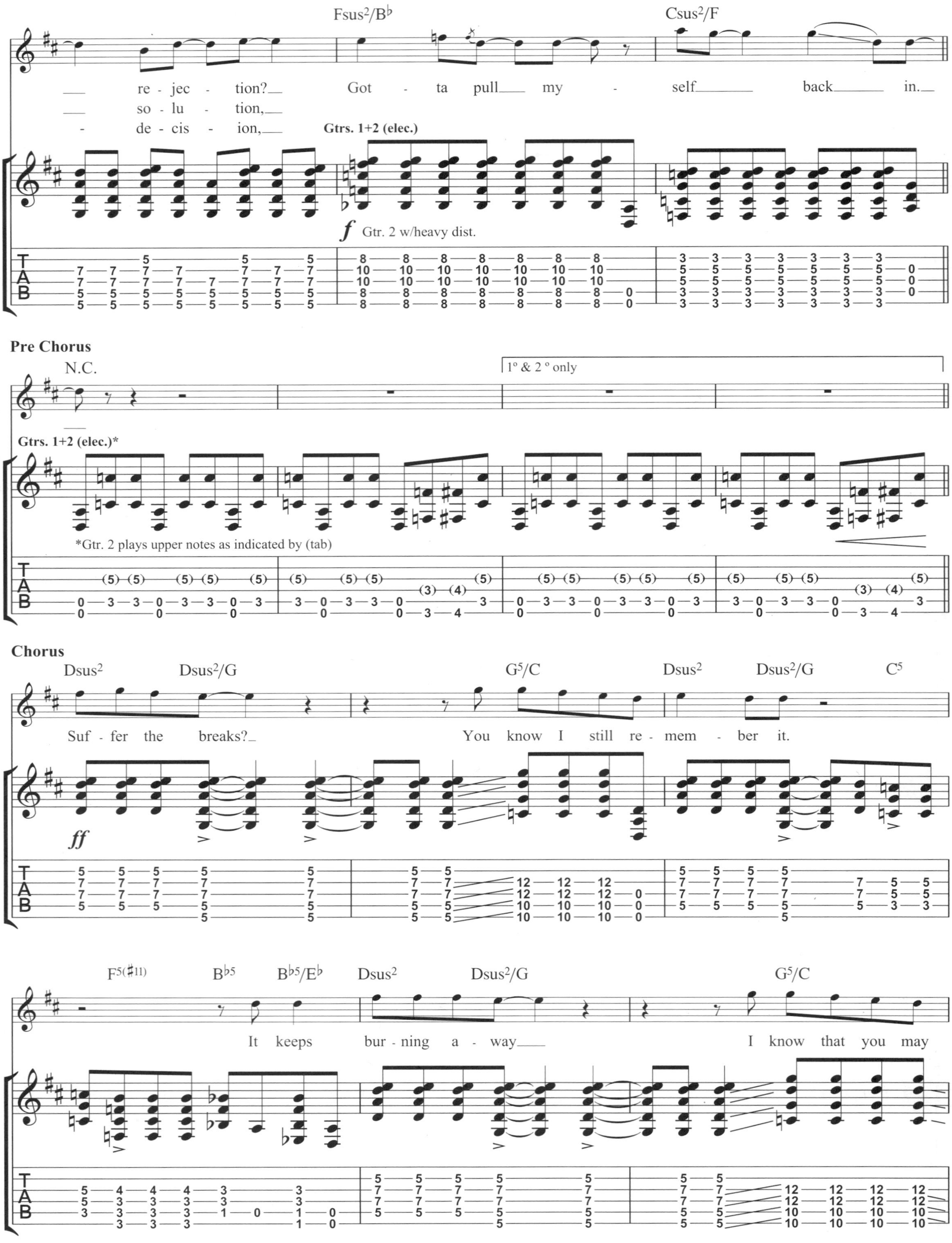
Fsus2/B♭
Csus2/F
re - jec - tion? Got - ta pull my - self back in.
so - lu - tion,
de - cis - ion,
Gtrs. 1+2 (elec.)
Gtr. 2 w/heavy dist.
Pre Chorus
N.C.
1º & 2 º only
Gtrs. 1+2 (elec.)*
*Gtr. 2 plays upper notes as indicated by (tab)
Chorus
Dsus2
Dsus2/G
G5/C
C5
Suf - fer the breaks? You know I still re - mem - ber it.
F5(♯11)
B♭5
B♭5/E♭
It keeps bur - ning a - way I know that you may

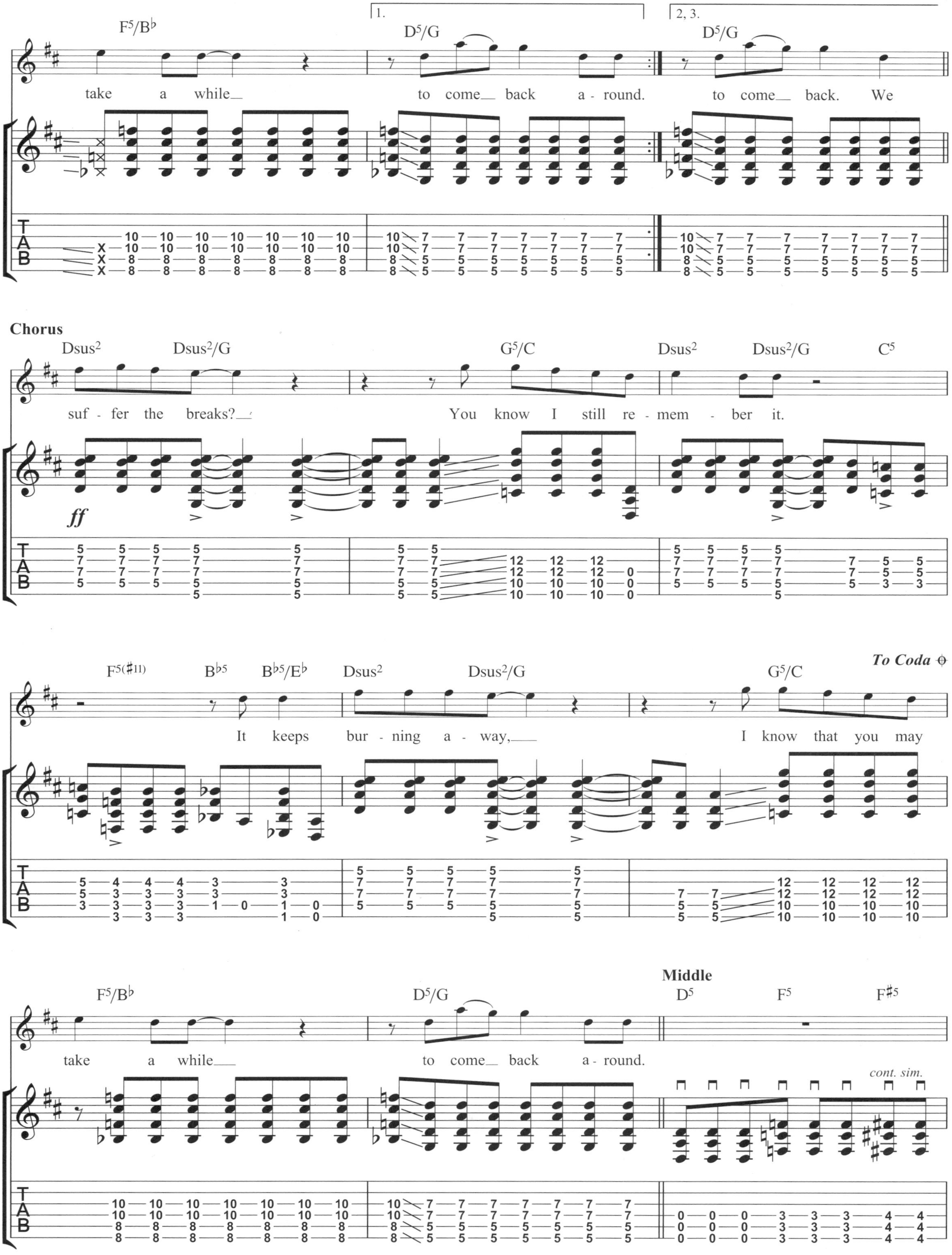

1.
2, 3.
F5/B♭ D5/G D5/G
take a while__ to come__ back a-round. to come__ back. We
Chorus
Dsus2 Dsus2/G G5/C Dsus2 Dsus2/G C5
suf-fer the breaks?__ You know I still re-mem-ber it.
ff
F5(♯11) B♭5 B♭5/E♭ Dsus2 Dsus2/G G5/C
To Coda
It keeps bur-ning a-way,__ I know that you may
F5/B♭ D5/G
Middle
D5 F5 F♯5
take a while__ to come__ back a-round.
cont. sim.

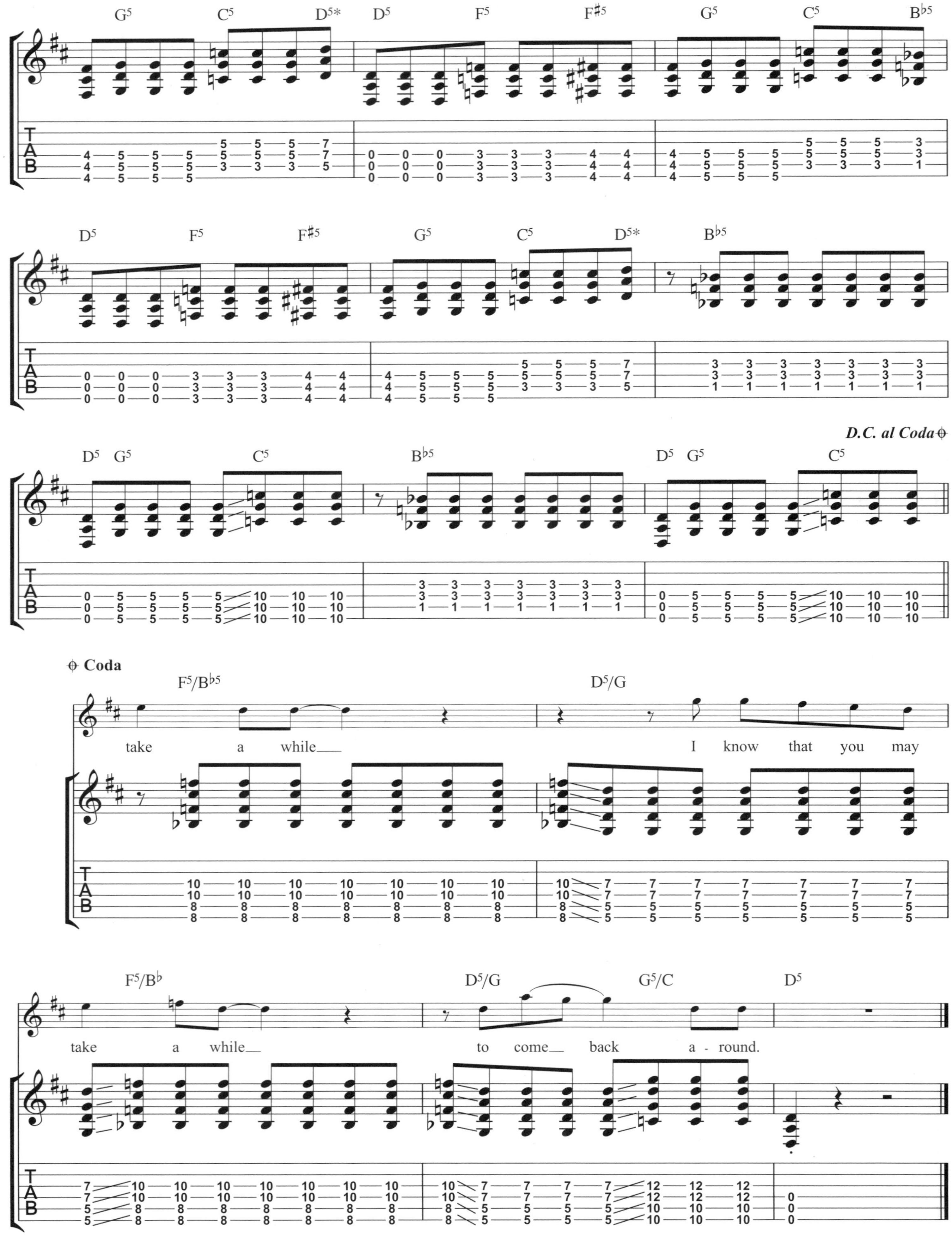
G5 C5 D5* D5 F5 F♯5 G5 C5 B♭5
D5 F5 F♯5 G5 C5 D5* B♭5
D.C. al Coda
D5 G5 C5 B♭5 D5 G5 C5
Coda
F5/B♭5 D5/G
take a while I know that you may
F5/B♭ D5/G G5/C D5
take a while to come back a - round.

DEAD IN THE WATER

WORDS & MUSIC BY DAVID GRAY

All Gtrs. Capo 1st fret

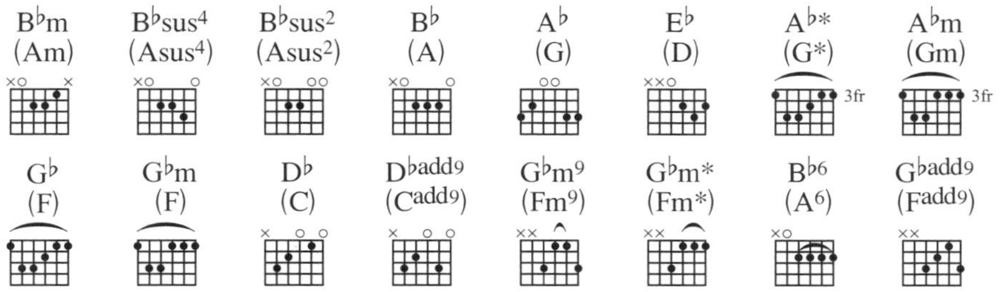

Intro ♩ = 100

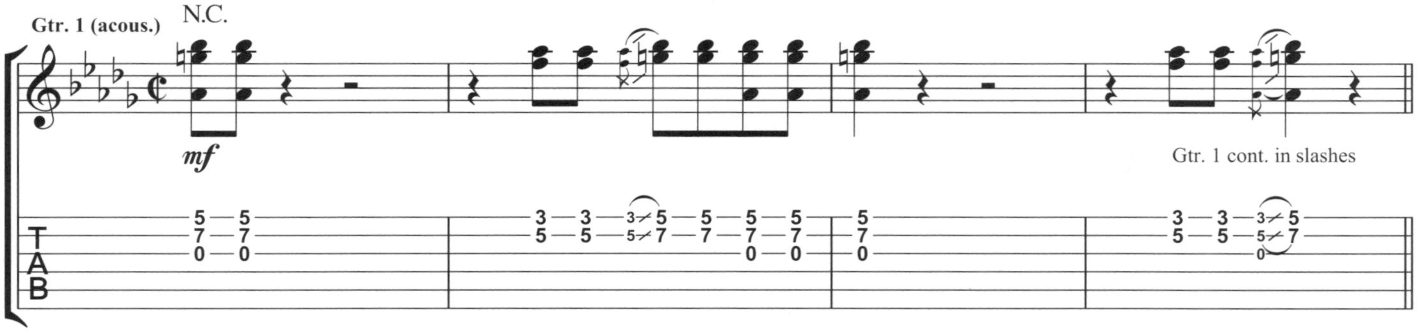

*Symbols in parentheses represent chord names with respect to capoed guitar (TAB 0 = 1st fret). Symbols above represent actual sounding chords.

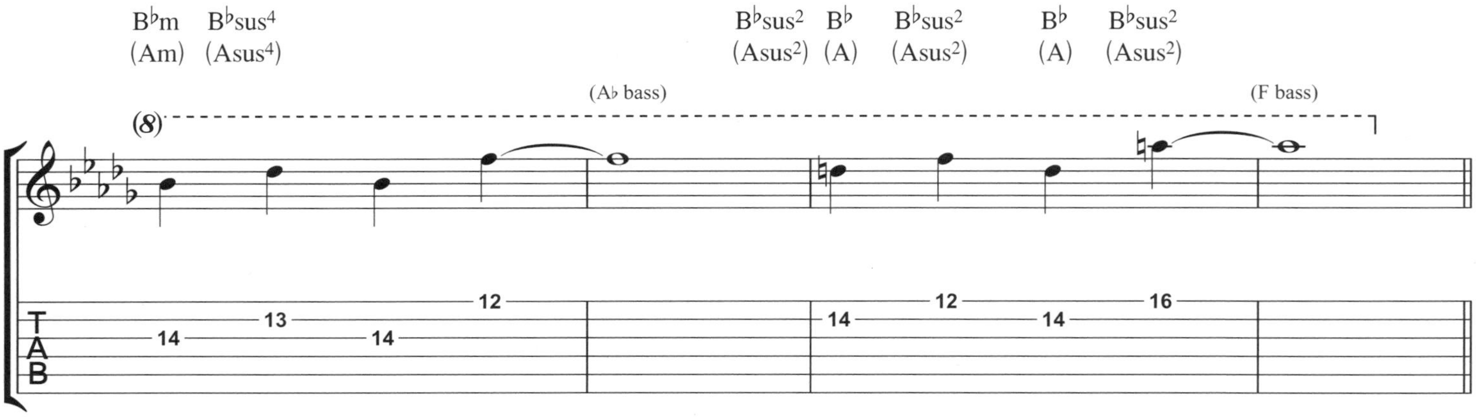

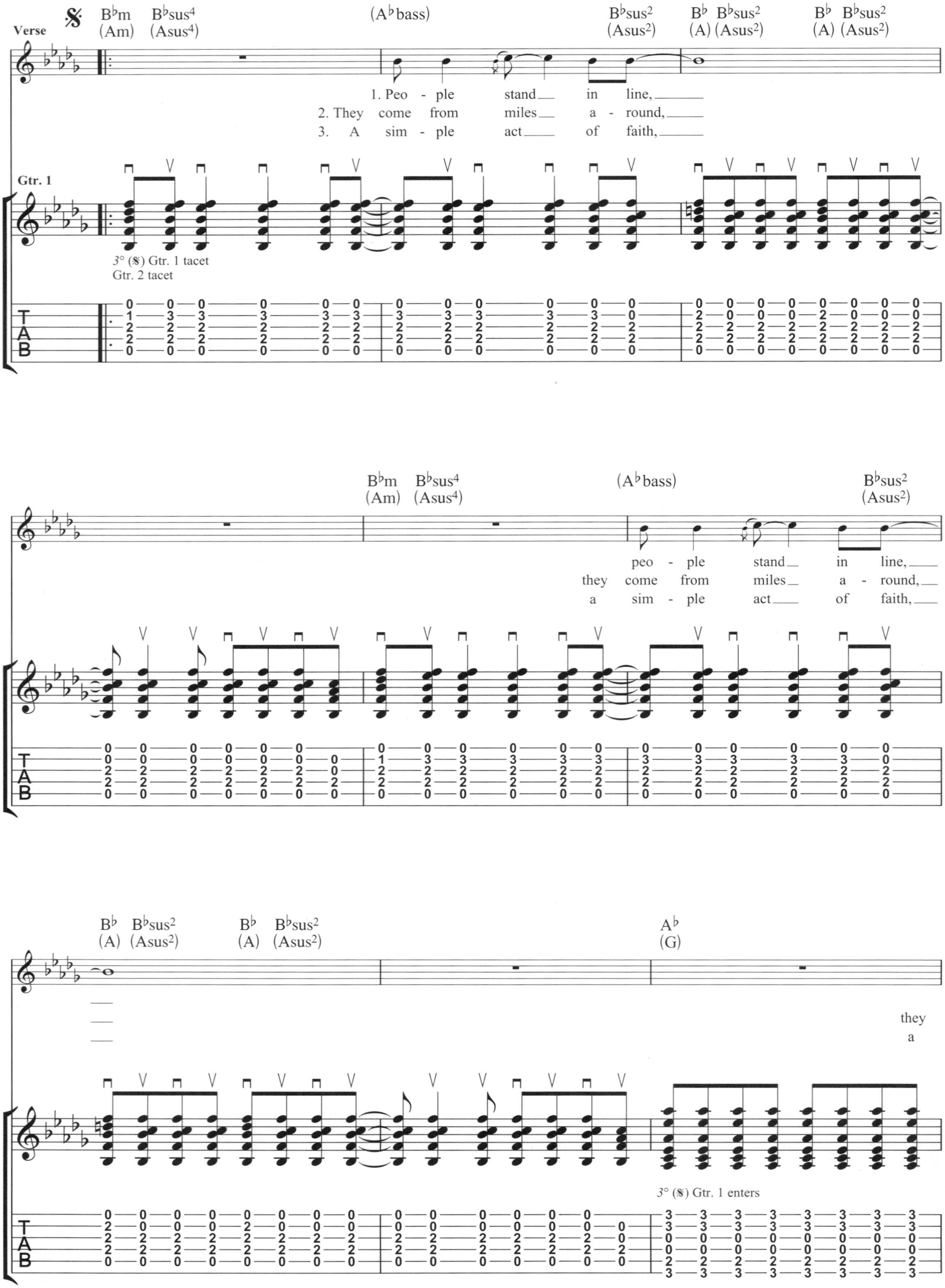
Verse
B♭m (Am) B♭sus4 (Asus4) (A♭bass) B♭sus2 (Asus2) B♭ (A) B♭sus2 (Asus2) B♭ (A) B♭sus2 (Asus2)
1. People stand in line,
2. They come from miles around,
3. A simple act of faith,
Gtr. 1
3° (𝄋) Gtr. 1 tacet
Gtr. 2 tacet
B♭m (Am) B♭sus4 (Asus4) (A♭bass) B♭sus2 (Asus2)
people stand in line,
they come from miles around,
a simple act of faith,
B♭ (A) B♭sus2 (Asus2) B♭ (A) B♭sus2 (Asus2) A♭ (G)
they
a
3° (𝄋) Gtr. 1 enters

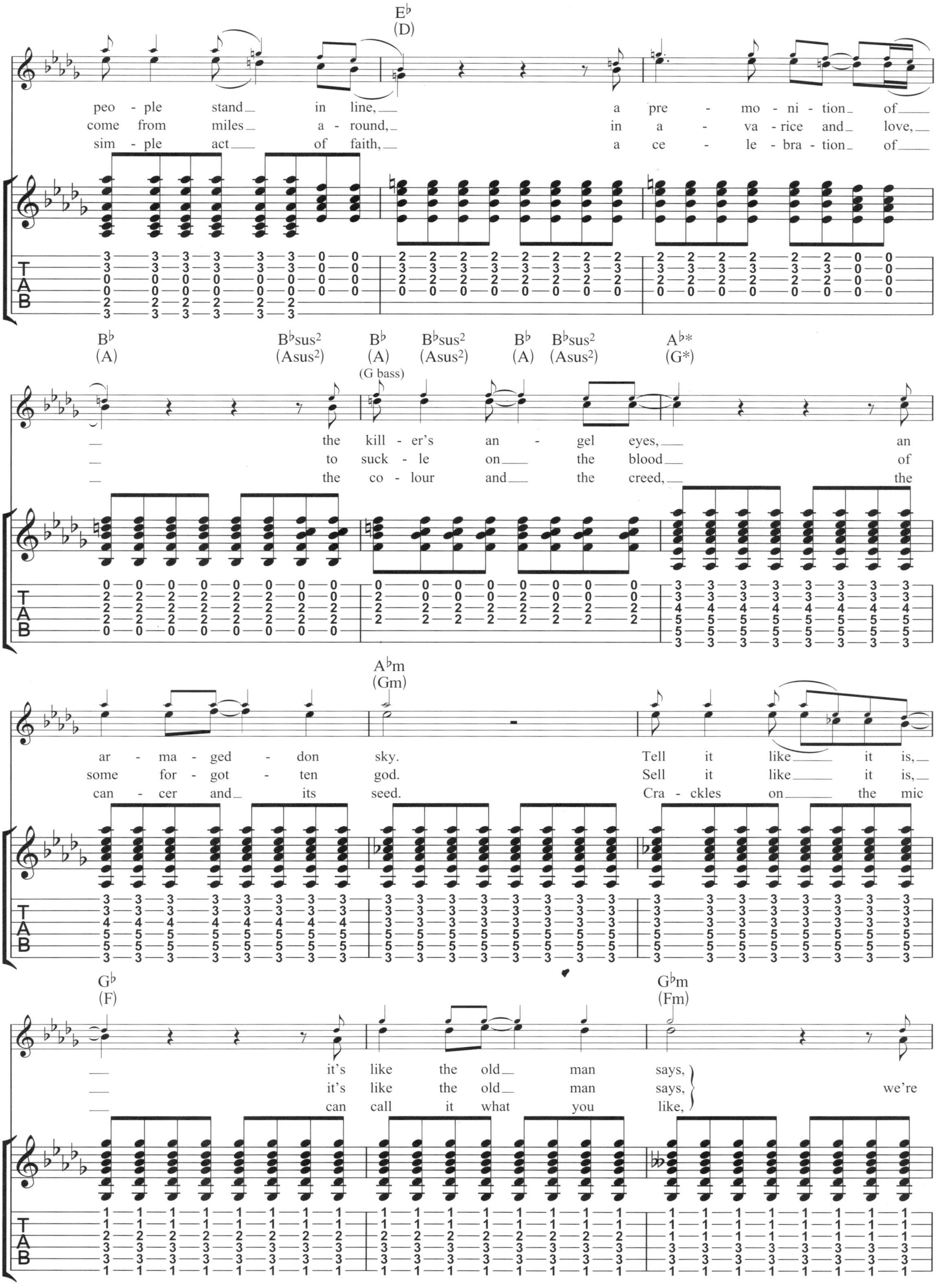
E♭ (D)
peo - ple stand in line, a pre - mo - ni - tion of
come from miles a - round, in a - va - rice and love,
sim - ple act of faith, a ce - le - bra - tion of
B♭ (A) B♭sus2 (Asus2) B♭ (A) (G bass) B♭sus2 (Asus2) B♭ (A) B♭sus2 (Asus2) A♭* (G*)
the kill - er's an - gel eyes, an
to suck - le on the blood of
the co - lour and the creed, the
A♭m (Gm)
ar - ma - ged - don sky. Tell it like it is,
some for - got - ten god. Sell it like it is,
can - cer and its seed. Cra - ckles on the mic
G♭ (F) G♭m (Fm)
it's like the old man says,
it's like the old man says, we're
can call it what you like,

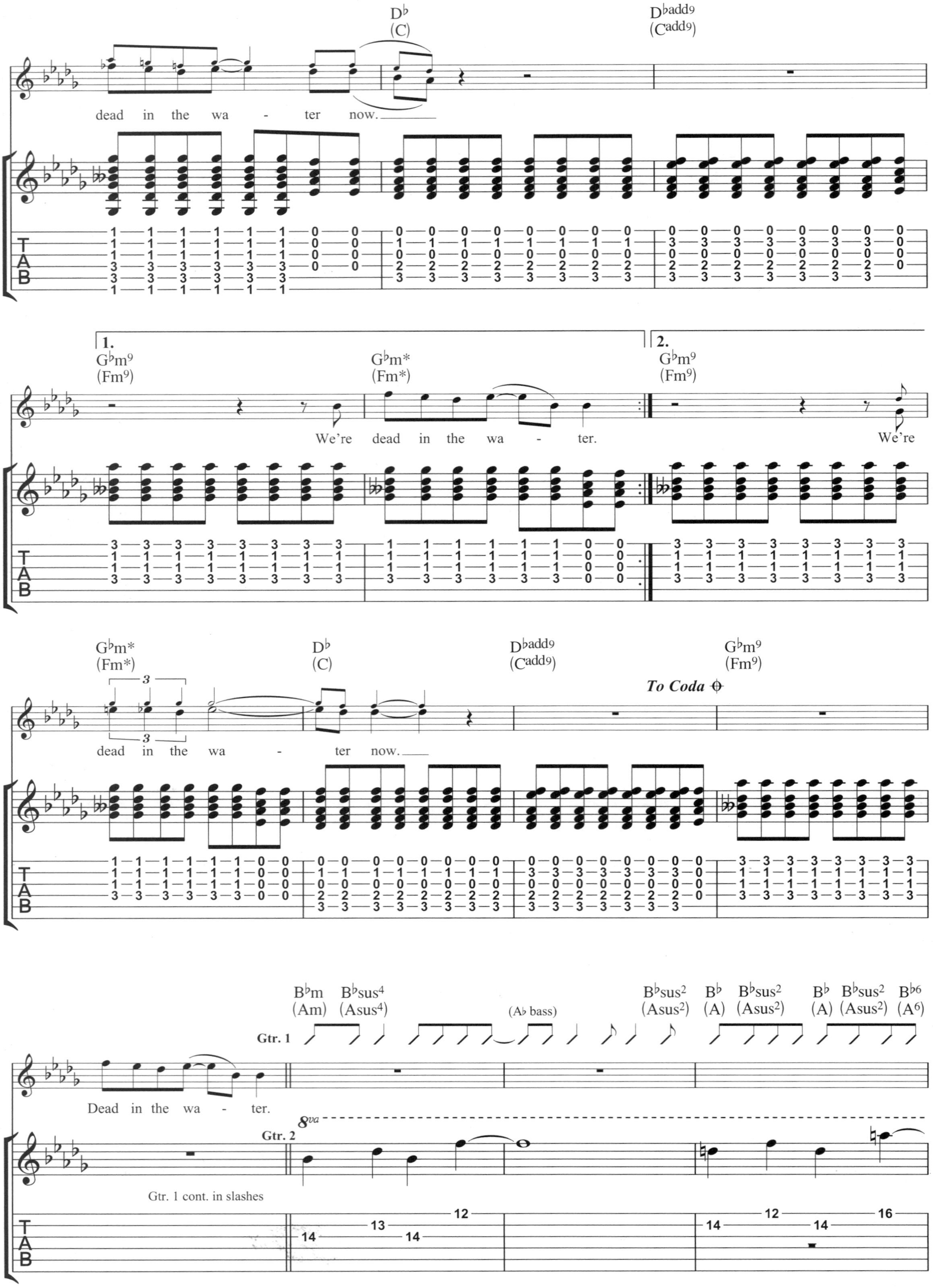
D♭ (C)
D♭add9 (Cadd9)
dead in the wa - ter now.
1.
G♭m9 (Fm9)
G♭m* (Fm*)
We're dead in the wa - ter.
2.
G♭m9 (Fm9)
We're
G♭m* (Fm*)
D♭ (C)
D♭add9 (Cadd9)
G♭m9 (Fm9)
To Coda
dead in the wa - ter now.
B♭m (Am)
B♭sus4 (Asus4)
(A♭ bass)
B♭sus2 (Asus2)
B♭ (A)
B♭sus2 (Asus2)
B♭ (A)
B♭sus2 (Asus2)
B♭6 (A6)
Gtr. 1
Dead in the wa - ter.
Gtr. 2
Gtr. 1 cont. in slashes

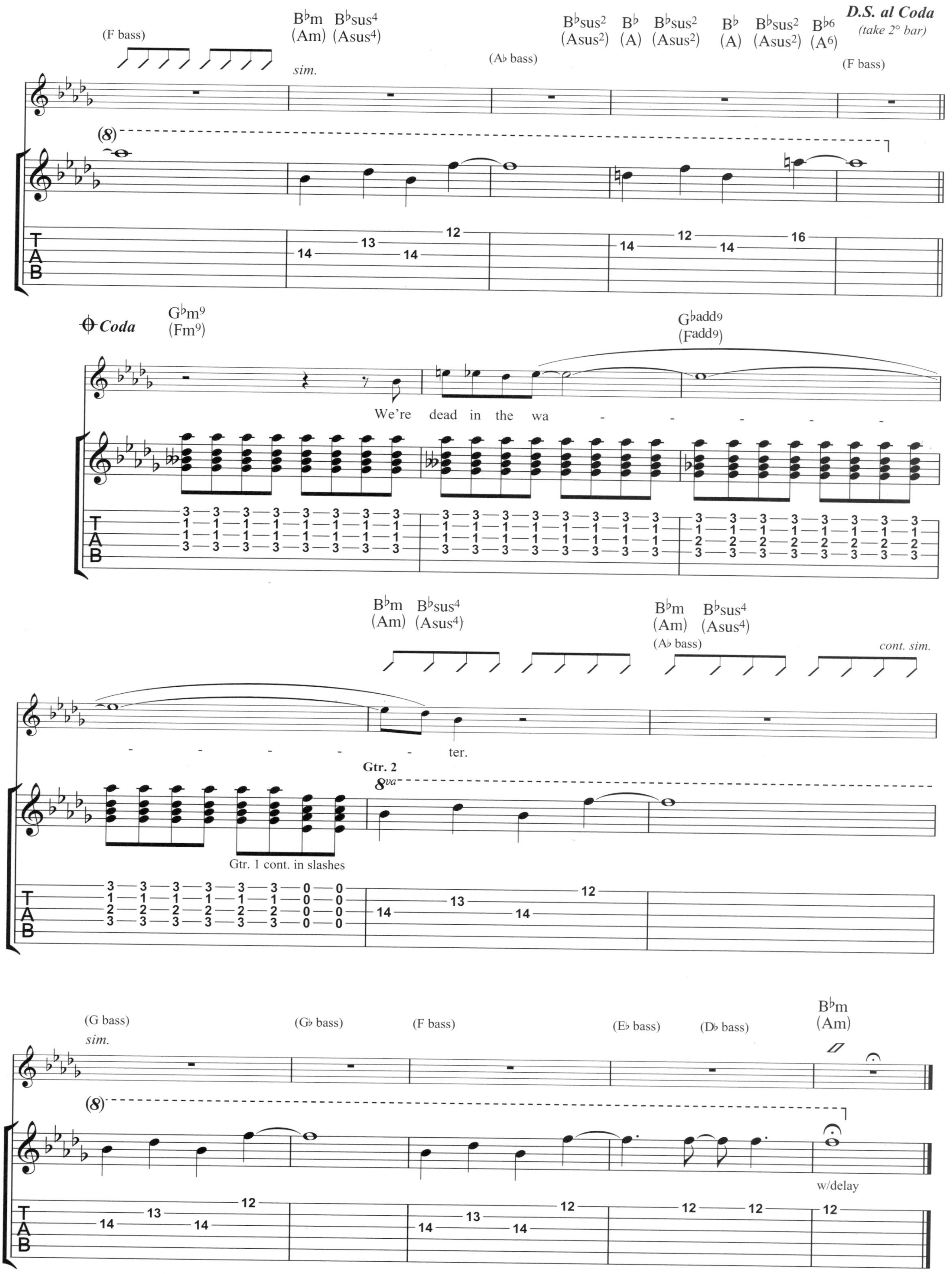
D.S. al Coda
(take 2° bar)
(F bass)
B♭m (Am)
B♭sus4 (Asus4)
sim.
(A♭ bass)
B♭sus2 (Asus2)
B♭ (A)
B♭6 (A6)
Coda
G♭m9 (Fm9)
G♭add9 (Fadd9)
We're dead in the wa - - - - - - - - - - ter.
Gtr. 2
8va
Gtr. 1 cont. in slashes
cont. sim.
(G bass)
(G♭ bass)
(E♭ bass)
(D♭ bass)
w/delay
T
A
B

ELEVATION

MUSIC BY U2
LYRICS BY BONO

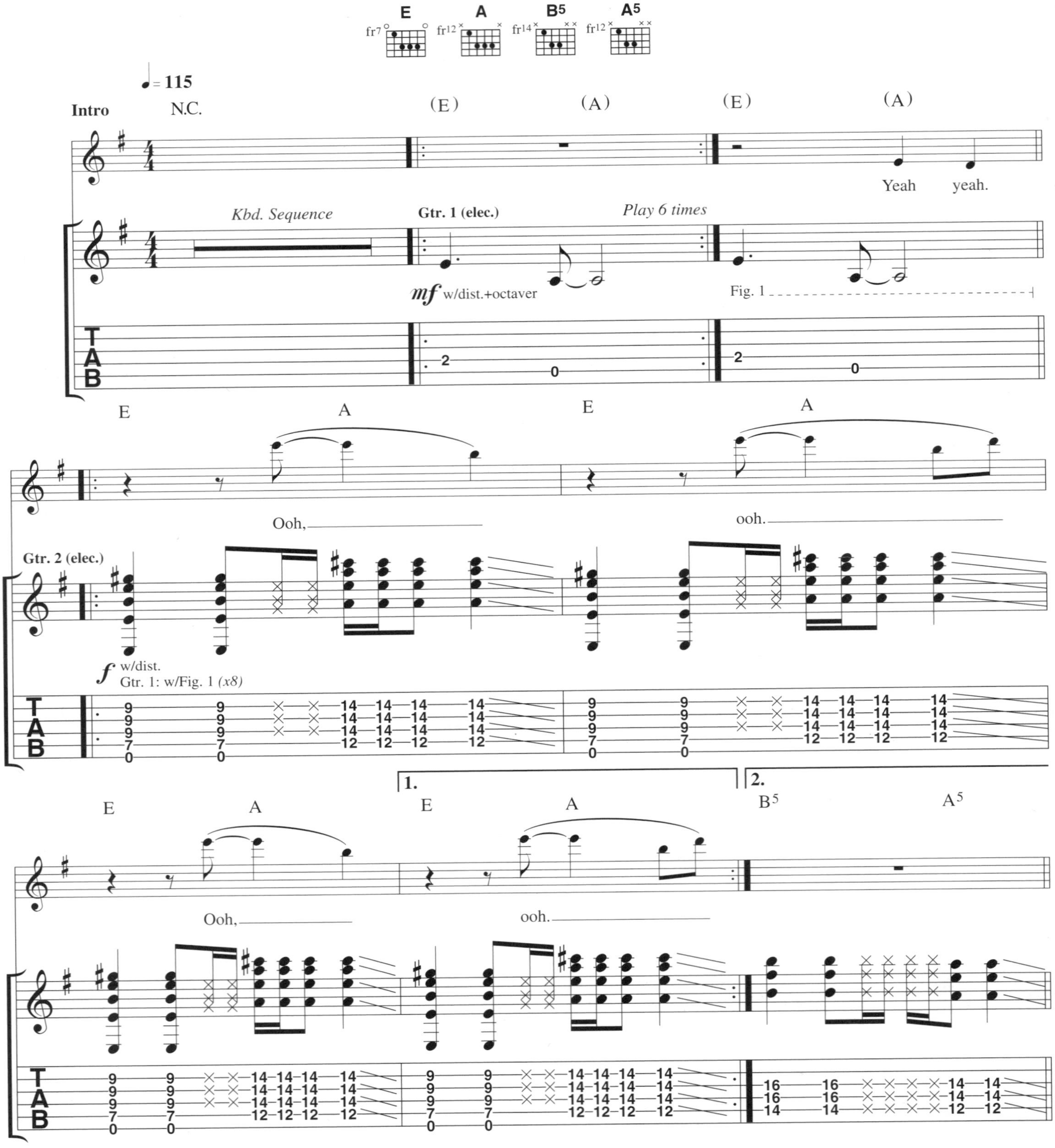

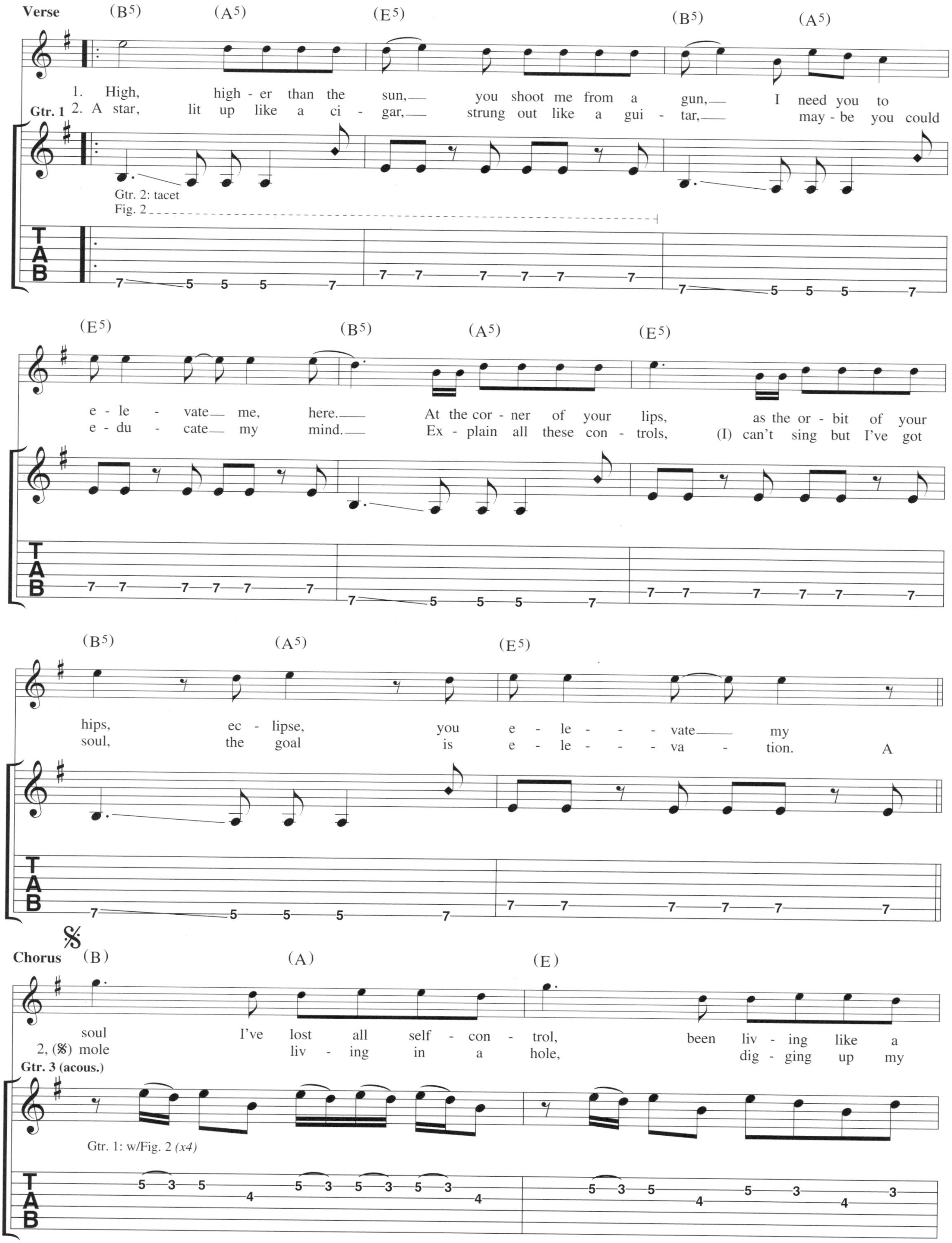
Verse
(B5) (A5) (E5) (B5) (A5)
1. High, high - er than the sun,— you shoot me from a gun,— I need you to
2. A star, lit up like a ci - gar,— strung out like a gui - tar,— may - be you could
Gtr. 1
Gtr. 2: tacet
Fig. 2
T A B
7 5 5 5 7 7 7 7 7 7 7 7 5 5 5 7
(E5) (B5) (A5) (E5)
e - le - vate— me, here.— At the cor - ner of your lips, as the or - bit of your
e - du - cate— my mind.— Ex - plain all these con - trols, (I) can't sing but I've got
7 7 7 7 7 7 7 5 5 5 7 7 7 7 7 7 7
(B5) (A5) (E5)
hips, ec - lipse, you e - le - - - vate— my
soul, the goal is e - le - - - va - tion. A
7 5 5 5 7 7 7 7 7 7 7
Chorus
(B) (A) (E)
soul I've lost all self - con - trol, been liv - ing like a
2, (𝄋) mole liv - ing in a hole, dig - ging up my
Gtr. 3 (acous.)
Gtr. 1: w/Fig. 2 (x4)
5 3 5 4 5 3 5 3 5 3 4 5 3 5 4 5 3 4 3

(B) (A) (E)
mole. Now, go - ing down, ex - - - ca - va - tion. I
soul go - ing down, ex - - - ca - va - tion. I
(B) (A) (E)
and I in the sky, you make me feel like I can
and I in the sky, you make me feel like I can
(B) (A) (E) To Coda
fly so high, e - - - le - va - - - tion.
fly so high, e - - - le - va - - - tion.
1.
(B) (A) (E) (B) (A) (E)
2. A
Gtr. 3: tacet

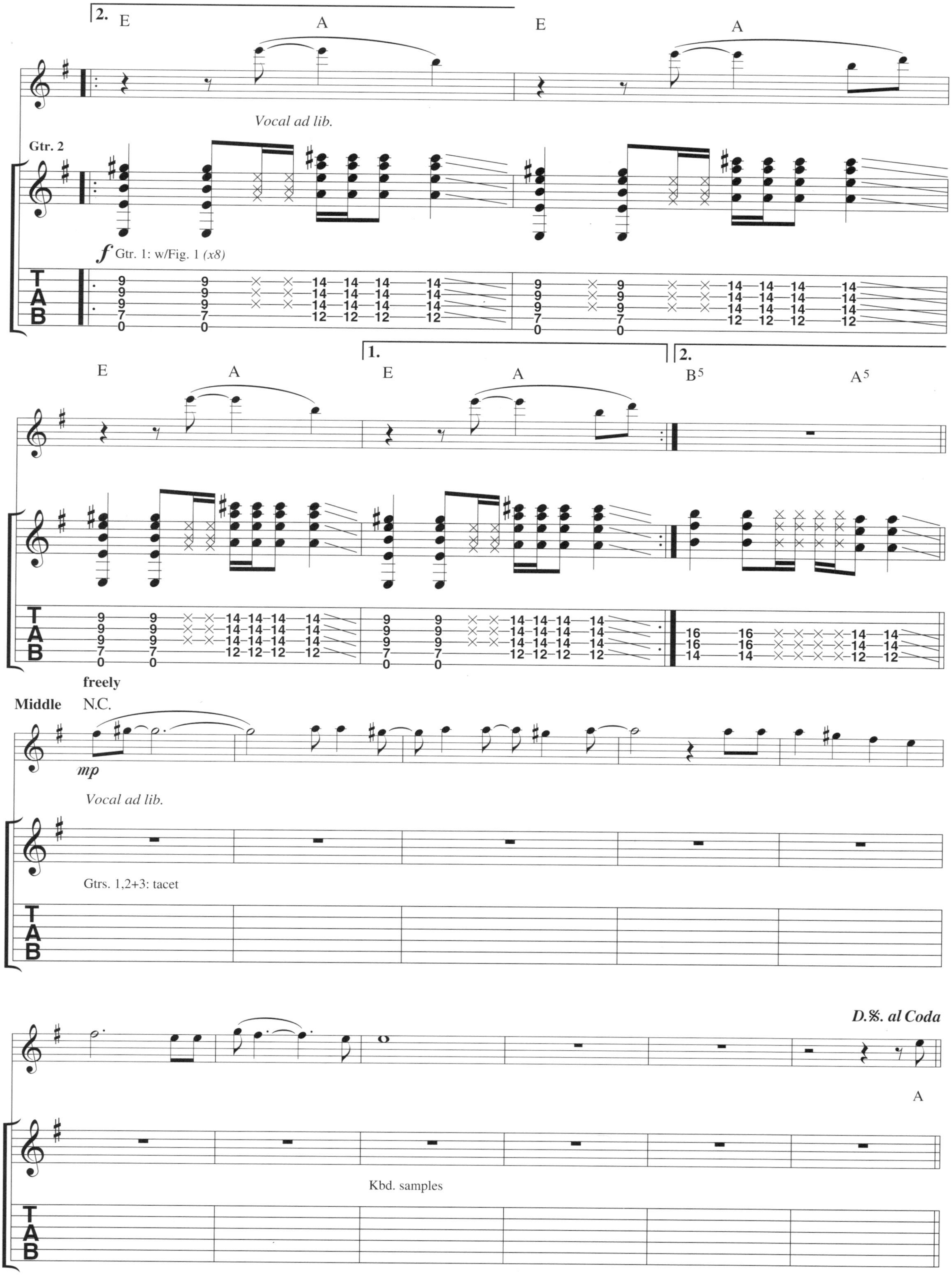
2.
E
A
Vocal ad lib.
Gtr. 2
Gtr. 1: w/Fig. 1 (x8)
1.
2.
B5
A5
freely
Middle
N.C.
Vocal ad lib.
Gtrs. 1,2+3: tacet
D.%. al Coda
Kbd. samples

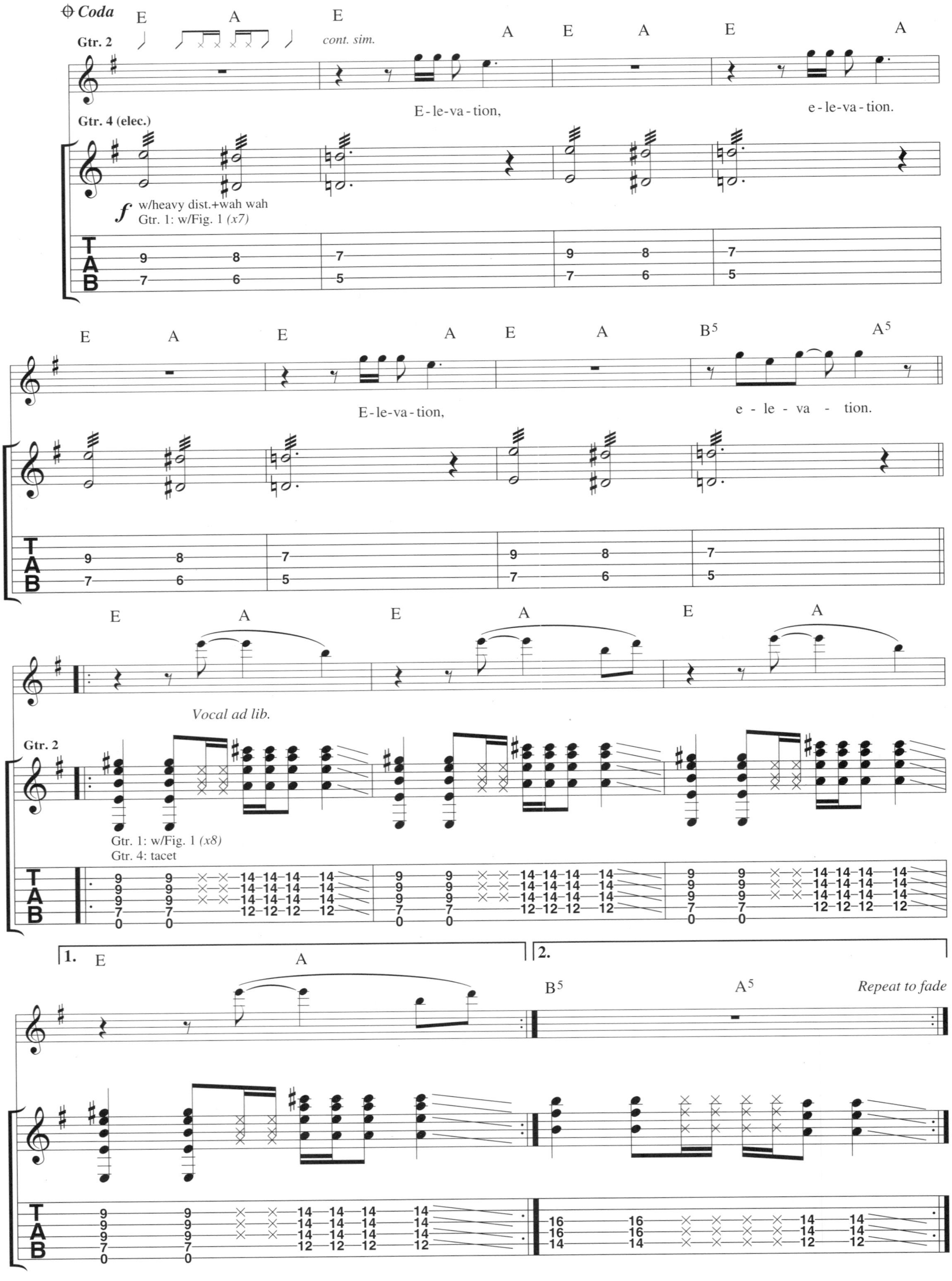
Coda
E A E A E A E A
Gtr. 2
cont. sim.
E-le-va-tion, e-le-va-tion.
Gtr. 4 (elec.)
f w/heavy dist.+wah wah
Gtr. 1: w/Fig. 1 (x7)
E A E A E A B5 A5
E-le-va-tion, e - le - va - tion.
E A E A E A
Vocal ad lib.
Gtr. 2
Gtr. 1: w/Fig. 1 (x8)
Gtr. 4: tacet
1. E A
2. B5 A5
Repeat to fade

ENVY

WORDS & MUSIC BY TIM WHEELER

*Symbols in parentheses represent chord names with respect to capoed guitar (TAB 0 = 2nd fret). Symbols above represent actual sounding chords.

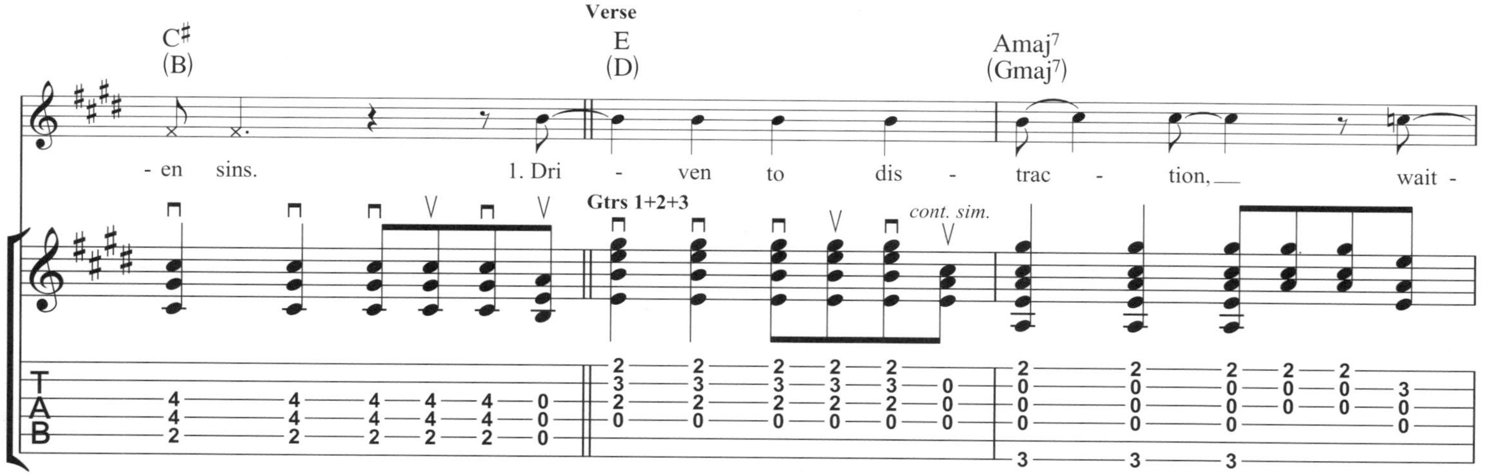

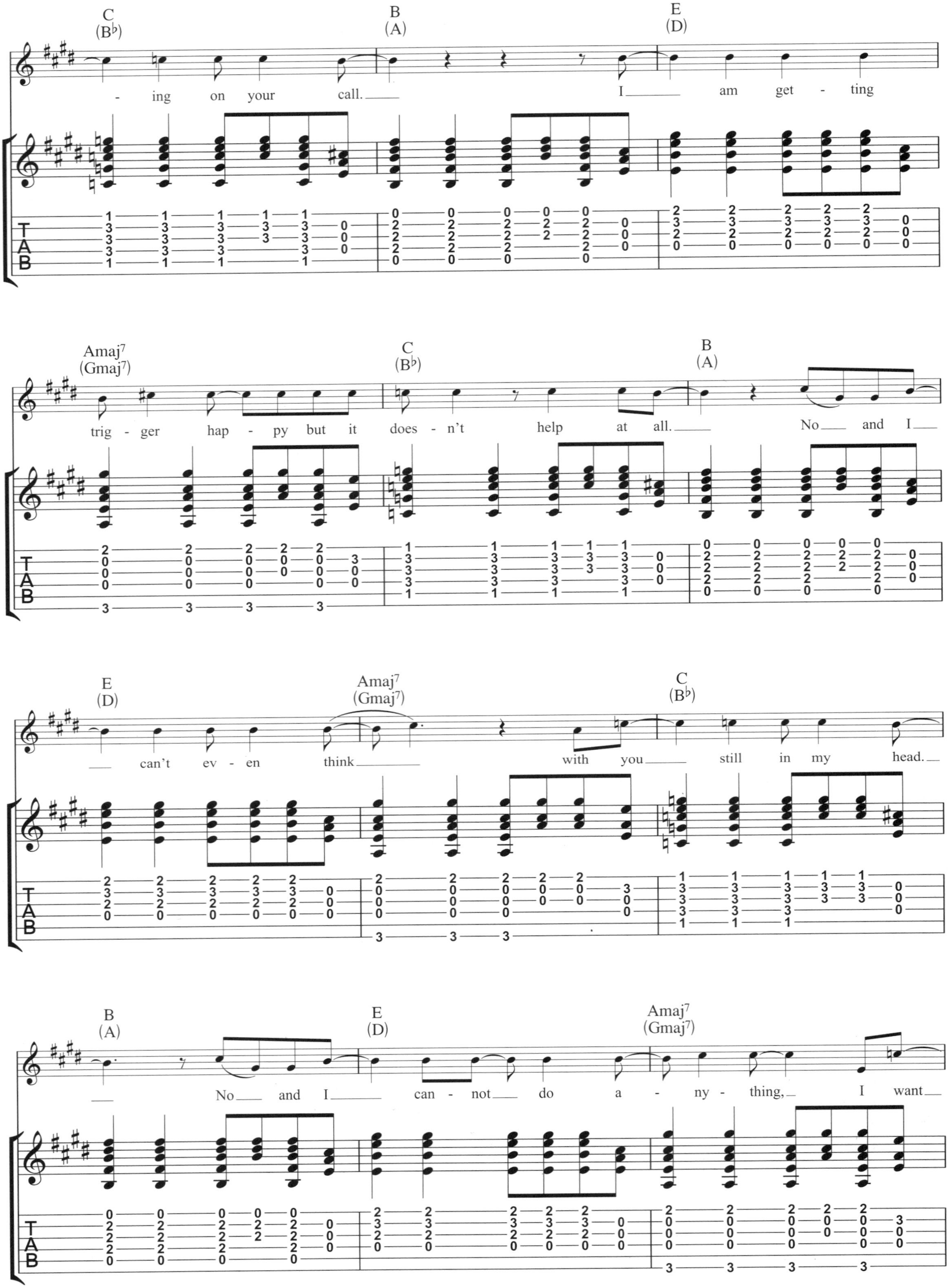
C (B♭)
B (A)
E (D)
- ing on your call. I am get - ting
Amaj7 (Gmaj7)
C (B♭)
B (A)
trig - ger hap - py but it does - n't help at all. No and I
E (D)
Amaj7 (Gmaj7)
C (B♭)
can't ev - en think with you still in my head.
B (A)
E (D)
Amaj7 (Gmaj7)
No and I can - not do a - ny - thing, I want

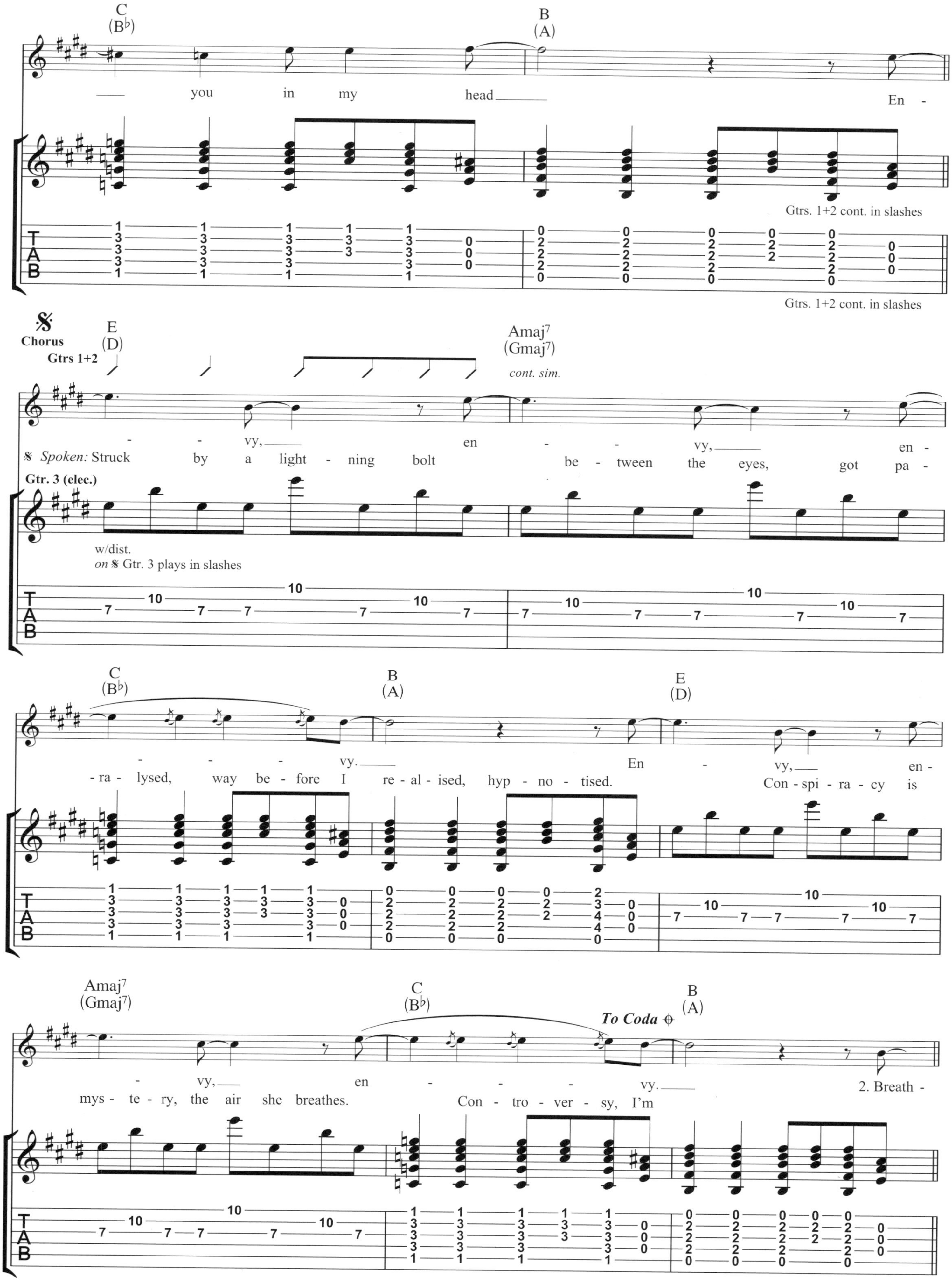
C (B♭)
you in my head
B (A)
En-
Gtrs. 1+2 cont. in slashes
Chorus
Gtrs 1+2
E (D)
Amaj7 (Gmaj7)
cont. sim.
-vy, envy, en-
Spoken: Struck by a lightning bolt between the eyes, got pa-
Gtr. 3 (elec.)
w/dist.
on 𝄋 Gtr. 3 plays in slashes
C (B♭)
B (A)
E (D)
-vy. Envy, en-
-ralysed, way before I re-al-ised, hyp-no-tised. Con-spi-ra-cy is
Amaj7 (Gmaj7)
C (B♭)
To Coda
B (A)
-vy, en-vy. 2. Breath-
mys-te-ry, the air she breathes. Con-tro-ver-sy, I'm

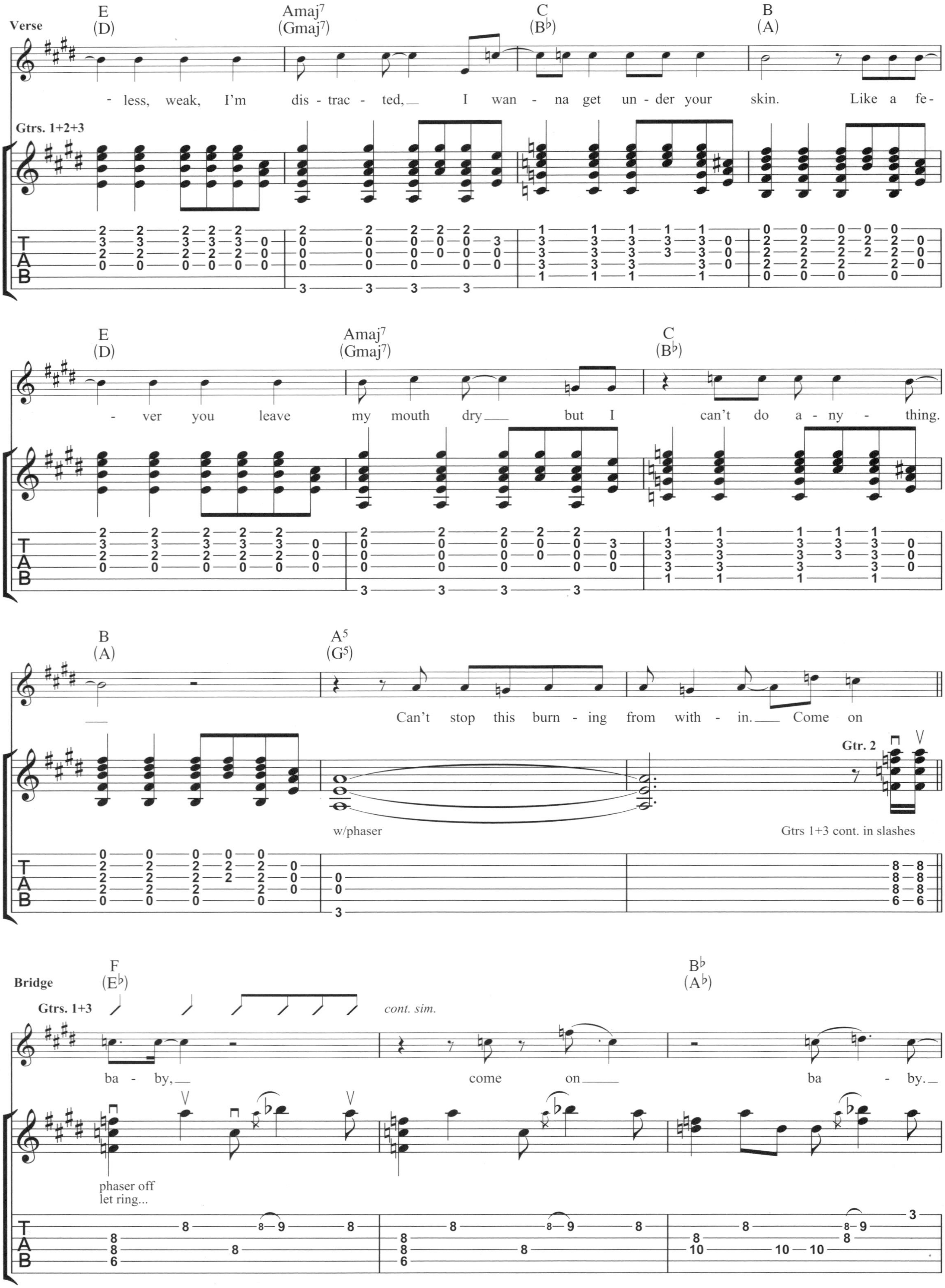
Verse
E
(D)
Amaj7
(Gmaj7)
C
(B♭)
B
(A)
-less, weak, I'm dis-trac-ted, I wan-na get un-der your skin. Like a fe-
Gtrs. 1+2+3
E
(D)
Amaj7
(Gmaj7)
C
(B♭)
-ver you leave my mouth dry but I can't do a-ny-thing.
B
(A)
A5
(G5)
Can't stop this burn-ing from with-in. Come on
Gtr. 2
w/phaser
Gtrs 1+3 cont. in slashes
Bridge
F
(E♭)
B♭
(A♭)
Gtrs. 1+3
cont. sim.
ba-by, come on ba-by.
phaser off
let ring...

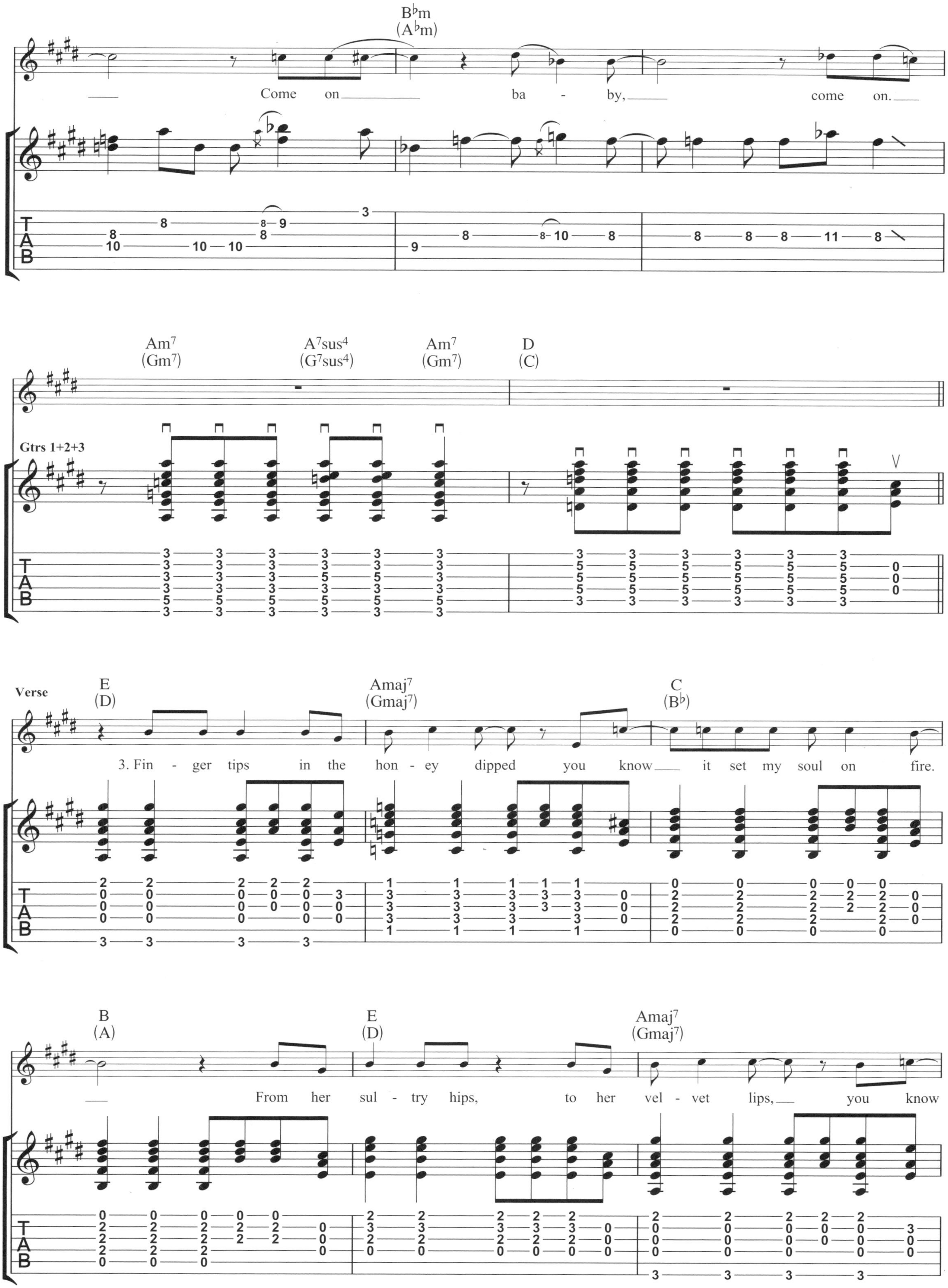
B♭m
(A♭m)
Come on baby, come on.
Am7
(Gm7)
A7sus4
(G7sus4)
Am7
(Gm7)
D
(C)
Gtrs 1+2+3
Verse
E
(D)
Amaj7
(Gmaj7)
C
(B♭)
3. Finger tips in the honey dipped you know it set my soul on fire.
B
(A)
E
(D)
Amaj7
(Gmaj7)
From her sultry hips, to her velvet lips, you know

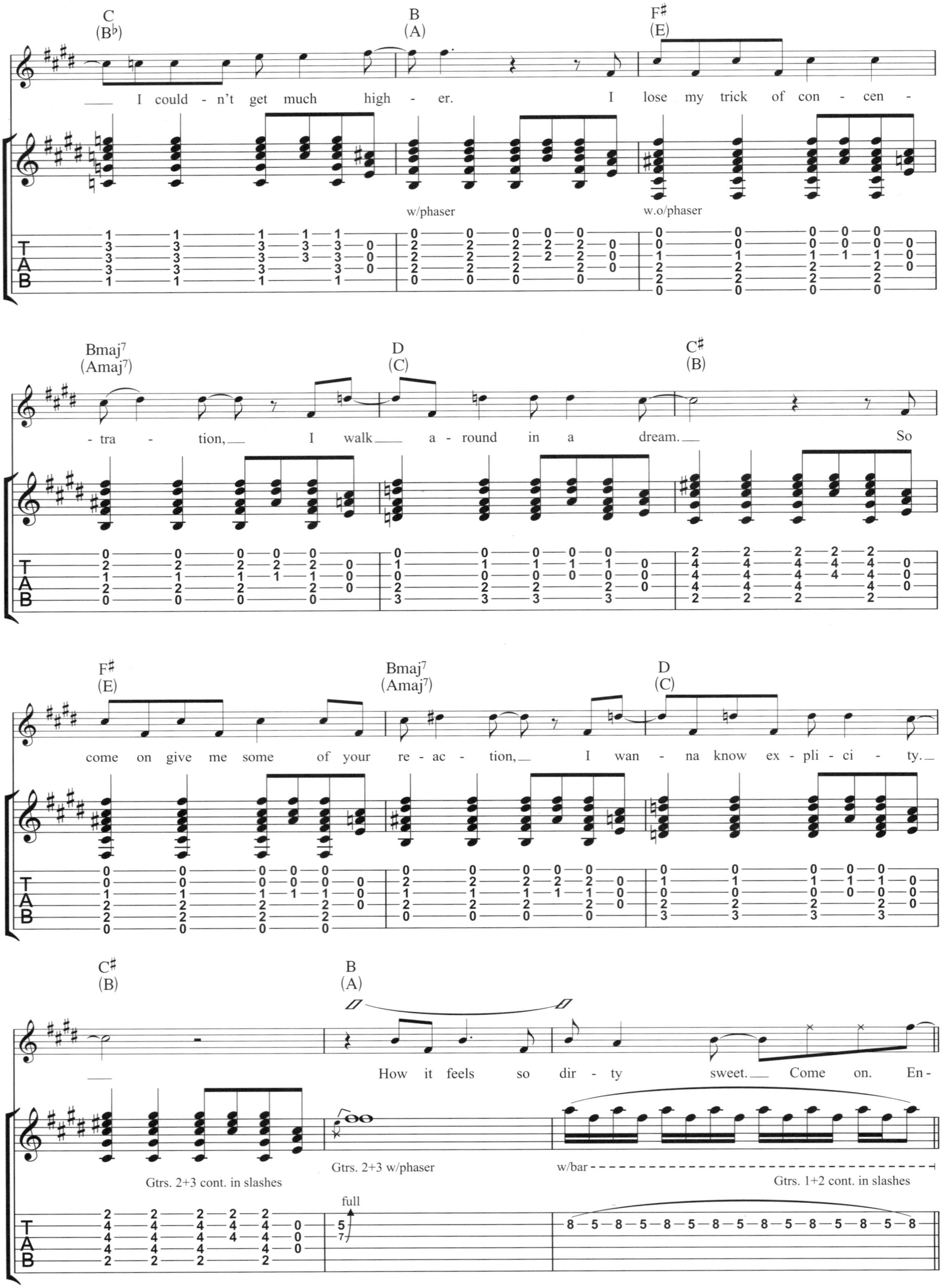
C (B♭)
B (A)
F♯ (E)
I couldn't get much high - er. I lose my trick of con - cen -
w/phaser
w.o/phaser
Bmaj7 (Amaj7)
D (C)
C♯ (B)
- tra - tion, I walk a - round in a dream. So
F♯ (E)
Bmaj7 (Amaj7)
D (C)
come on give me some of your re - ac - tion, I wan - na know ex - pli - ci - ty.
C♯ (B)
B (A)
How it feels so dir - ty sweet. Come on. En -
Gtrs. 2+3 cont. in slashes
Gtrs. 2+3 w/phaser
w/bar
Gtrs. 1+2 cont. in slashes
full

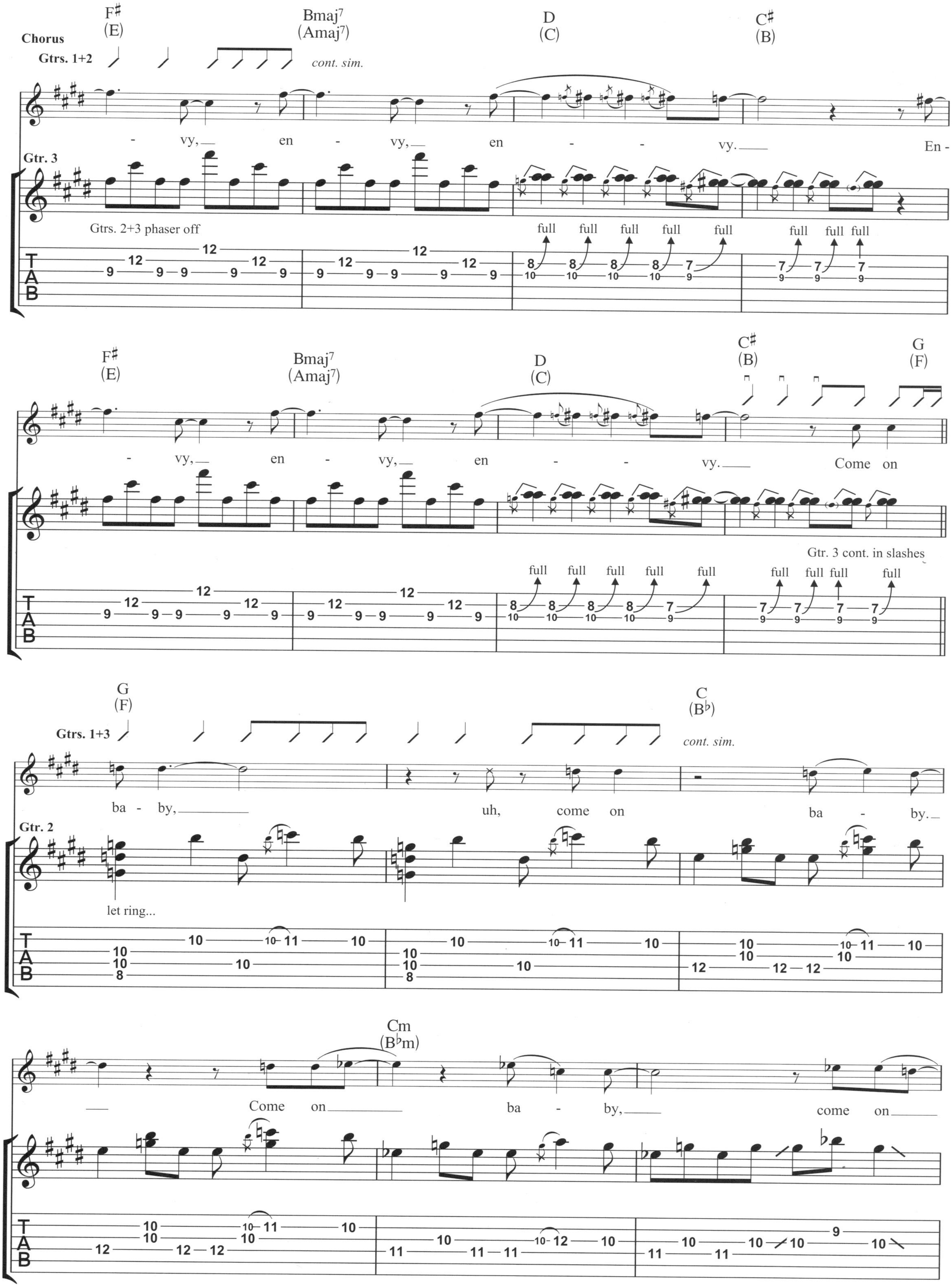
Chorus
Gtrs. 1+2
F♯ (E)
Bmaj7 (Amaj7)
D (C)
C♯ (B)
cont. sim.
-vy, en - vy, en - - vy. En -
Gtr. 3
Gtrs. 2+3 phaser off
full
-vy, en - vy, en - - vy. Come on
G (F)
Gtr. 3 cont. in slashes
Gtrs. 1+3
C (B♭)
ba - by, uh, come on ba - by.
Gtr. 2
let ring...
Cm (B♭m)
Come on ba - by, come on

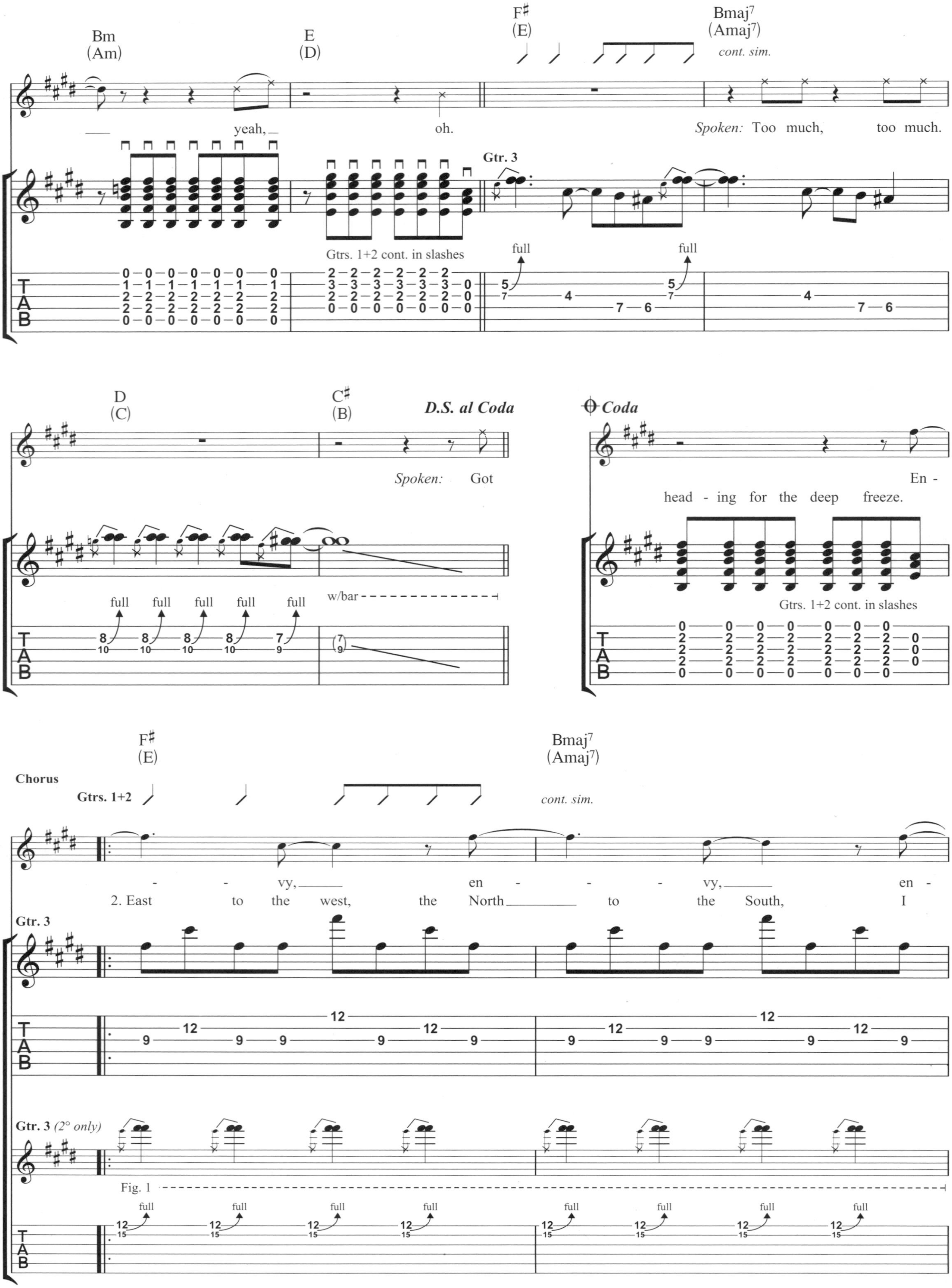
Bm (Am)
E (D)
F♯ (E)
Bmaj7 (Amaj7)
cont. sim.
yeah, oh.
Spoken: Too much, too much.
Gtr. 3
Gtrs. 1+2 cont. in slashes
full
D (C)
C♯ (B)
D.S. al Coda
Spoken: Got
w/bar
Coda
En - heading for the deep freeze.
Gtrs. 1+2 cont. in slashes
Chorus
Gtrs. 1+2
F♯ (E)
Bmaj7 (Amaj7)
cont. sim.
- - vy, en - - - vy, en -
2. East to the west, the North to the South, I
Gtr. 3
Gtr. 3 (2° only)
Fig. 1
full

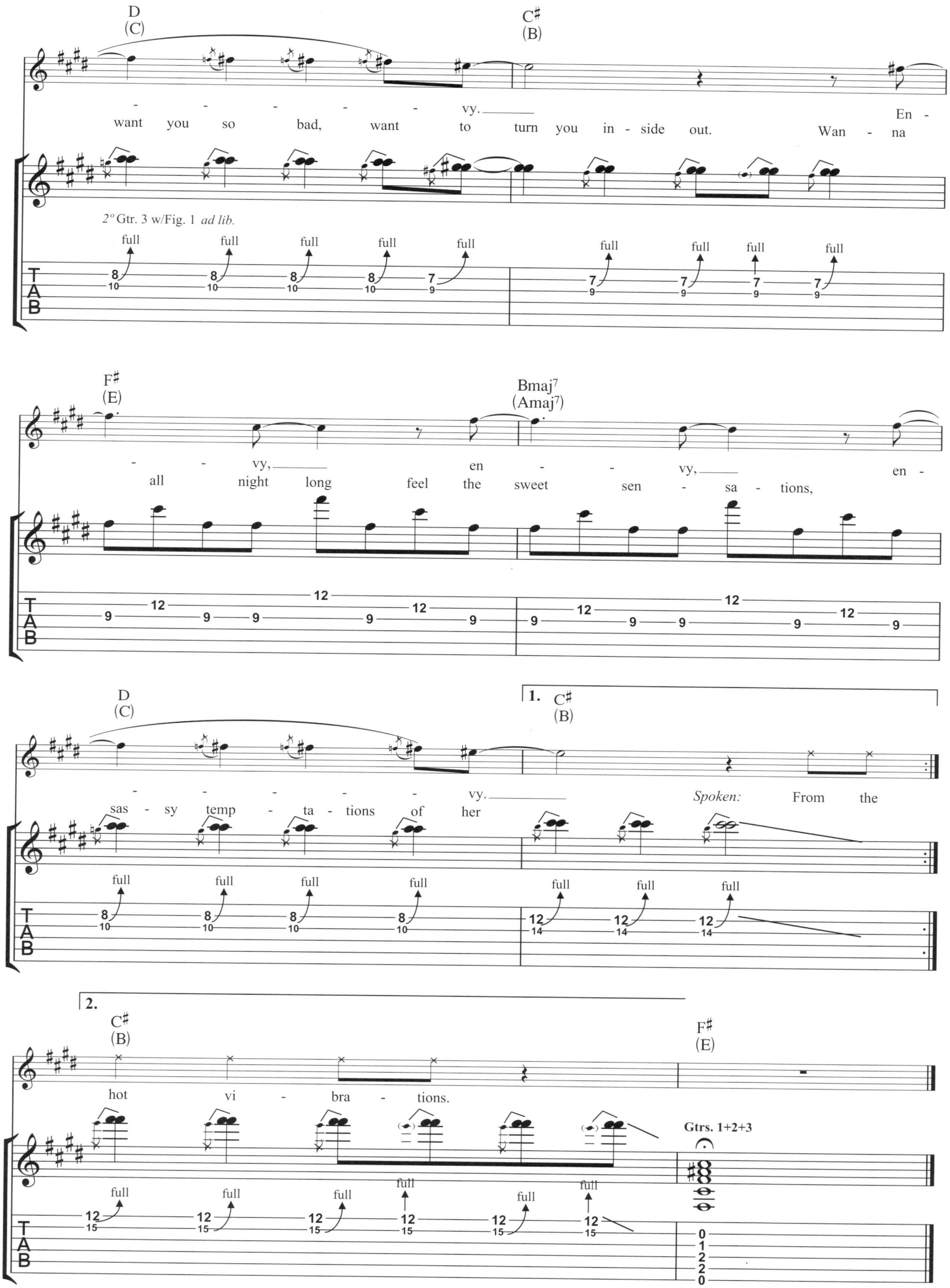
D
(C)
C♯
(B)
- - - - - vy.
En -
want you so bad, want to turn you in - side out. Wan - na
2° Gtr. 3 w/Fig. 1 ad lib.
full
F♯
(E)
Bmaj7
(Amaj7)
- - vy,
en - - vy,
en -
all night long feel the sweet sen - sa - tions,
D
(C)
1.
C♯
(B)
- - - - - vy.
sas - sy temp - ta - tions of her
Spoken: From the
2.
C♯
(B)
F♯
(E)
hot vi - bra - tions.
Gtrs. 1+2+3
T
A
B

EVERYDAY

WORDS & MUSIC BY JON BON JOVI, RICHIE SAMBORA & ANDREAS CARLSSON

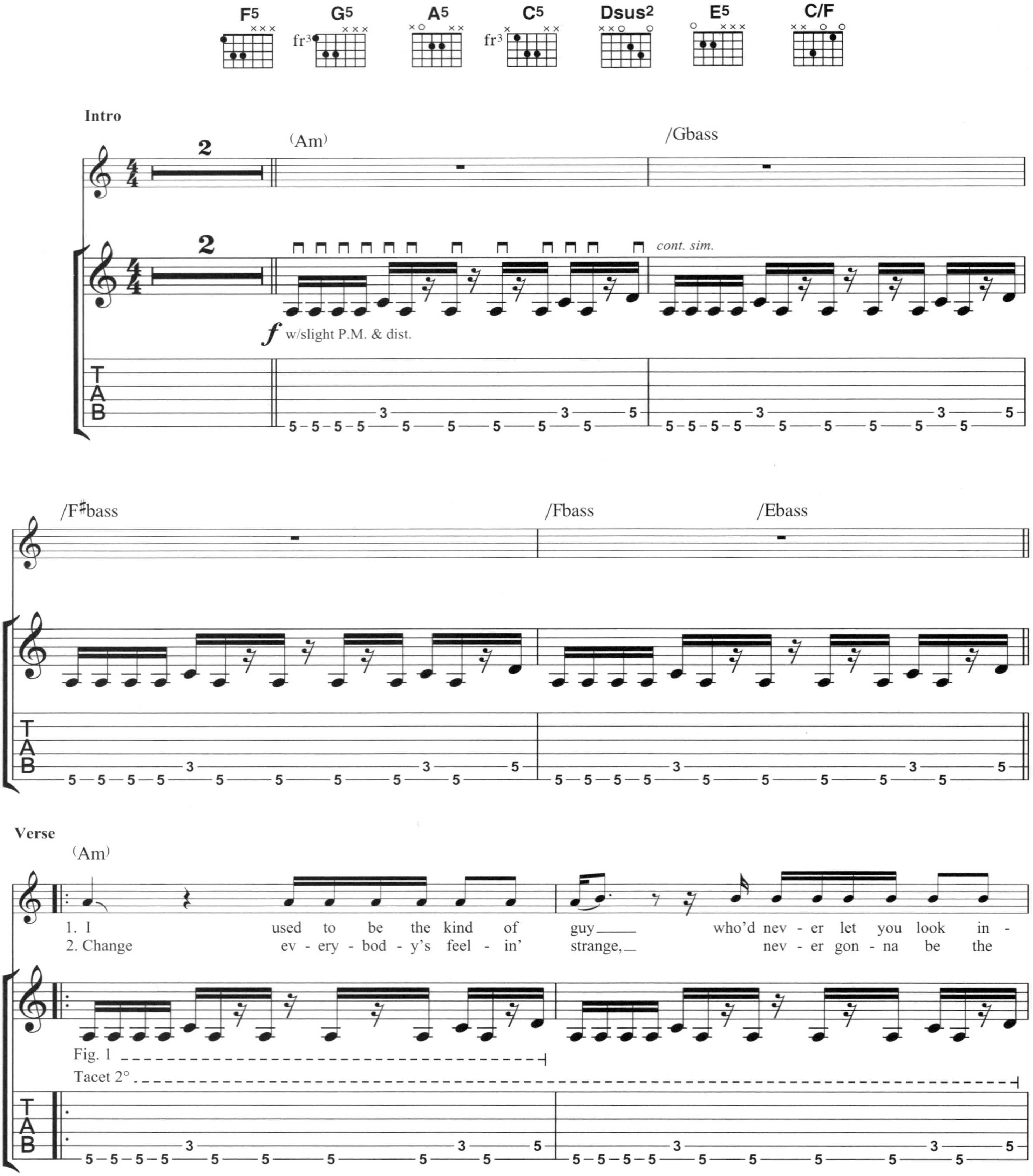

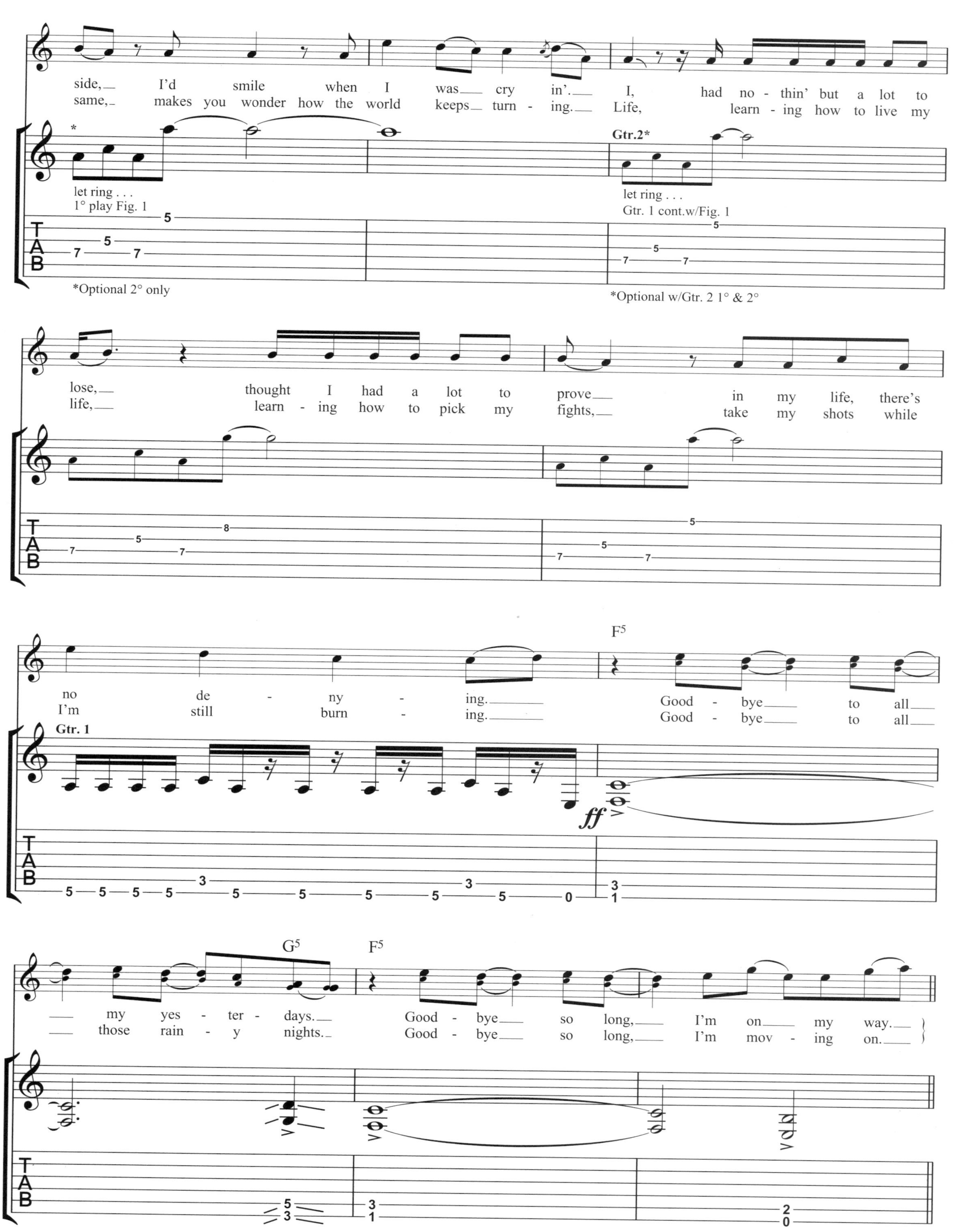
side, I'd smile when I was cry in'. I, had no - thin' but a lot to
same, makes you wonder how the world keeps turn - ing. Life, learn - ing how to live my
let ring . . .
1° play Fig. 1
Gtr.2*
let ring . . .
Gtr. 1 cont.w/Fig. 1
*Optional 2° only
*Optional w/Gtr. 2 1° & 2°
lose, thought I had a lot to prove in my life, there's
life, learn - ing how to pick my fights, take my shots while
no de - ny - ing. Good - bye to all
I'm still burn - ing. Good - bye to all
F5
Gtr. 1
ff
my yes - ter - days. Good - bye so long, I'm on my way.
those rain - y nights. Good - bye so long, I'm mov - ing on.
G5
F5

Chorus
A5 C5 G5
I had e - nough of cry - in', bleed - in', sweat - in', dy - in'. For - give me when I say, gon - na
*Optional w/Gtr. 2
F5 E5 A5 C5
live my life ev - ery day. I'm gon - na touch the sky and I spread these wings and fly.
G5 F5 G5 1. A5
I ain't here to play, gon - na live my life ev - ery day.
2° They can
P.M.
2. Dsus2 C/F
guess, take the wheel, I just made my - self a deal, there ain't no - thin' gon - na get in my
mf
let ring . . .

Solo
(Am)
/Gbass
/F♯bass
way. Ev - ery day.
Gtr.1 w/Fig.1
ff
full
1/2
3
/Fbass
/Ebass
A5
let ring . . . .
G5
let ring . . . .
D5
T
A
B

F5
E5
8va
full
Chorus
F5
A5
Good - bye, so long I'm mov - ing on. I had enough of cry - in',
C5
G5
F5
E5
bleed - in', sweat - in', dy - in'. For - give me when I say, gon - na live my life ev - ery day.
A5
C5
G5
I'm gon - na touch the sky and I spread these wings and fly. I ain't here to play, gon - na

F5 G5 A5 C5
live my life ev - ery day. I, oh I, oh
G5 F5 E5 A5
I, I'm gon - na live my life ev - ery day. I, (gon - na touch the sky. oh
C5 G5 F5 N.C.
I oh I, I'm gon - na live my life ev - ery day.
spread those wings and fly.)
T
A
B

GET FREE

WORDS & MUSIC BY CRAIG NICHOLLS

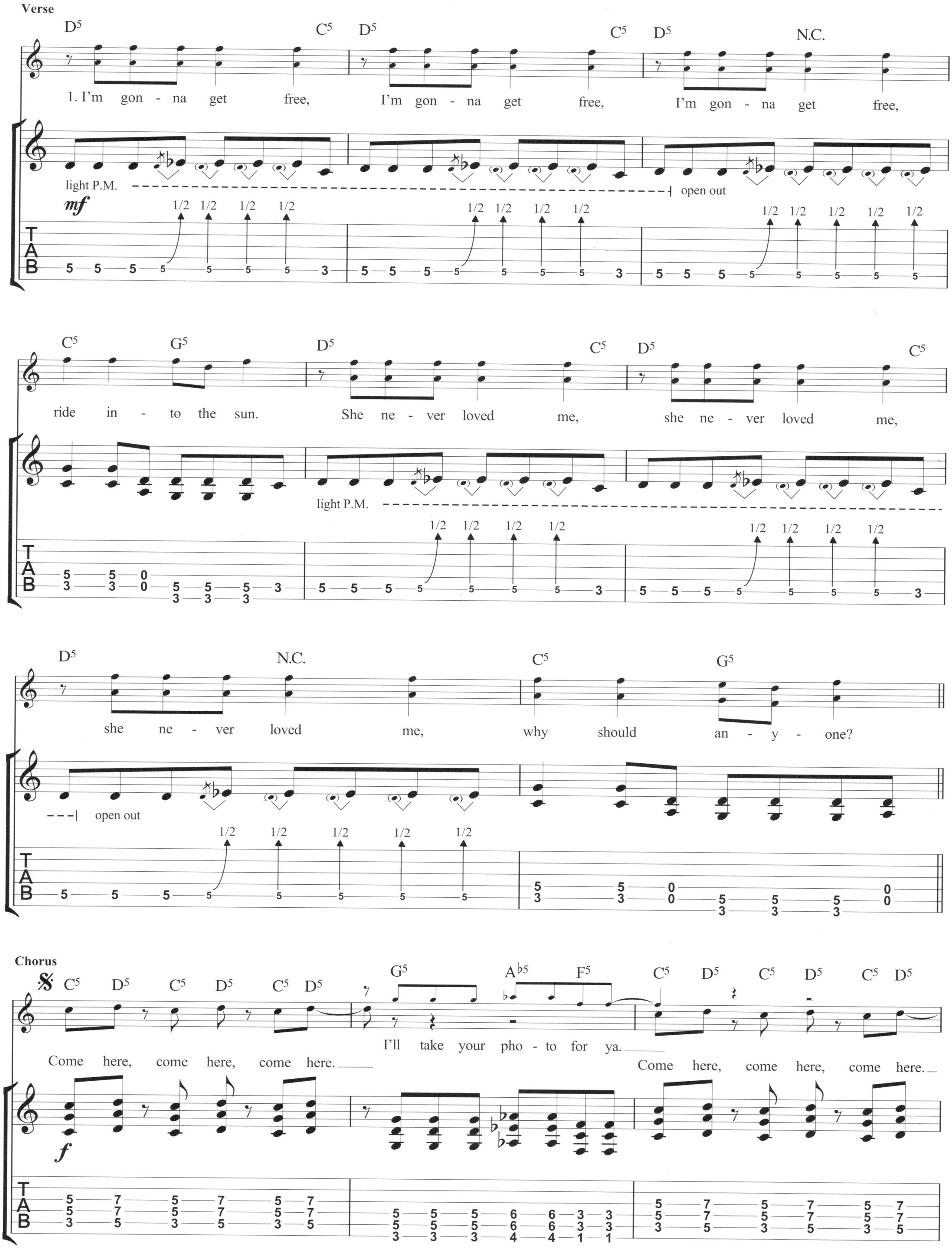
Verse
D5 C5 D5 C5 D5 N.C.
1. I'm gon - na get free, I'm gon - na get free, I'm gon - na get free,
light P.M. open out
mf
C5 G5 D5 C5 D5 C5
ride in - to the sun. She ne - ver loved me, she ne - ver loved me,
light P.M.
D5 N.C. C5 G5
she ne - ver loved me, why should an - y - one?
open out
Chorus
C5 D5 C5 D5 C5 D5 G5 A♭5 F5 C5 D5 C5 D5 C5 D5
I'll take your pho - to for ya.
Come here, come here, come here.
Come here, come here, come here.
f

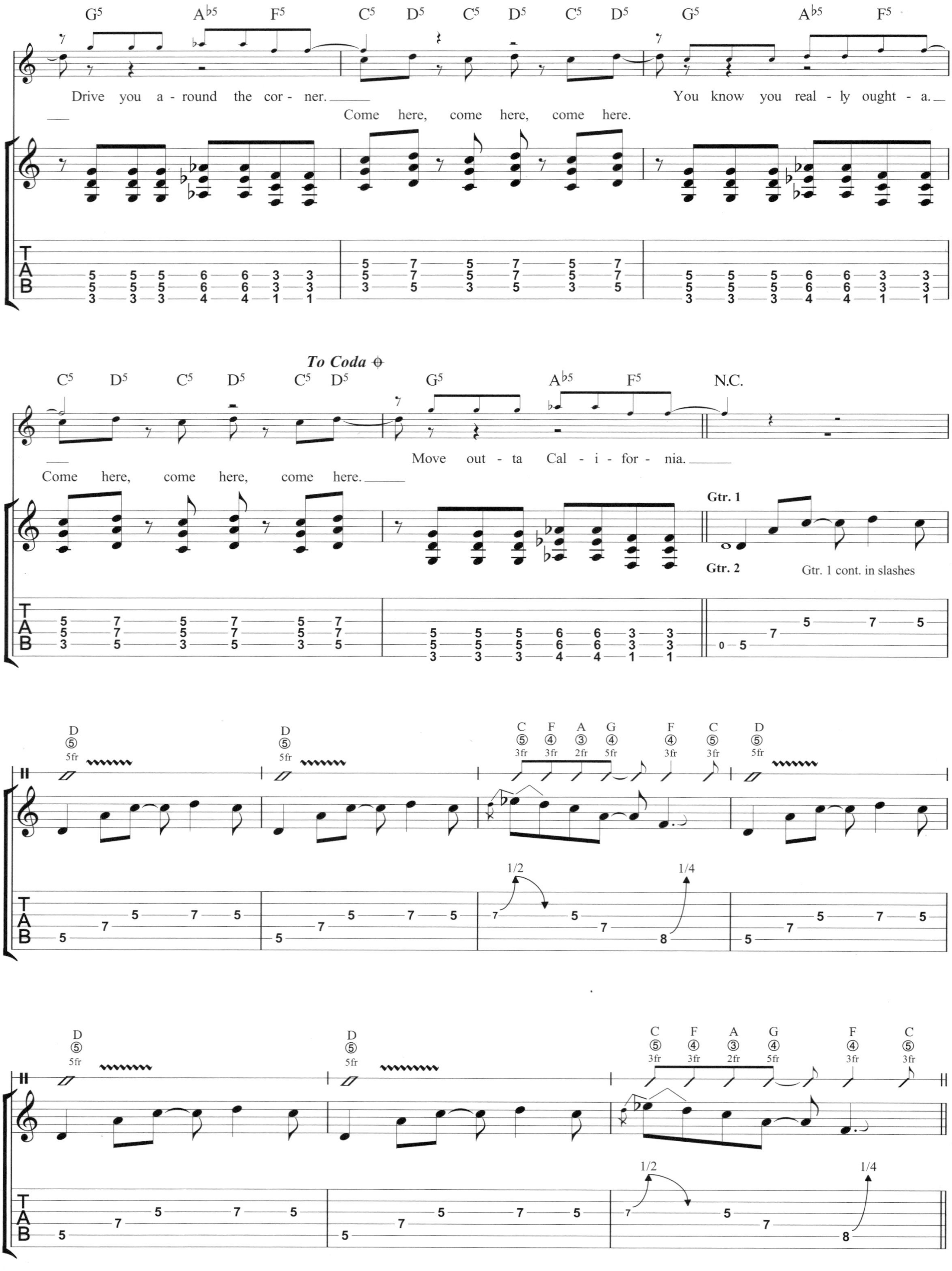
G5 A♭5 F5 C5 D5 C5 D5 C5 D5 G5 A♭5 F5
Drive you a-round the cor-ner.
Come here, come here, come here.
You know you real-ly ought-a.
To Coda
C5 D5 C5 D5 C5 D5 G5 A♭5 F5 N.C.
Come here, come here, come here.
Move out-ta Cal-i-for-nia.
Gtr. 1
Gtr. 2
Gtr. 1 cont. in slashes
D 5fr
C 3fr F 3fr A 2fr G 5fr F 3fr C 3fr
1/2
1/4

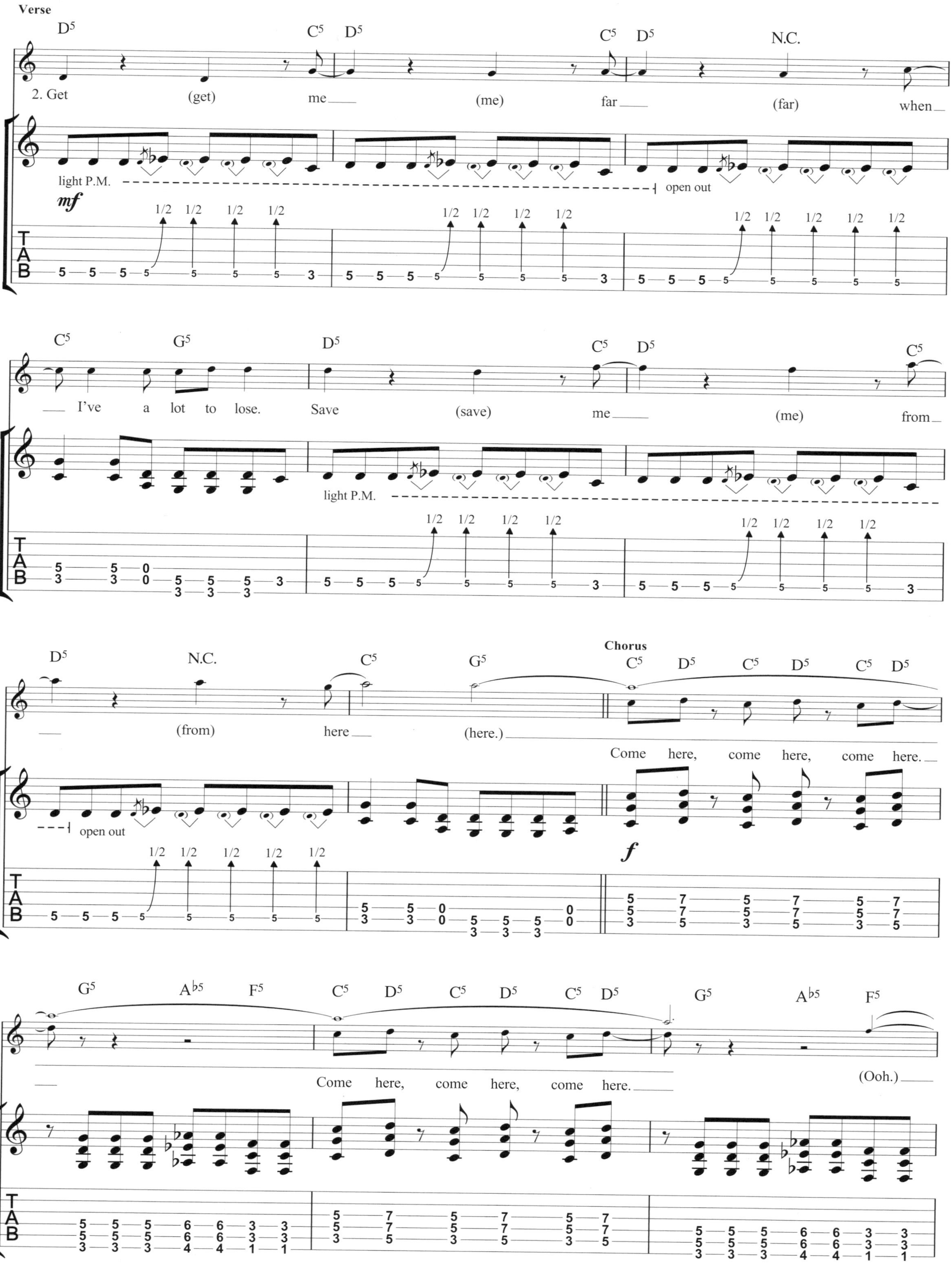
Verse
D5 C5 D5 C5 D5 N.C.
2. Get (get) me (me) far (far) when
light P.M.
open out
mf
C5 G5 D5 C5 D5 C5
I've a lot to lose. Save (save) me (me) from
light P.M.
D5 N.C. C5 G5
(from) here (here.)
open out
Chorus
C5 D5 C5 D5 C5 D5
Come here, come here, come here.
f
G5 A♭5 F5 C5 D5 C5 D5 C5 D5 G5 A♭5 F5
Come here, come here, come here.
(Ooh.)

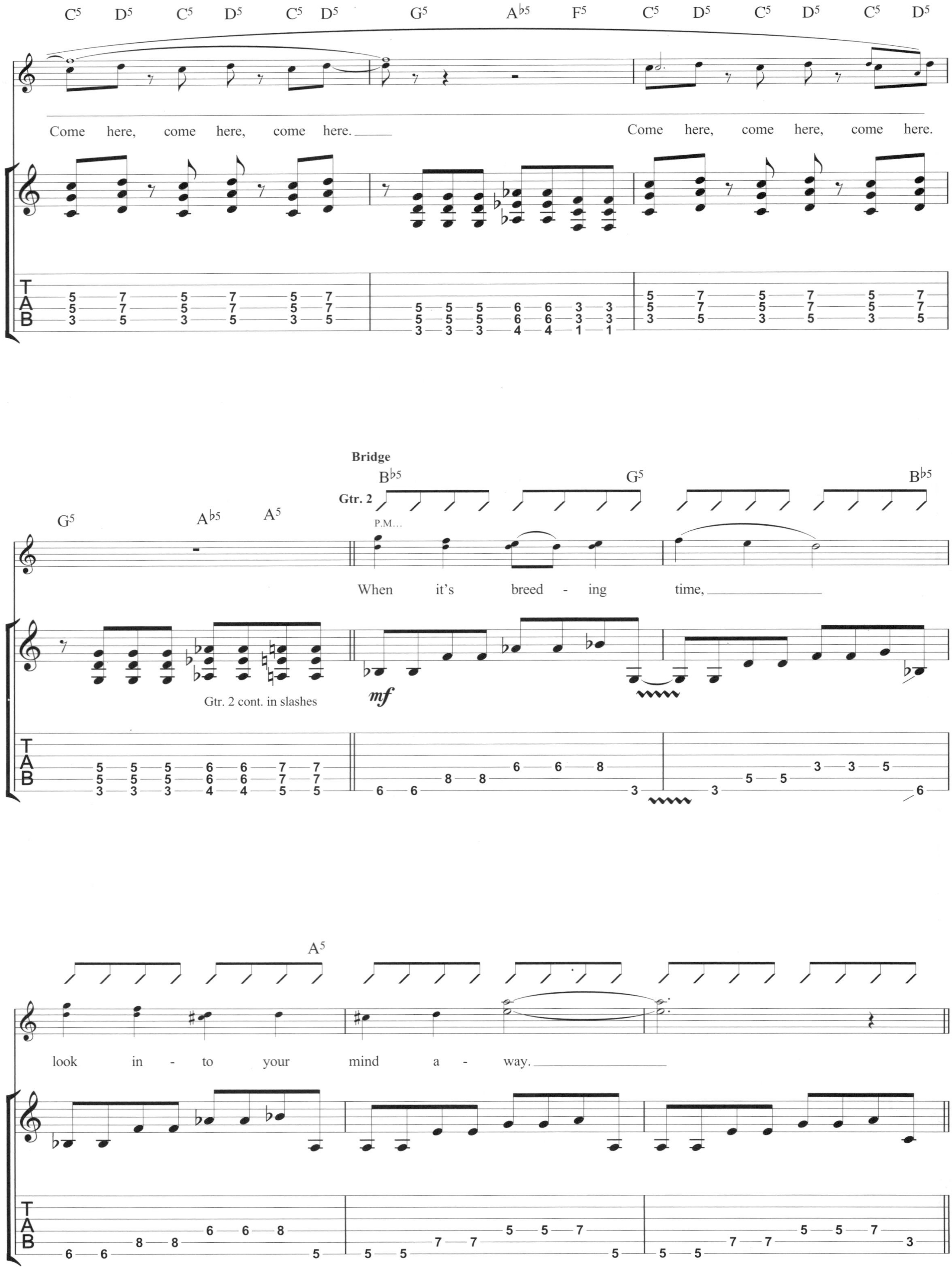
C5 D5 C5 D5 C5 D5 G5 A♭5 F5 C5 D5 C5 D5 C5 D5
Come here, come here, come here.
Come here, come here, come here.
G5 A♭5 A5
Gtr. 2 cont. in slashes
Bridge
B♭5 G5 B♭5
Gtr. 2
P.M...
When it's breed - ing time,
mf
A5
look in - to your mind a - way.

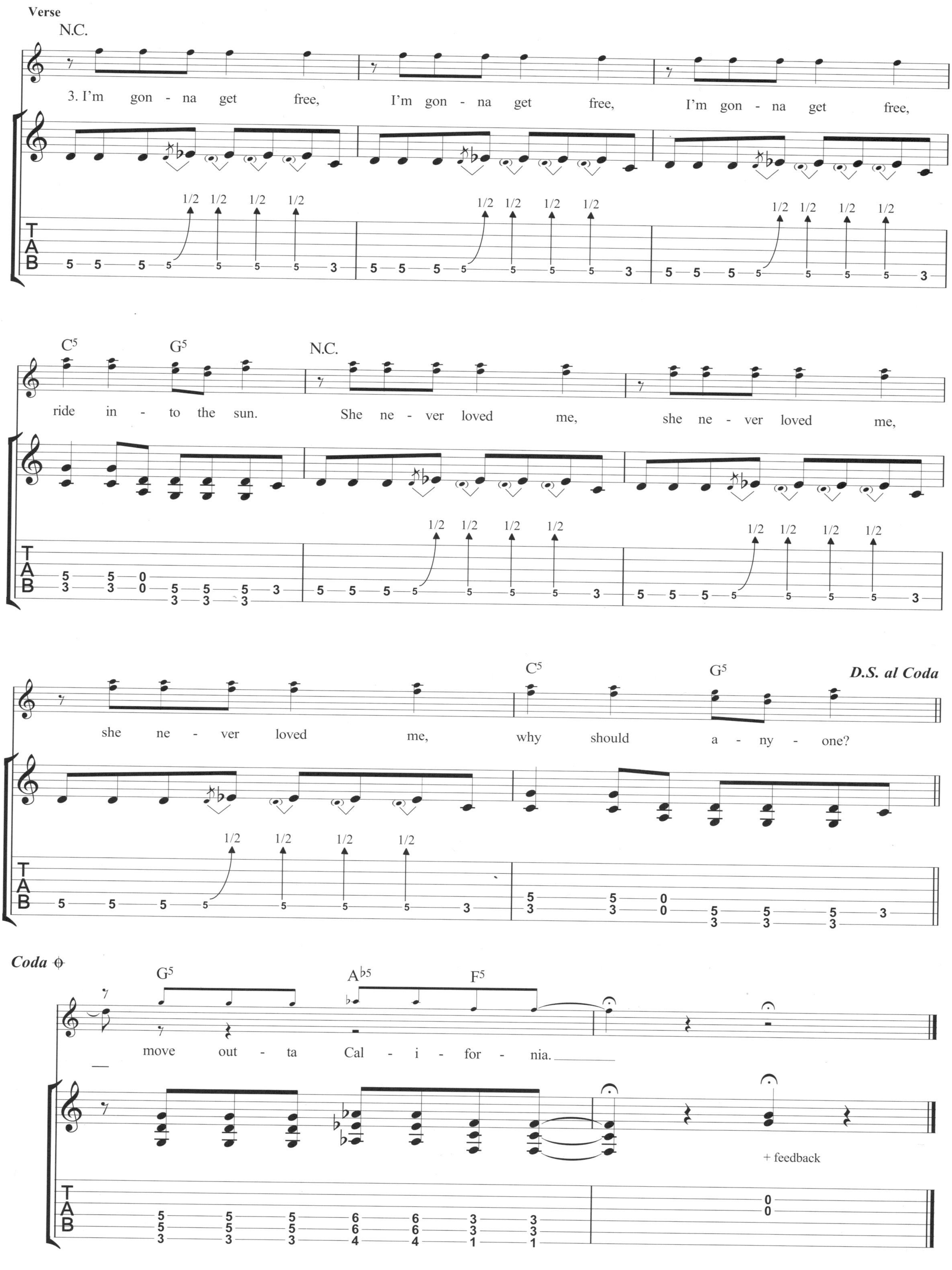
Verse
N.C.
3. I'm gon - na get free, I'm gon - na get free, I'm gon - na get free,
C5 G5 N.C.
ride in - to the sun. She ne - ver loved me, she ne - ver loved me,
C5 G5 D.S. al Coda
she ne - ver loved me, why should a - ny - one?
Coda
G5 A♭5 F5
move out - ta Cal - i - for - nia.
+ feedback

In My Place

Words & Music by Guy Berryman, Jon Buckland, Will Champion & Chris Martin

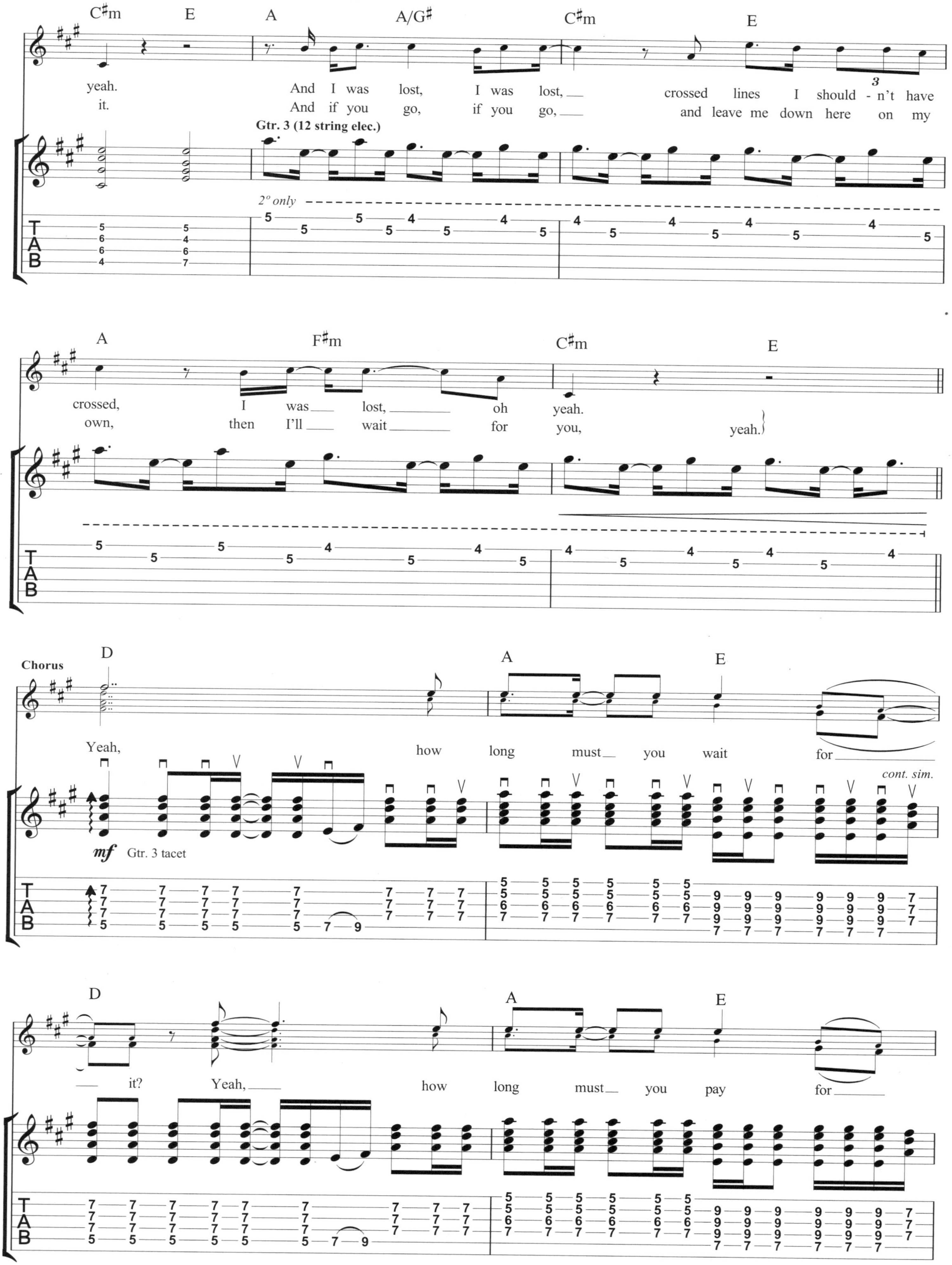
C♯m E A A/G♯ C♯m E
yeah. And I was lost, I was lost, crossed lines I should - n't have
it. And if you go, if you go, and leave me down here on my
Gtr. 3 (12 string elec.)
2° only
A F♯m C♯m E
crossed, I was lost, oh yeah.
own, then I'll wait for you, yeah.
Chorus
D A E
Yeah, how long must you wait for
mf Gtr. 3 tacet
cont. sim.
D A E
it? Yeah, how long must you pay for

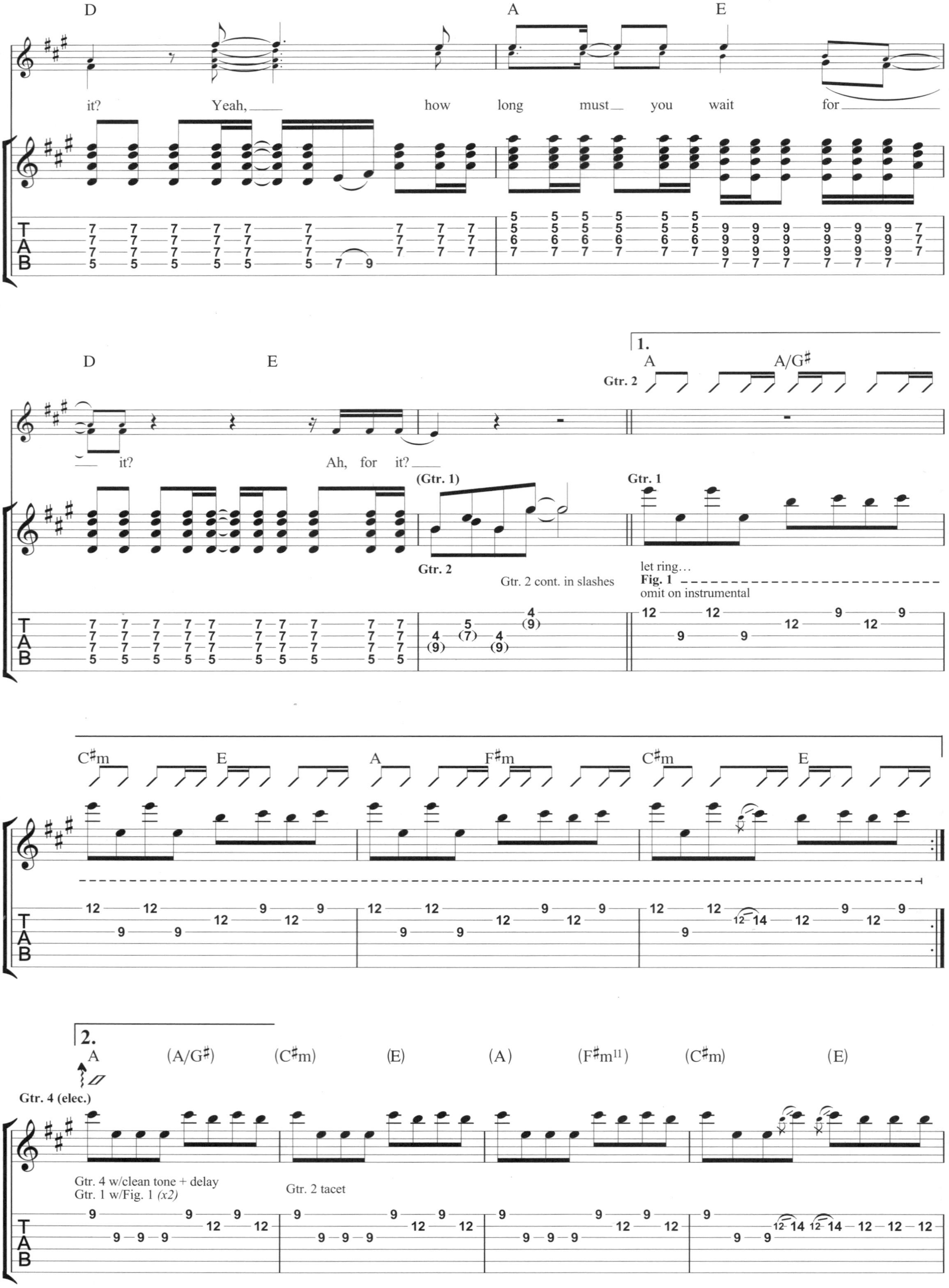
D
A
E
it? Yeah, how long must you wait for
D
E
it? Ah, for it?
1.
A
A/G♯
Gtr. 2
(Gtr. 1)
Gtr. 2
Gtr. 2 cont. in slashes
Gtr. 1
let ring…
Fig. 1
omit on instrumental
C♯m
E
A
F♯m
C♯m
E
2.
A
(A/G♯)
(C♯m)
(E)
(A)
(F♯m11)
(C♯m)
(E)
Gtr. 4 (elec.)
Gtr. 4 w/clean tone + delay
Gtr. 1 w/Fig. 1 (x2)
Gtr. 2 tacet

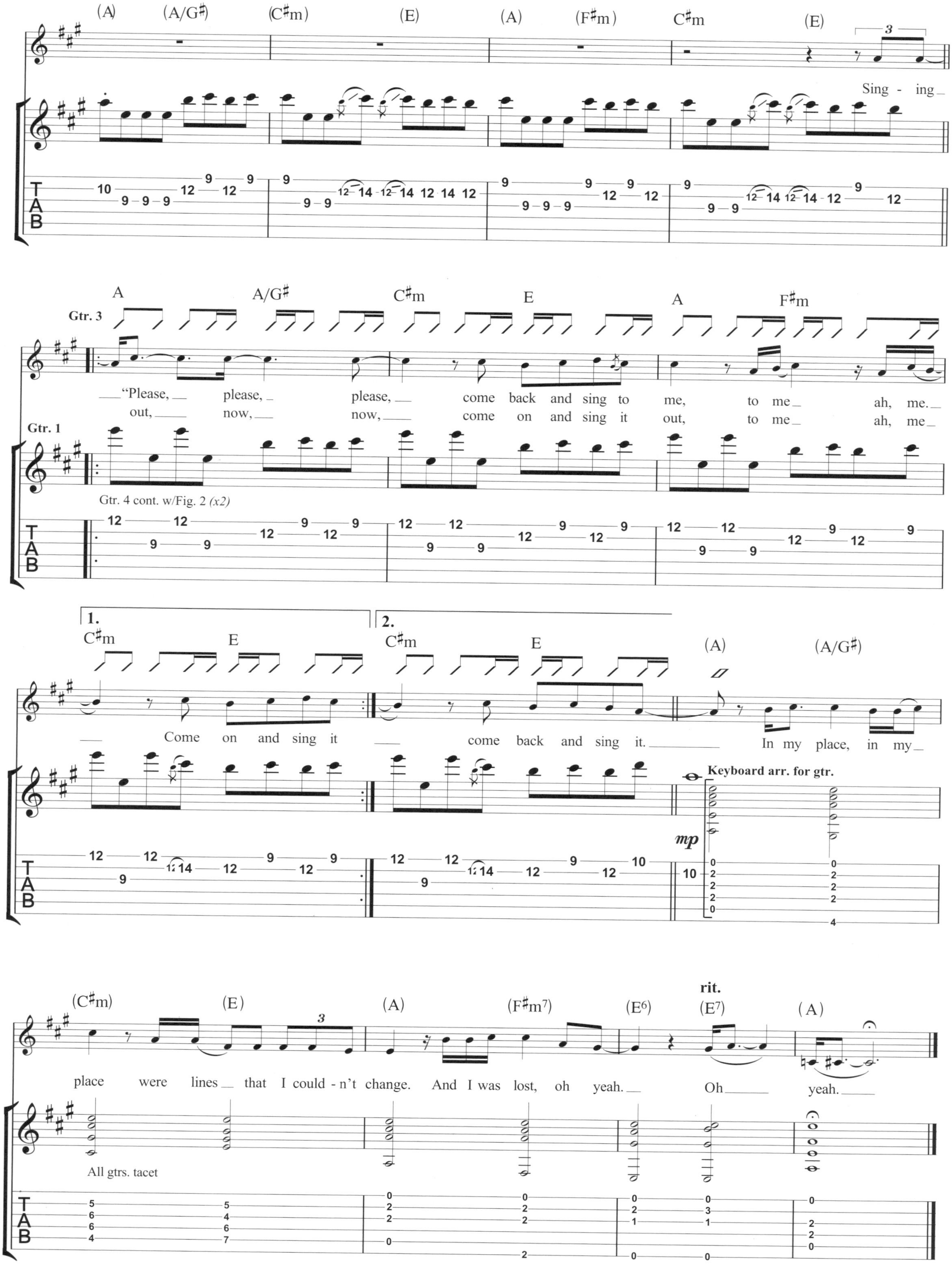
(A) (A/G♯) (C♯m) (E) (A) (F♯m) C♯m (E)
Sing - ing
A A/G♯ C♯m E A F♯m
Gtr. 3
"Please, please, please, come back and sing to me, to me ah, me.
out, now, now, come on and sing it out, to me ah, me
Gtr. 1
Gtr. 4 cont. w/Fig. 2 (x2)
1. C♯m E
2. C♯m E (A) (A/G♯)
Come on and sing it come back and sing it. In my place, in my
Keyboard arr. for gtr.
mp
(C♯m) (E) (A) (F♯m7) (E6) rit. (E7) (A)
place were lines that I could - n't change. And I was lost, oh yeah. Oh yeah.
All gtrs. tacet
TAB

I AM MINE

WORDS & MUSIC BY EDDIE VEDDER

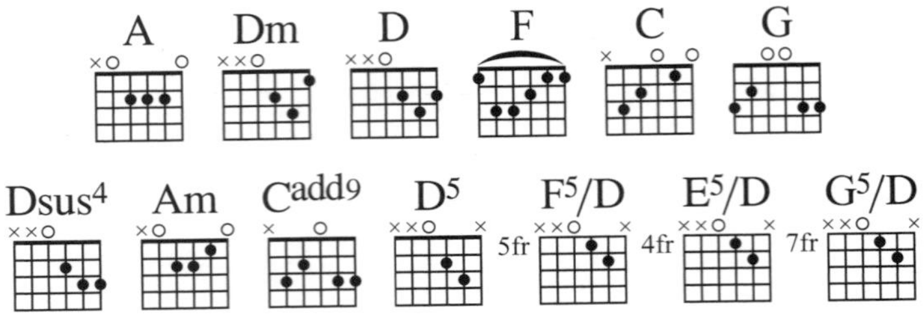

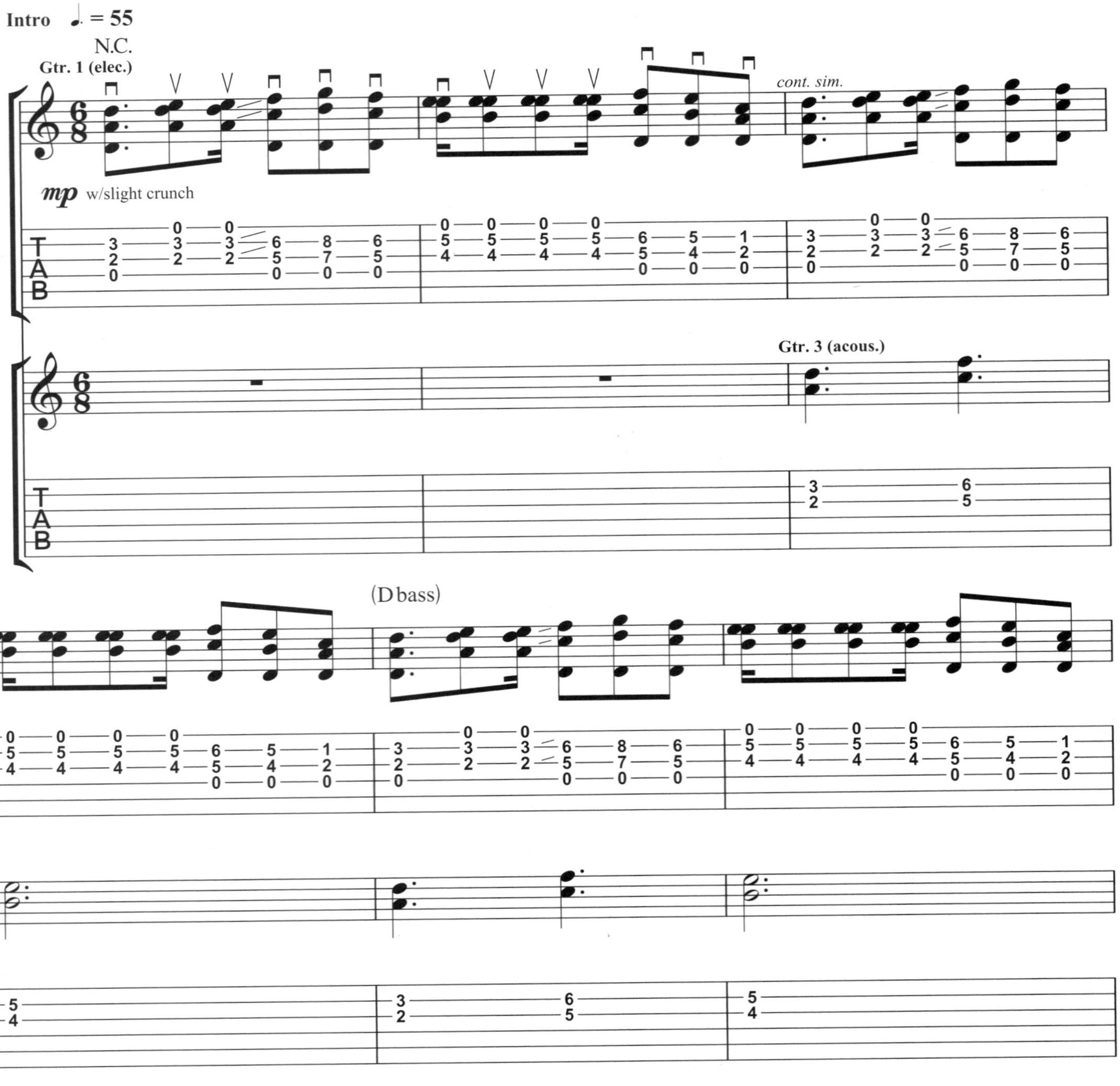

A
Gtr. 2 (elec.)
1. The
Gtr. 2 w/slight overdrive
Gtr. 3 tacet
Verse
Dm* F C G Dm* F
self - ish they're all stand - ing in line, faith and in hope and to
Gtrs. 1 & 2 (composite part)
cont. sim.
mf
*Gtr. 2 plays D major
C G Dm* F C G
buy them - selves time. Me, I fig - ure as each breath goes by I

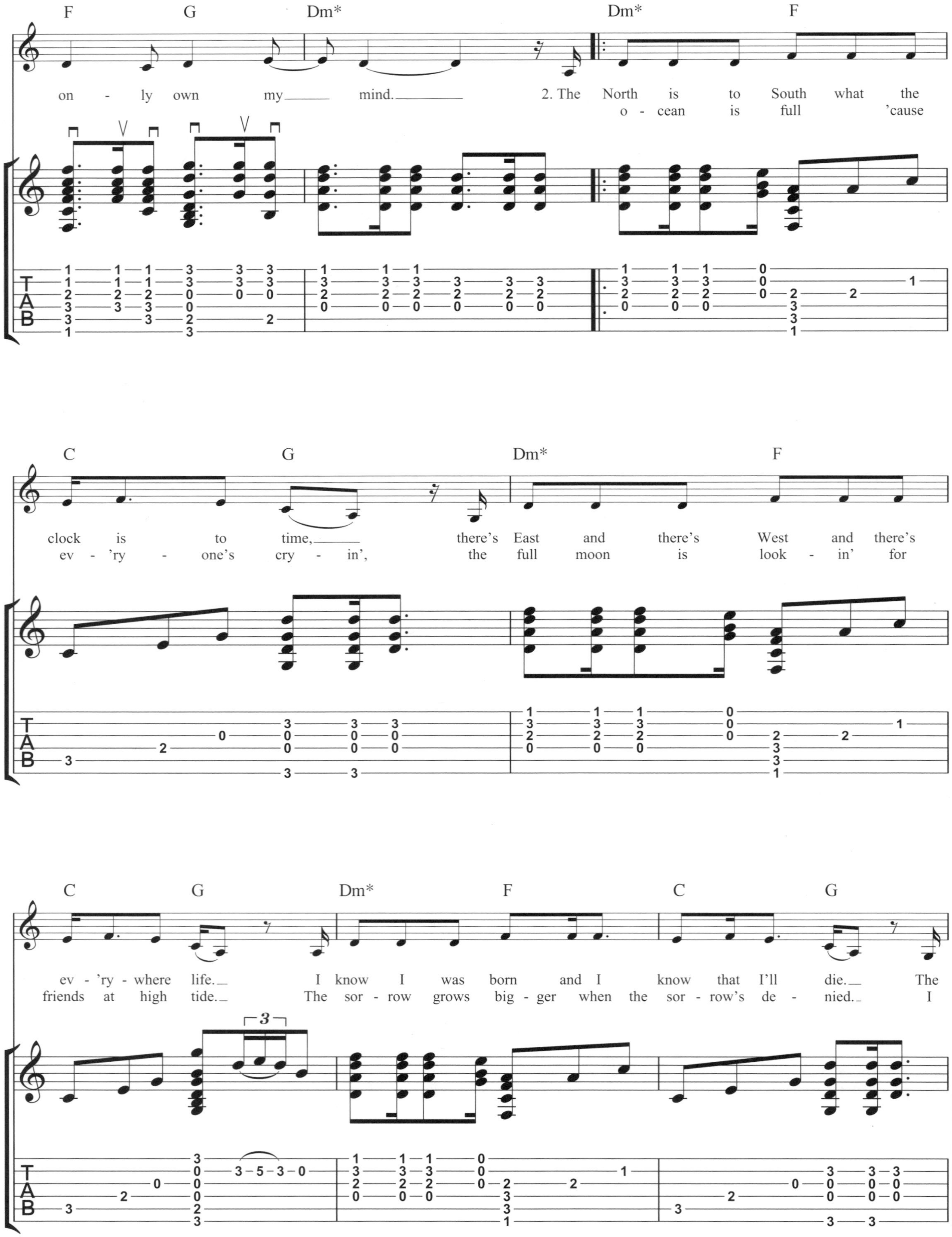
F G Dm* Dm* F
on - ly own my mind. 2. The North is to South what the
o - cean is full 'cause
C G Dm* F
clock is to time, there's East and there's West and there's
ev - 'ry - one's cry - in', the full moon is look - in' for
C G Dm* F C G
ev - 'ry - where life. I know I was born and I know that I'll die. The
friends at high tide. The sor - row grows big - ger when the sor - row's de - nied. I
T
A
B

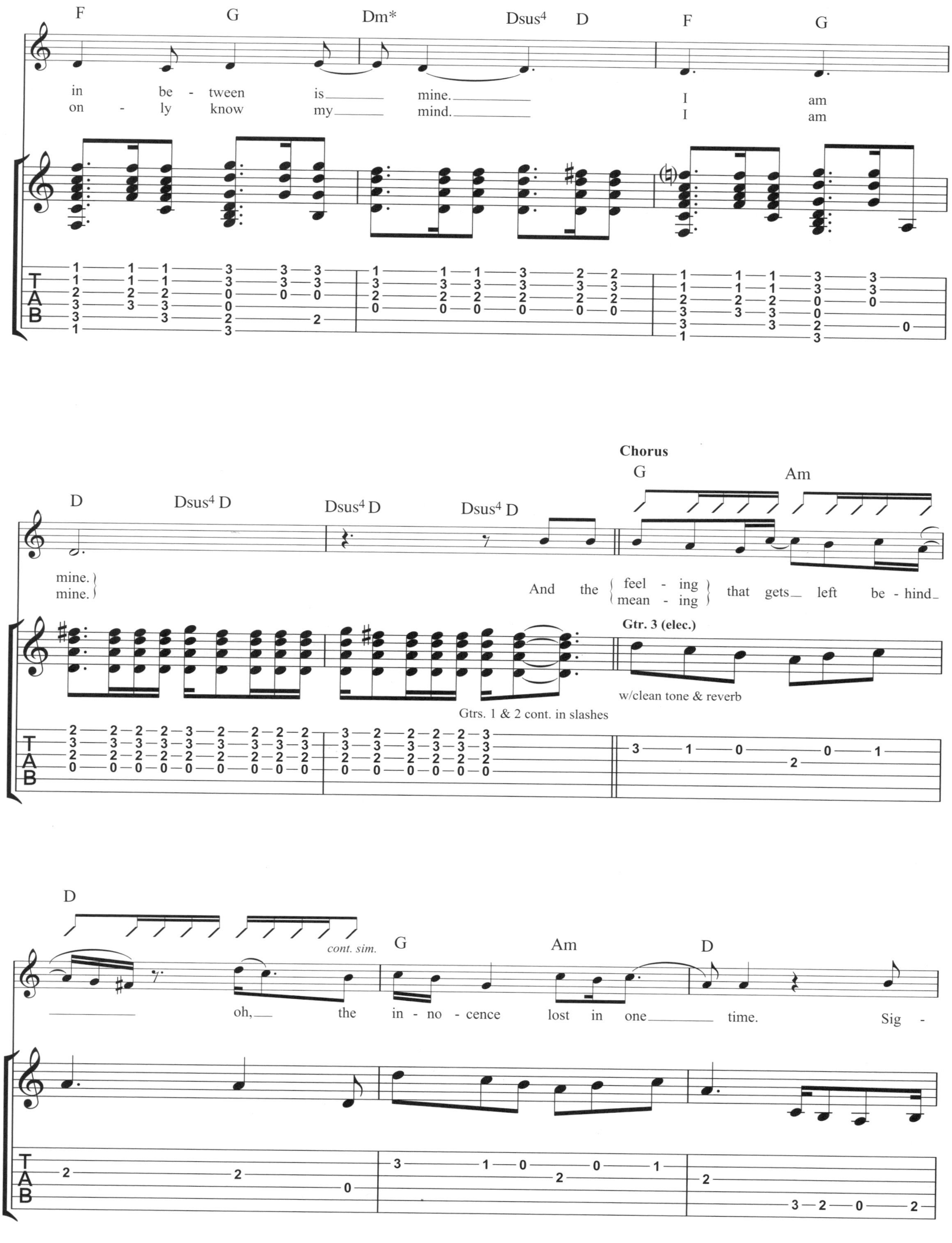
F G Dm* Dsus4 D F G
in be - tween is mine. I am
on - ly know my mind. I am
D Dsus4 D Dsus4 D Dsus4 D
Chorus
G Am
mine.
mine.
And the feel - ing / mean - ing that gets left be - hind
Gtr. 3 (elec.)
w/clean tone & reverb
Gtrs. 1 & 2 cont. in slashes
D
cont. sim.
G Am D
oh, the in - no - cence lost in one time. Sig -

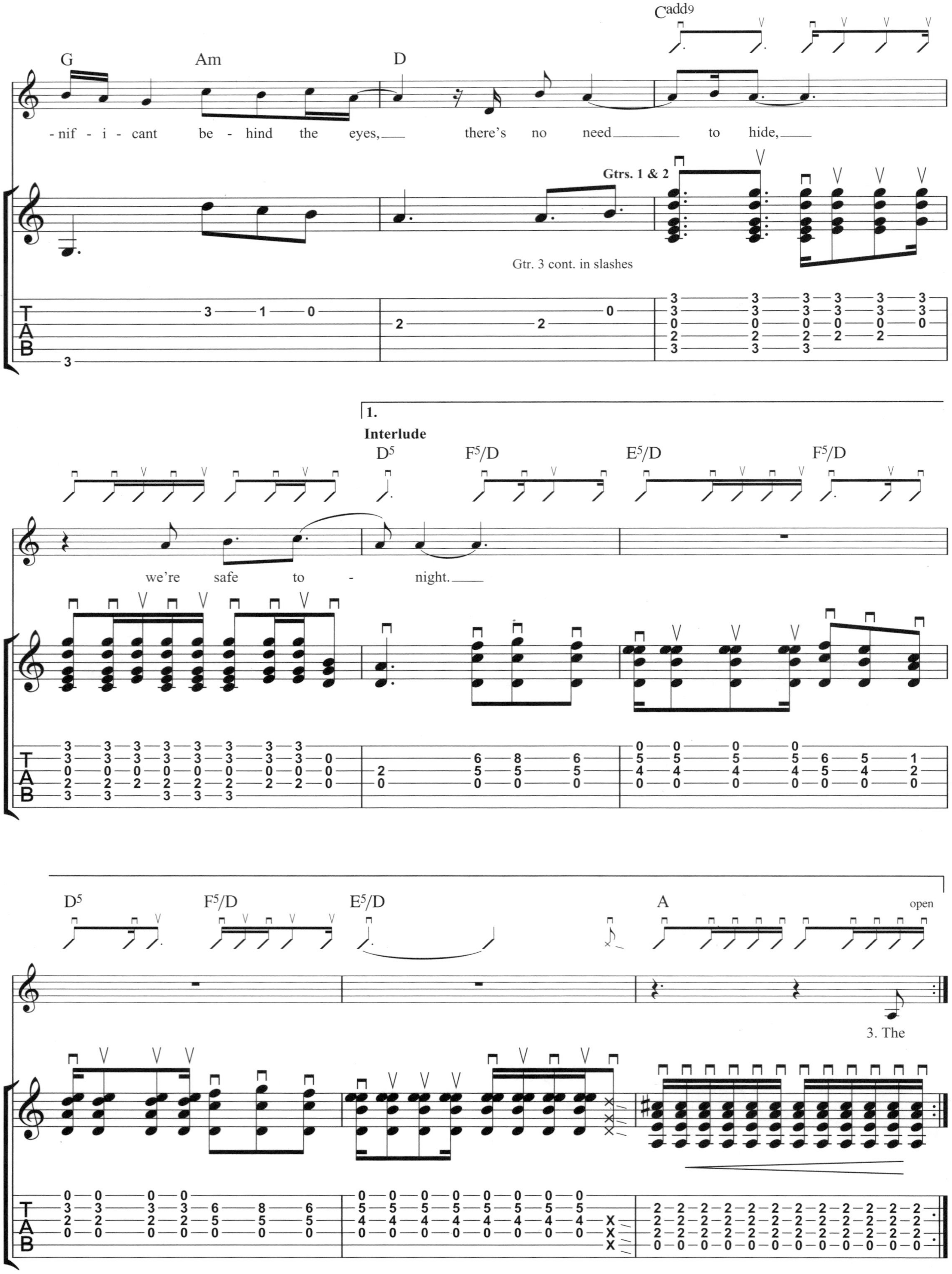
Cadd9
G
Am
D
-nif - i - cant be - hind the eyes, there's no need to hide,
Gtrs. 1 & 2
Gtr. 3 cont. in slashes
1.
Interlude
D5
F5/D
E5/D
F5/D
we're safe to - night.
D5
F5/D
E5/D
A
open
3. The

2.
Instrumental
D vocal tacet on repeats
F5/D G5/D F5/D
D
Cadd9
Play 3x
D
F5/D G5/D F5/D
- night,
woah!
Gtrs. 1, 2 & 3(elec.)*
f
*composite part
D
F5/D G5/D F5/D
D
F5/D G5/D F5/D
D
Cadd9
And the
Chorus
G
Am
D
cont. sim.
G
Am
feel - ings that get left be - hind oh, the in - no - cence bro - ken with
mean - ings that get left be - hind oh, the in - no - cence lost in one
Gtr. 3
D
G
Am
D
lies. Sig - nif - i - cance be - tween the lines we may need
time. We're all dif - fer - ent be - hind the eyes there's no need

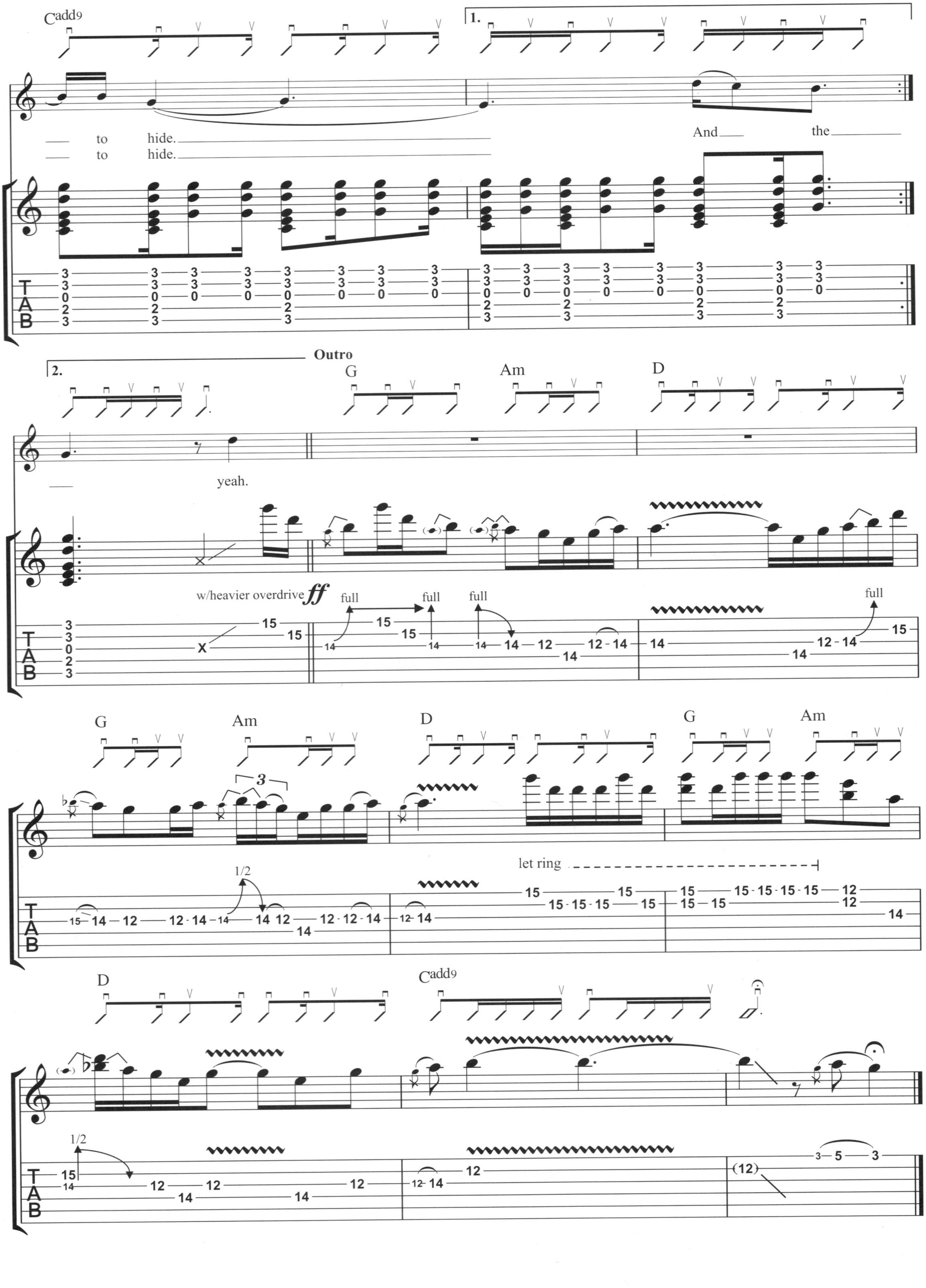
Cadd9
1.
to hide.
to hide.
And the
2.
Outro
G
Am
D
yeah.
w/heavier overdrive ff
full
let ring
1/2
Cadd9

IN YOUR WORLD

LYRICS & MUSIC BY MATTHEW BELLAMY

Gtr. 1 (elec)
6=E 3=G
5=A 2=B
4=E 1=E

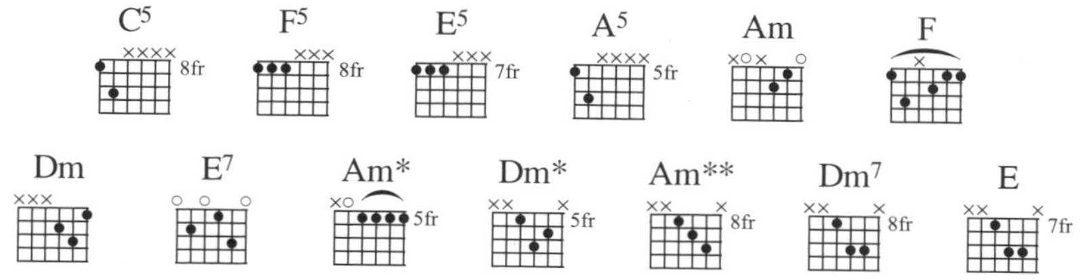

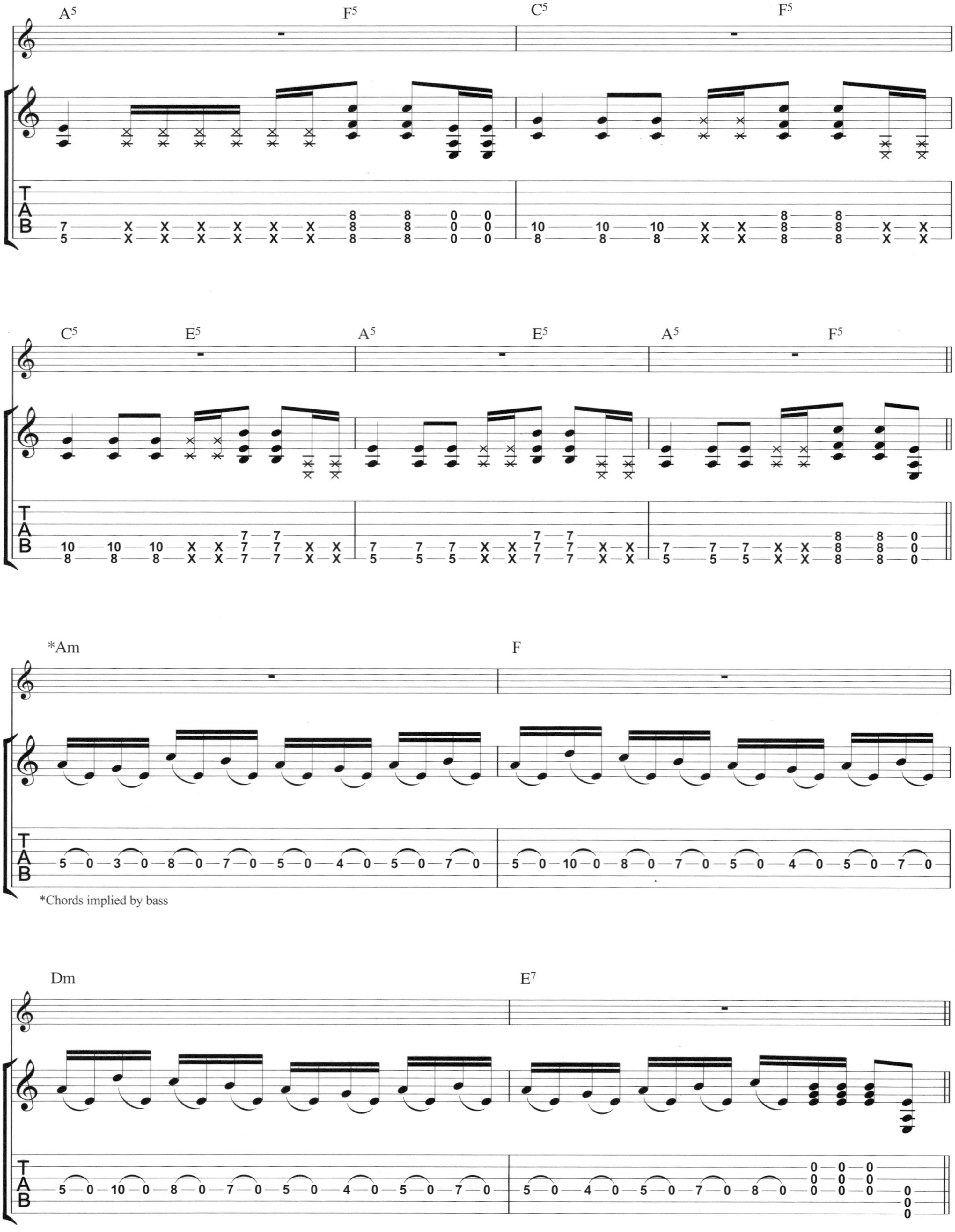
A5 F5 C5 F5
C5 E5 A5 E5 A5 F5
*Am F
*Chords implied by bass
Dm E7

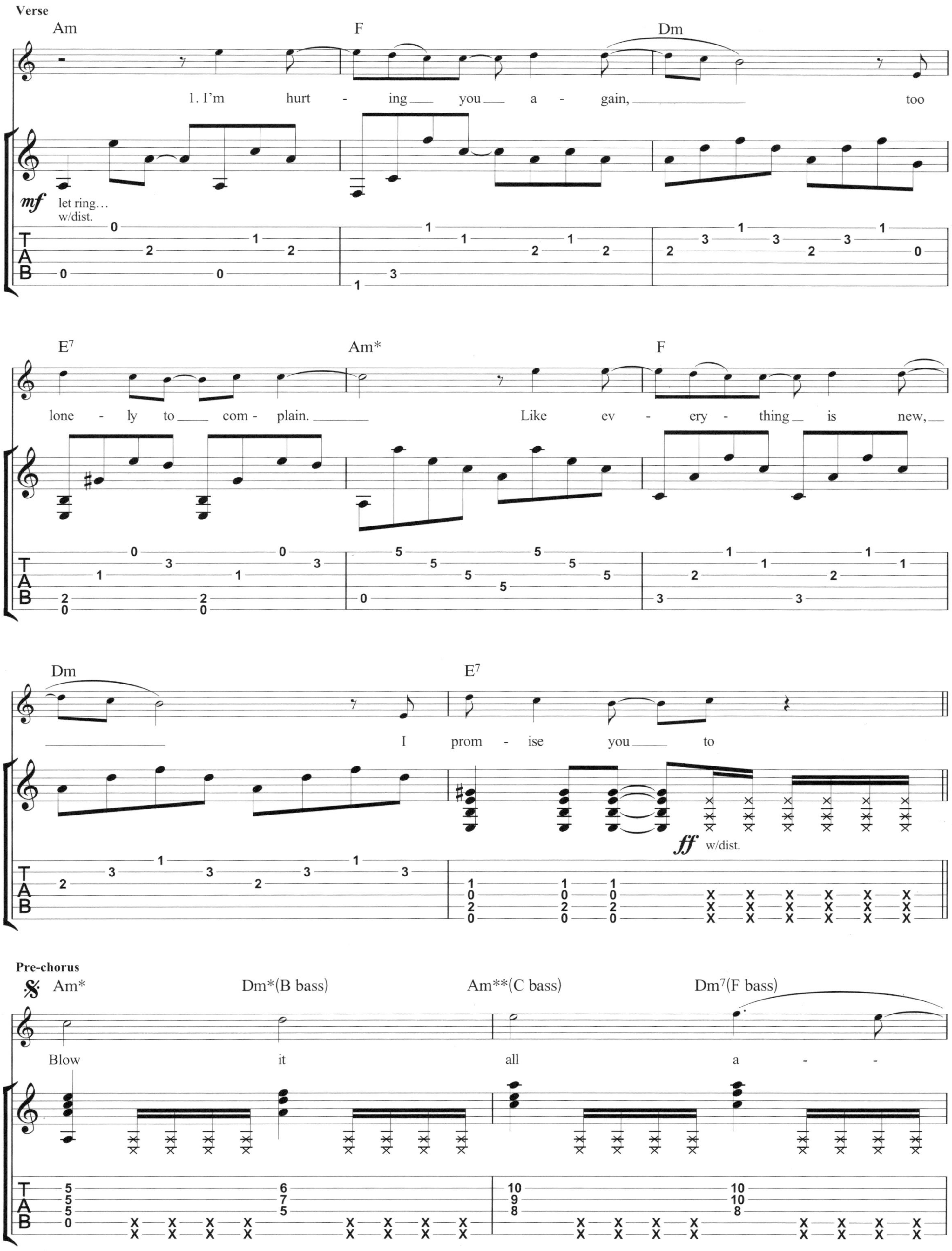
Verse
Am
F
Dm
1. I'm hurt - ing you a - gain, too
mf
let ring…
w/dist.
E7
Am*
F
lone - ly to com - plain. Like ev - ery - thing is new,
Dm
E7
I promise you to
ff w/dist.
Pre-chorus
Am*
Dm*(B bass)
Am**(C bass)
Dm7(F bass)
Blow it all a -

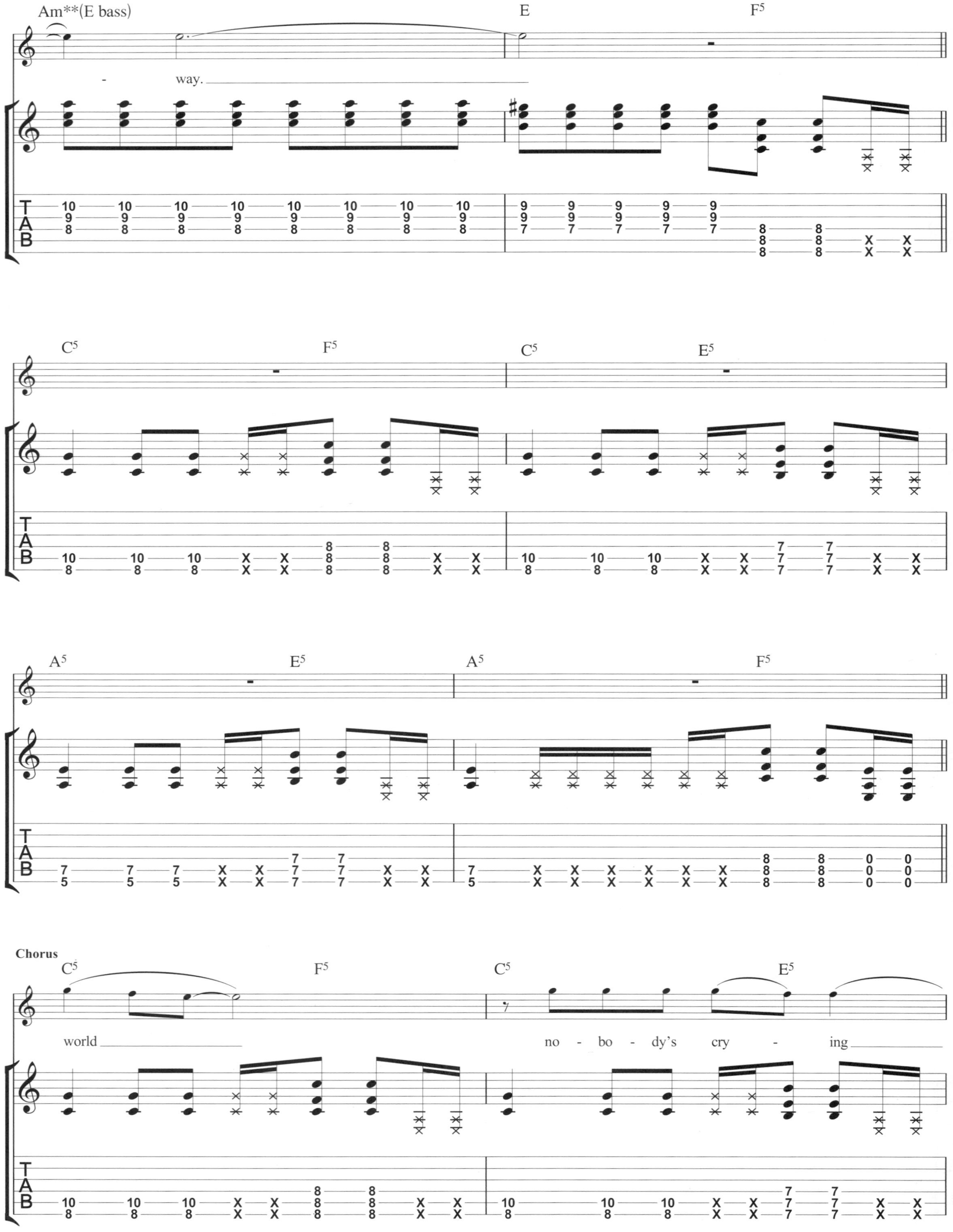
Am**(E bass)
E
F5
- way.
C5
F5
C5
E5
A5
E5
A5
F5
Chorus
C5
F5
C5
E5
world
no - bo - dy's cry - ing

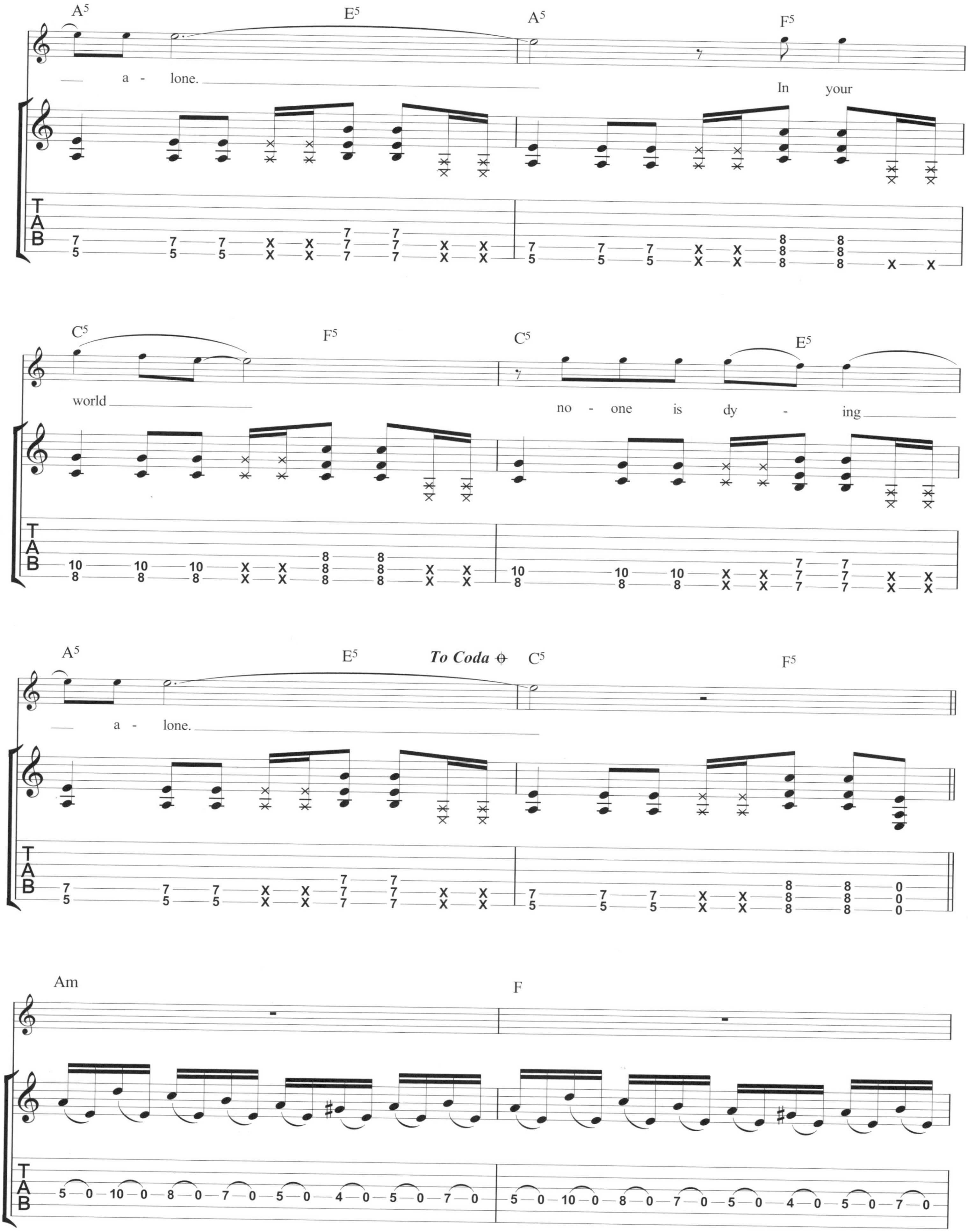
A5 E5 A5 F5
a - lone. In your
C5 F5 C5 E5
world no - one is dy - ing
A5 E5 To Coda C5 F5
a - lone.
Am F

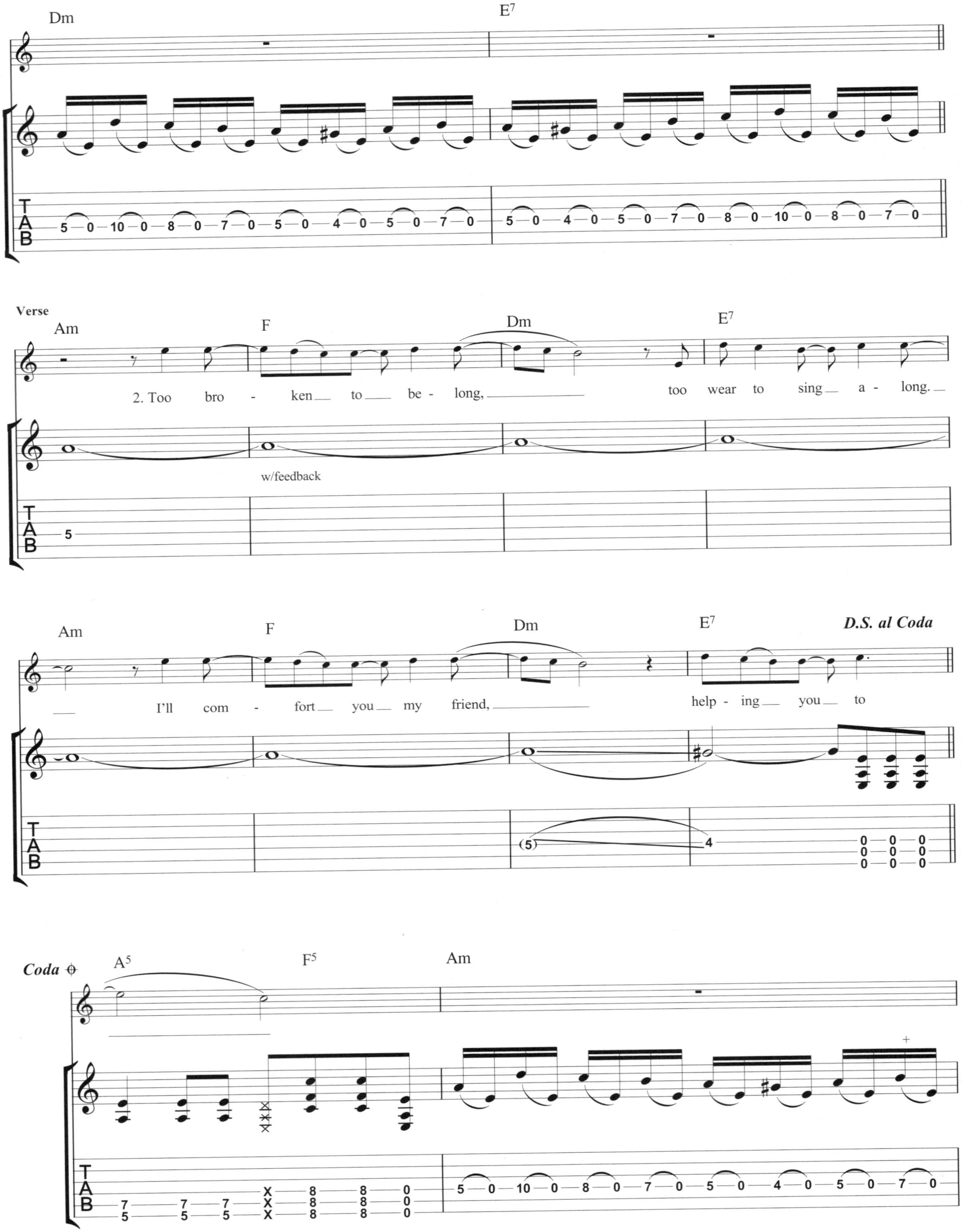
Dm
E7
Verse
Am
F
Dm
E7
2. Too bro - ken to be - long, too wear to sing a - long.
w/feedback
Am
F
Dm
E7
D.S. al Coda
I'll com - fort you my friend, help - ing you to
Coda
A5
F5
Am

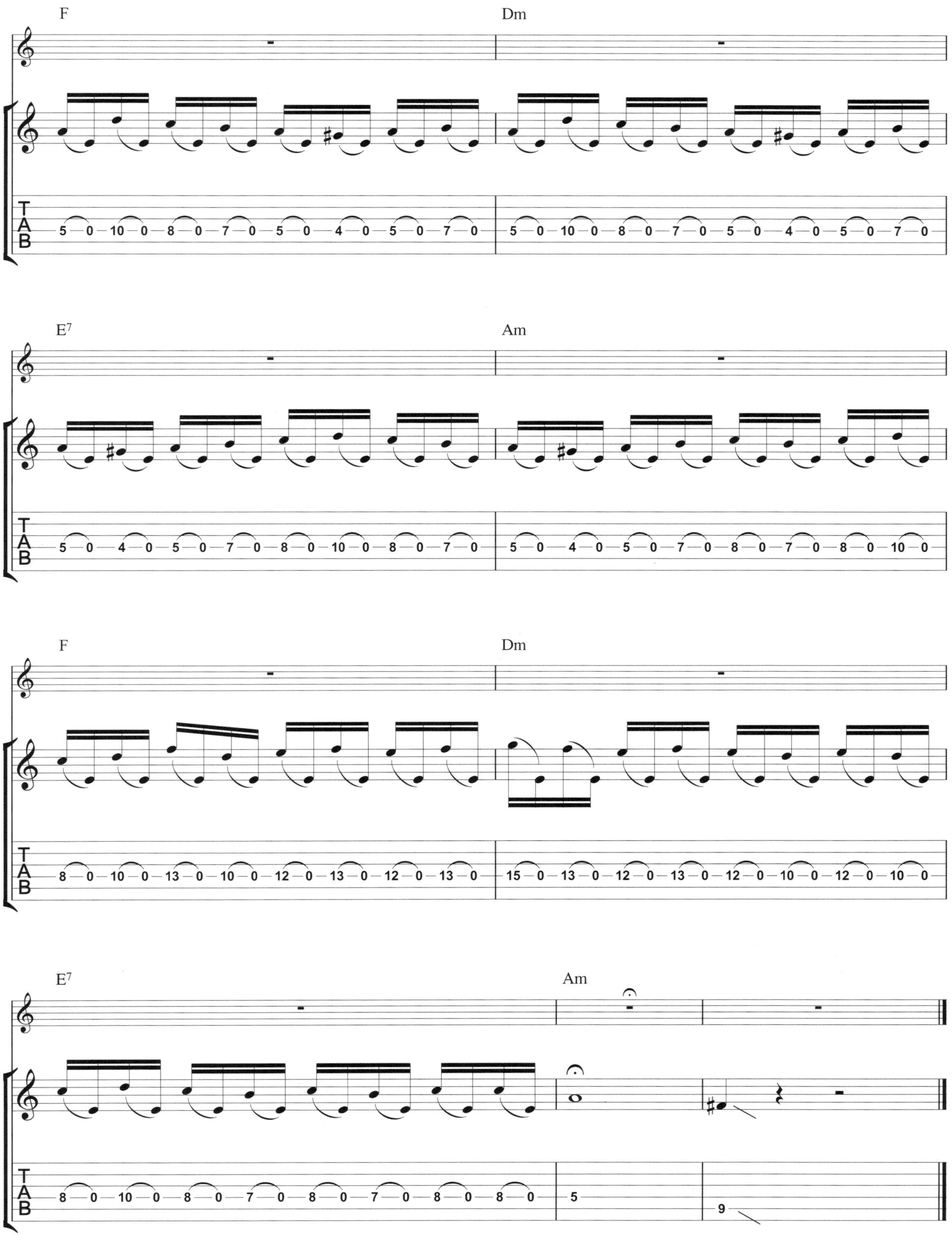
F
Dm
E7
Am
F
Dm
E7
Am

JUST A DAY

WORDS & MUSIC BY GRANT NICHOLAS

E5
A5
in my clothes a - gain, feel - ing head ex - plode from a night of gin.
with the freaks and frowns look - in' at the world through sil - ver clouds.
E5
An - oth - er night out late.
But they all come down.
A5
E5
I don't wan - na drink, don't wan - na be a clown,
I got - ta rise a - bove the e - mo - tion - al flame,
A5
got - ta get my feet back on the ground,
got - ta cut these ropes a - round my hands,

E5
C♯m
be - fore it pulls me in.
pull my - self around.
E5
How come it end - ed up like this?
C♯m
G♯m
And who's gon - na catch me when I'm
A
Aadd9
Chorus
(E)
(Badd11)
go - in' down to hit the ground a - gain? All

(Aadd9)
(C♯m7)
by my - self
(Wak-ing up at three in my clothes a-gain.)
(Esus2)
(Badd11)
'Cause I don't wan-na drag you down, hold you down,
(Aadd9)
(E)
(Badd11)
'cause you're a friend. I blame my -
(Aadd9)
(C♯m7)
(F♯7sus4)
- self.
(Feel my head ex - plode from a night of gin.)
I guess you think it's
T
A
B

1.
A5
fun - ny now, fun - ny now.
1. cont.
E5
A5
Do do do do do do do do. Do do do do do do do do.
B
Full
1. cont.
E5
A5
Do do do do do do do do. Do do do do do.
B
Full
2.
A5
fun - ny now, fun - ny now.

B5 C♯5 G♯5 A5
N.C. C♯5 B5 G♯5 A5
1. N.C.
2. A5 G♯5 F♯5
Chorus
(E) (B add11) (A add9)
All by my - self
(C♯m7) (E sus2)
'cause I don't wan - na drag you down,
TAB

(B add11) (Aadd9) (E)
drag you down, 'cause you're a friend. I
(B add11) (Aadd9)
blame my - self.
(C♯m7) (F♯7sus4) (A5)
I guess you think it's fun - ny now, fun - ny now.
(E) (B add11)
It's such a shame. All by my -
f

(Aadd9)
(C♯m7)
-self
'cause I don't wan - na
(Esus2)
(Badd11)
(Aadd9)
drag you down,
drag you down,
'cause you're a
(E)
(Badd11)
(Aadd9)
friend. I blame my - self.
(C♯m7)
1.
(F♯7sus4)
A5
I guess you think it's fun - ny now, fun -

1. cont.
2.
A5
- ny now. It's such a shame. fun - ny now, fun -
- ny now. Do do do do. Do do do do.
Do do do do. Do do do do. Do do do do.
Do do do do. Do do do do.

LITTLE BY LITTLE

WORDS & MUSIC BY NOEL GALLAGHER

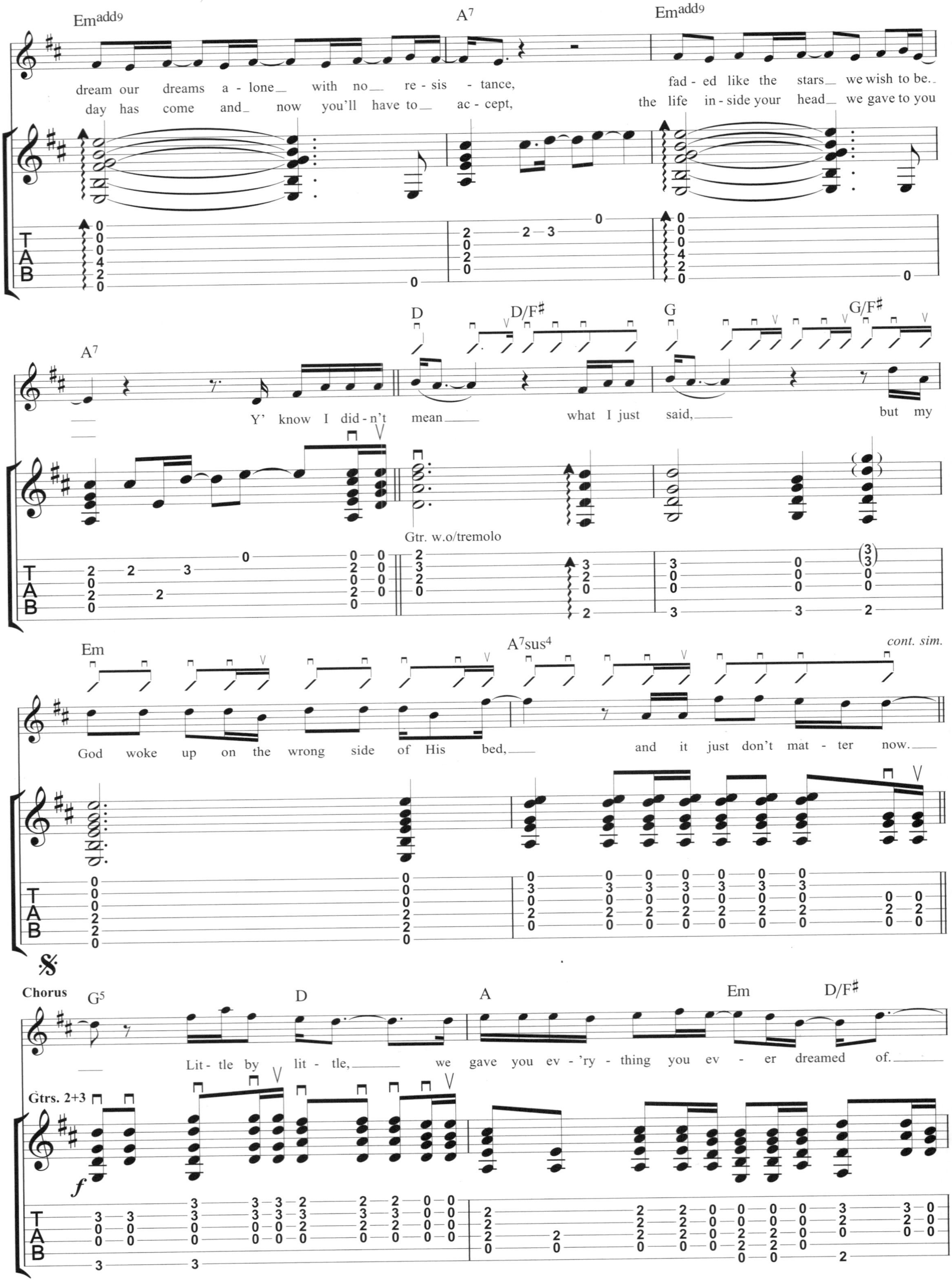
Emadd9
A7
Emadd9
dream our dreams a - lone with no re - sis - tance,
fad - ed like the stars we wish to be.
day has come and now you'll have to ac - cept,
the life in - side your head we gave to you
A7
D
D/F#
G
G/F#
Y' know I did - n't mean what I just said, but my
Gtr. w.o/tremolo
Em
A7sus4
cont. sim.
God woke up on the wrong side of His bed, and it just don't mat - ter now.
Chorus
G5
D
A
Em
D/F#
Lit - tle by lit - tle, we gave you ev - 'ry - thing you ev - er dreamed of.
Gtrs. 2+3
f
TAB

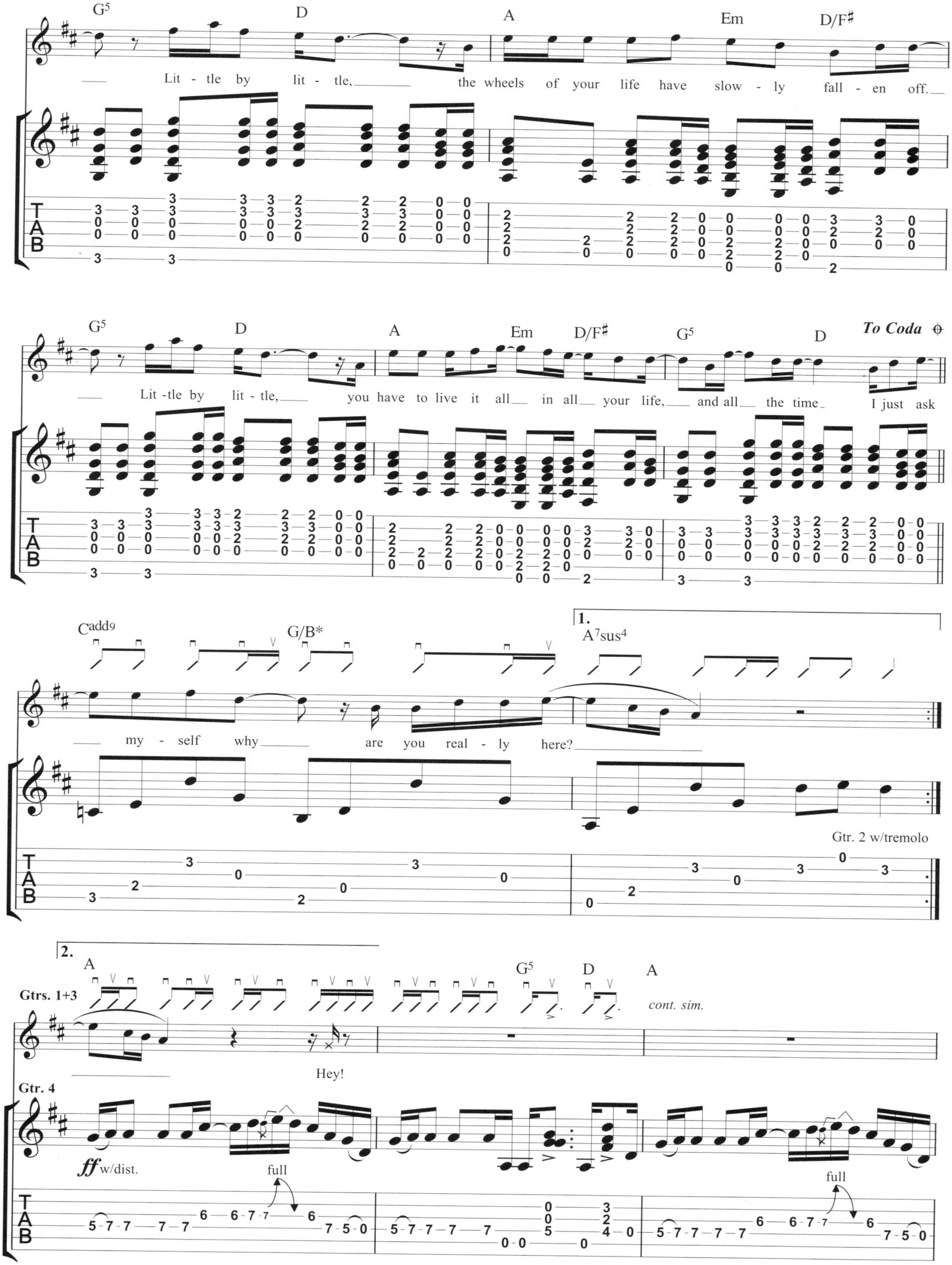
G5 D A Em D/F♯
Lit - tle by lit - tle, the wheels of your life have slow - ly fall - en off.
G5 D A Em D/F♯ G5 D
To Coda
Lit - tle by lit - tle, you have to live it all in all your life, and all the time I just ask
Cadd9 G/B* A7sus4
1.
my - self why are you real - ly here?
Gtr. 2 w/tremolo
2.
A G5 D A
Gtrs. 1+3
cont. sim.
Hey!
Gtr. 4
ff w/dist.
full
full

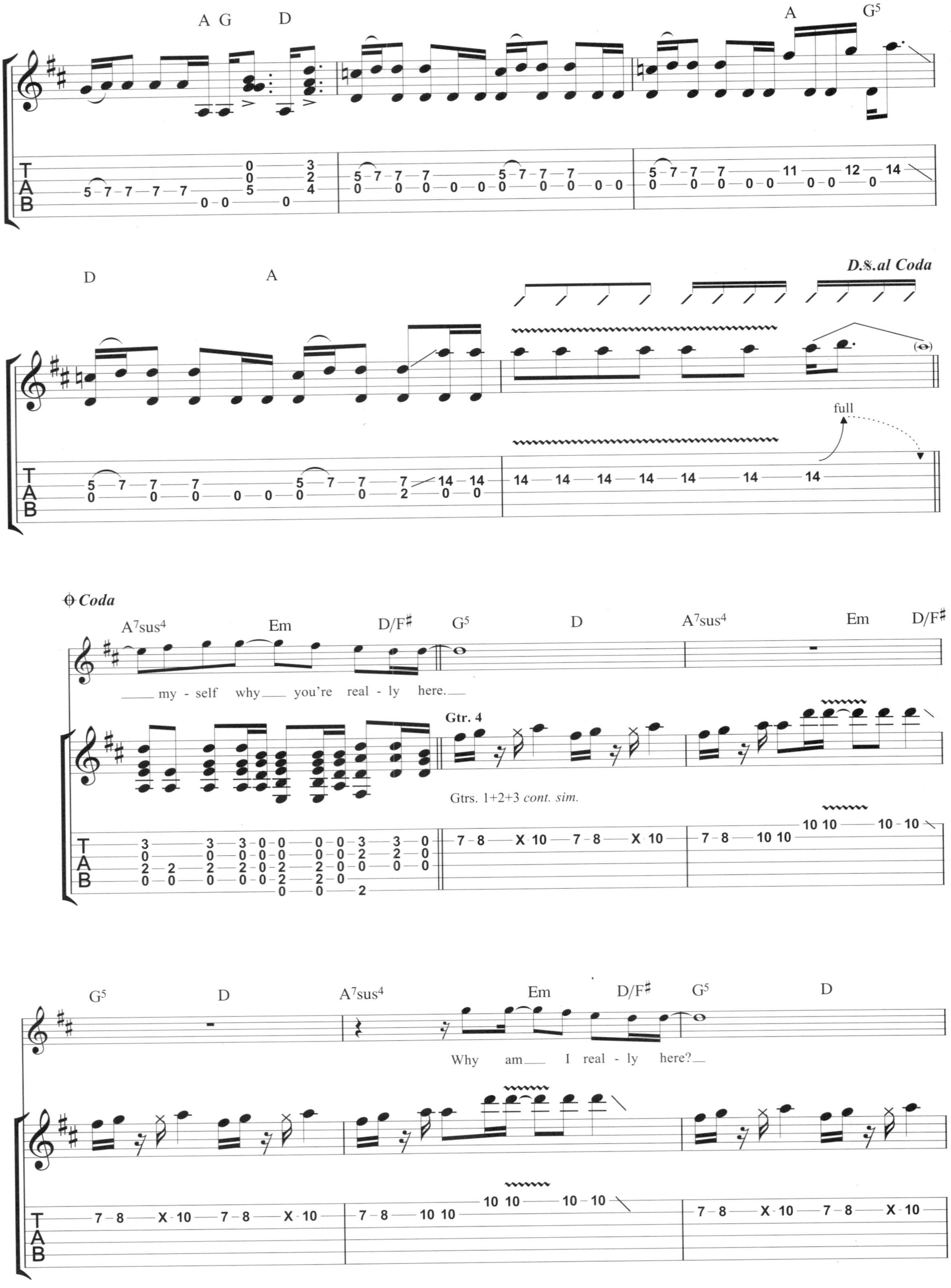
A G D
A G5
D A
D.𝄋.al Coda
full
Coda
A7sus4 Em D/F♯ G5 D A7sus4 Em D/F♯
my - self why you're real - ly here.
Gtr. 4
Gtrs. 1+2+3 cont. sim.
G5 D A7sus4 Em D/F♯ G5 D
Why am I real - ly here?

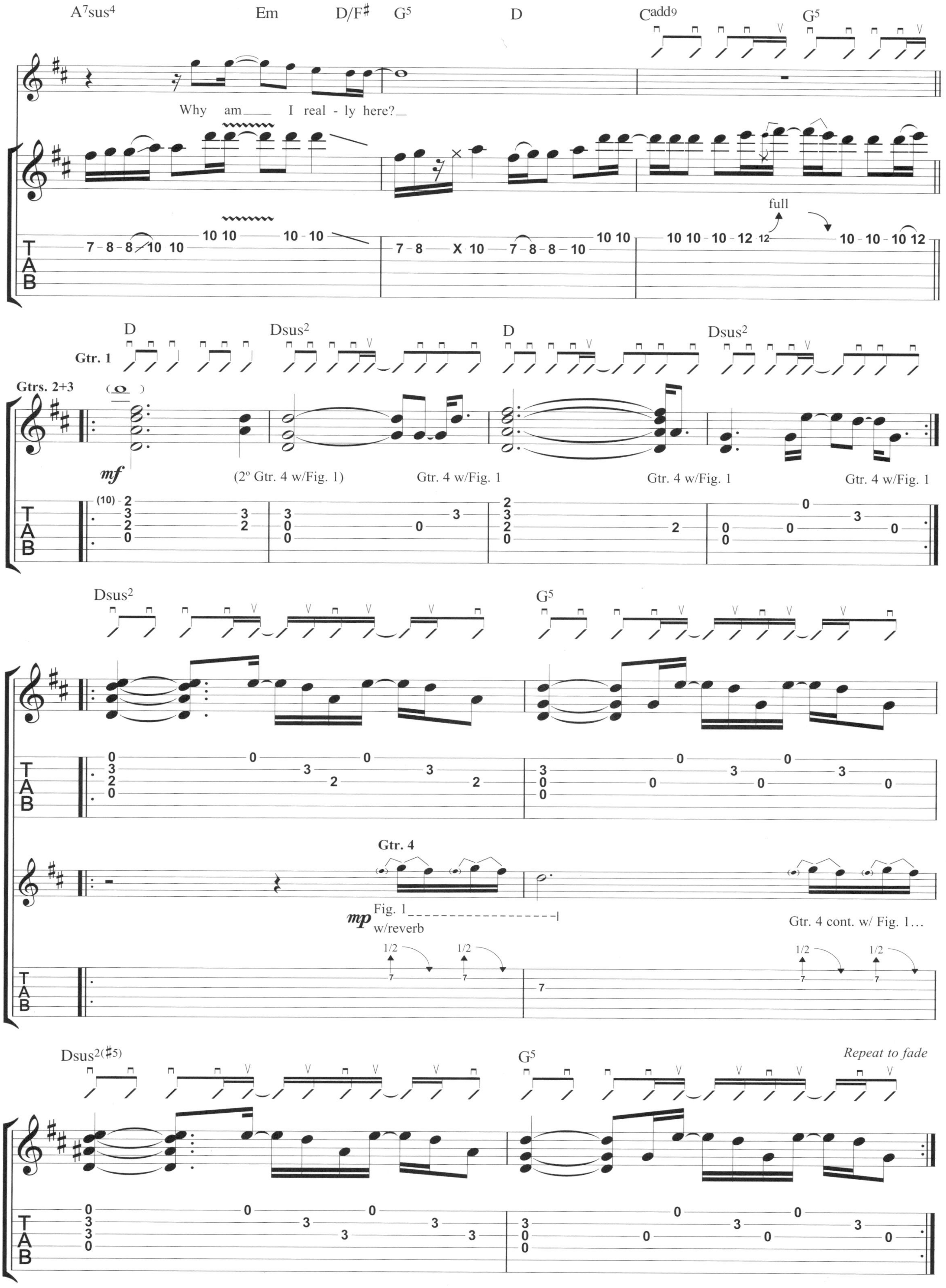
A7sus4 Em D/F♯ G5 D Cadd9 G5
Why am I real - ly here?
full
D Dsus2 D Dsus2
Gtr. 1
Gtrs. 2+3
mf
(2º Gtr. 4 w/Fig. 1)
Gtr. 4 w/Fig. 1
Gtr. 4 w/Fig. 1
Gtr. 4 w/Fig. 1
Dsus2 G5
Gtr. 4
mp
Fig. 1
w/reverb
Gtr. 4 cont. w/ Fig. 1…
Dsus2(♯5) G5
Repeat to fade

LEAFY MYSTERIES

WORDS & MUSIC BY PAUL WELLER

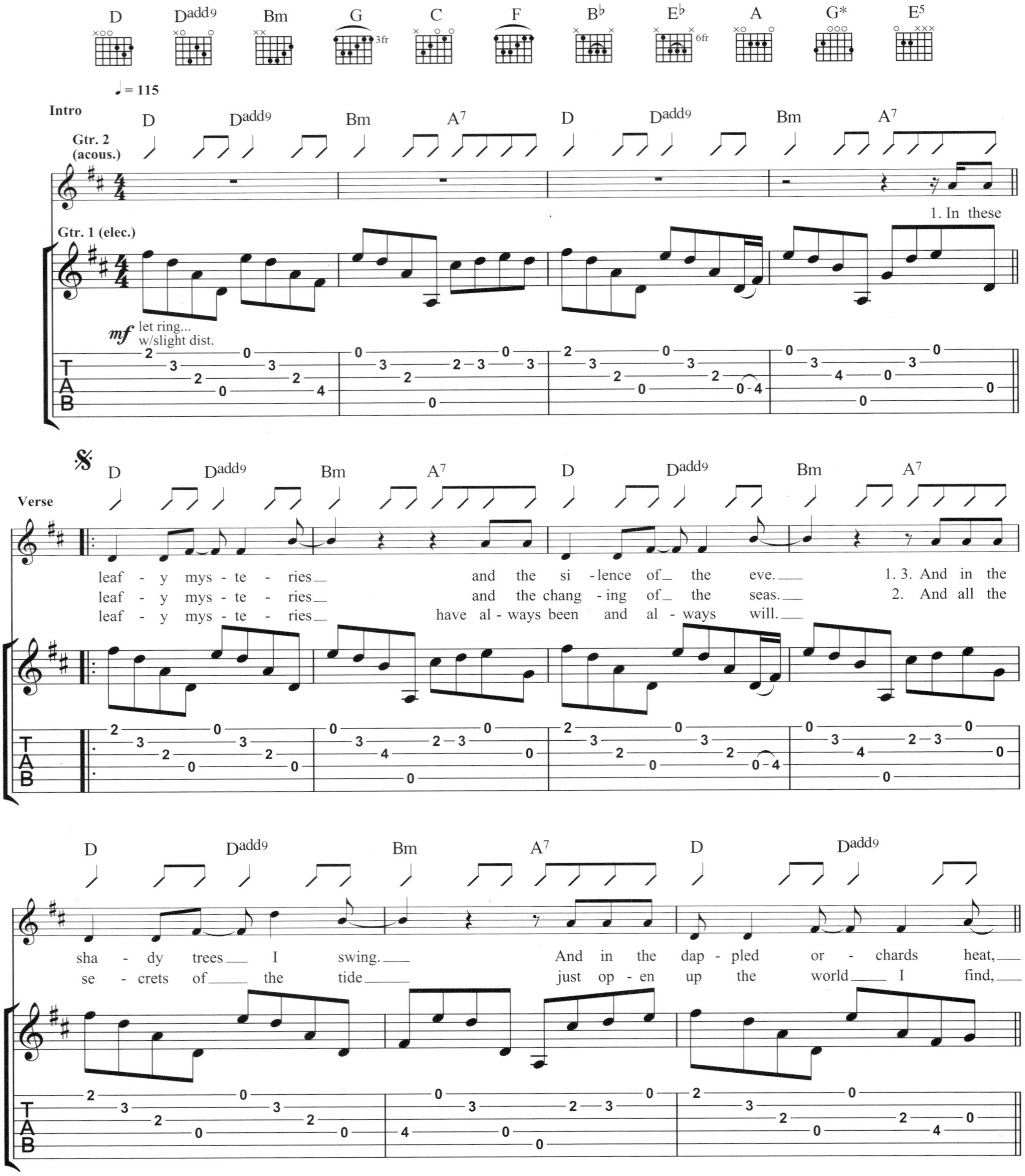

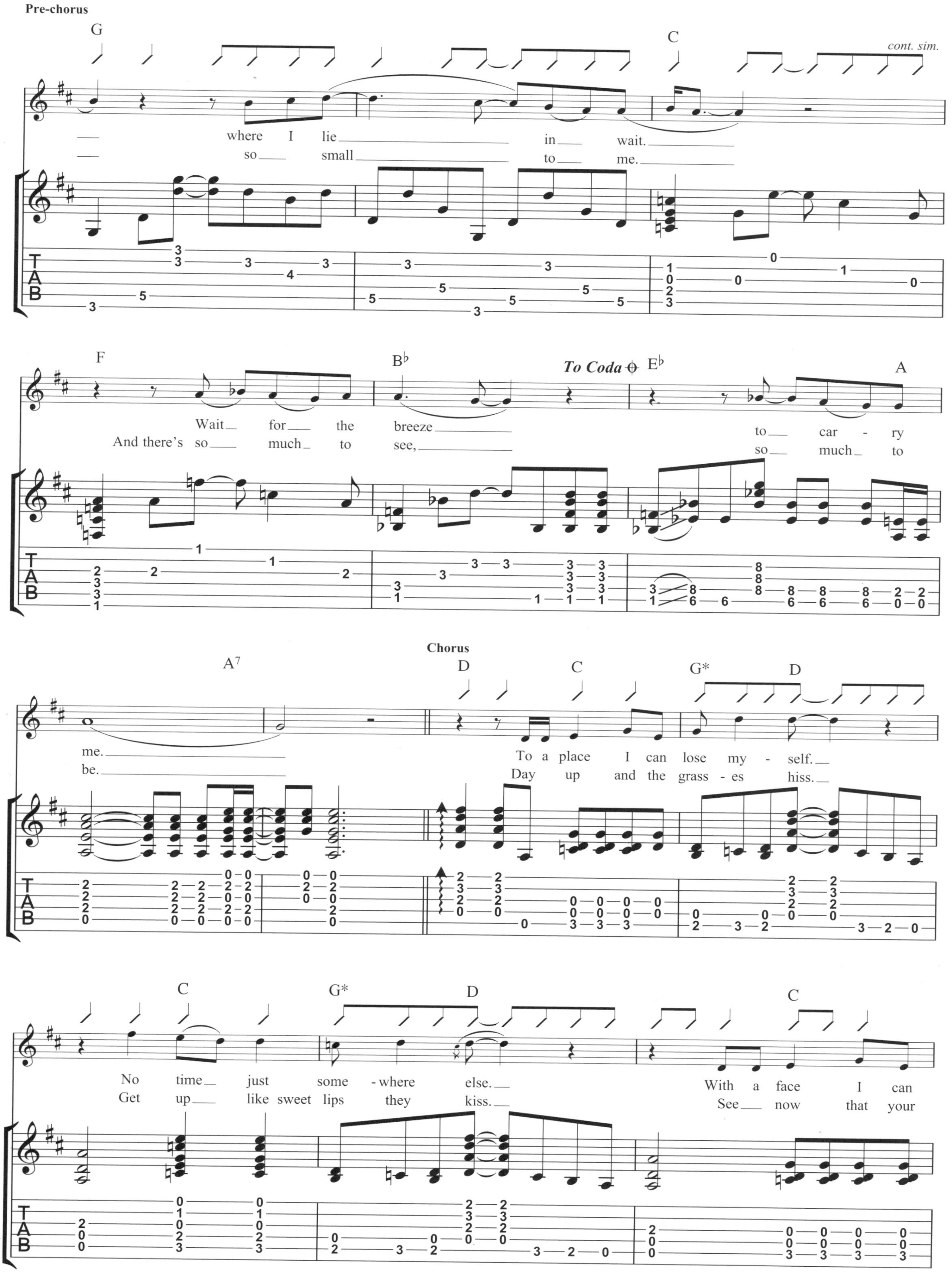
Pre-chorus
G
C
cont. sim.
where I lie in wait.
so small to me.
F
B♭
To Coda ⊕
E♭
A
Wait for the breeze to carry
And there's so much to see, so much to
A7
me.
be.
Chorus
D
C
G*
D
To a place I can lose myself.
Day up and the grasses hiss.
C
G*
D
C
No time just somewhere else.
Get up like sweet lips they kiss.
With a face I can
See now that your

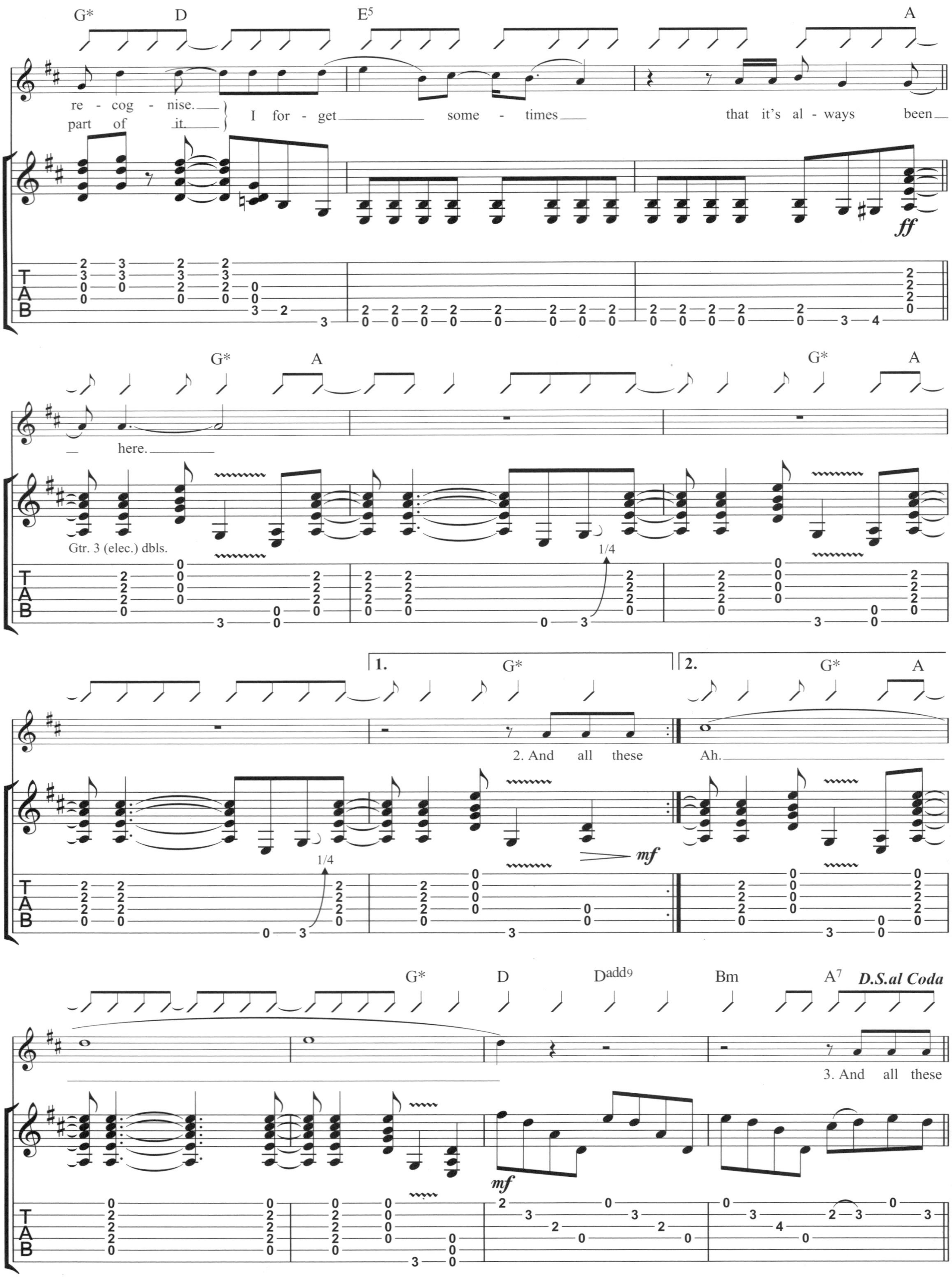
G* D E5 A
re - cog - nise.
part of it.
I for - get some - times that it's al - ways been
here.
Gtr. 3 (elec.) dbls.
G* A
1/4
1. G*
2. G* A
2. And all these
Ah.
mf
ff
G* D Dadd9 Bm A7 D.S.al Coda
3. And all these
T
A
B

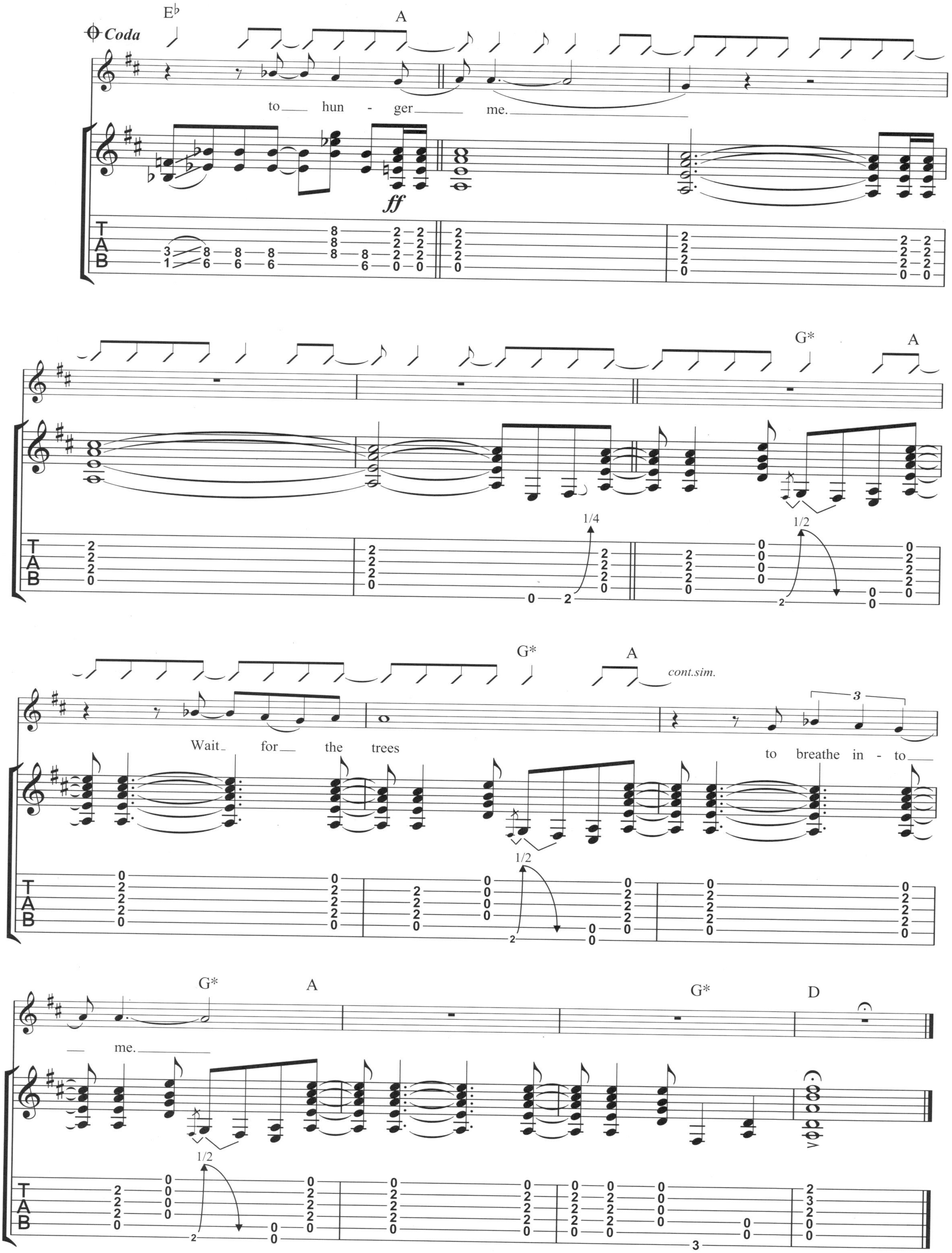
Coda
E♭
A
to hun - ger me.
ff
G*
A
cont.sim.
Wait for the trees
to breathe in - to
me.
G*
A
G*
D

LOST CAUSE

WORDS & MUSIC BY BECK HANSEN

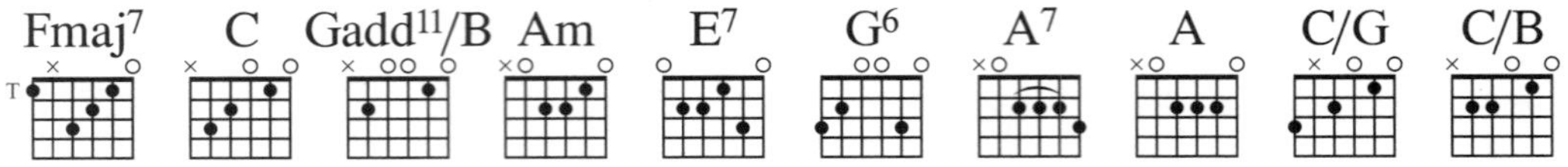

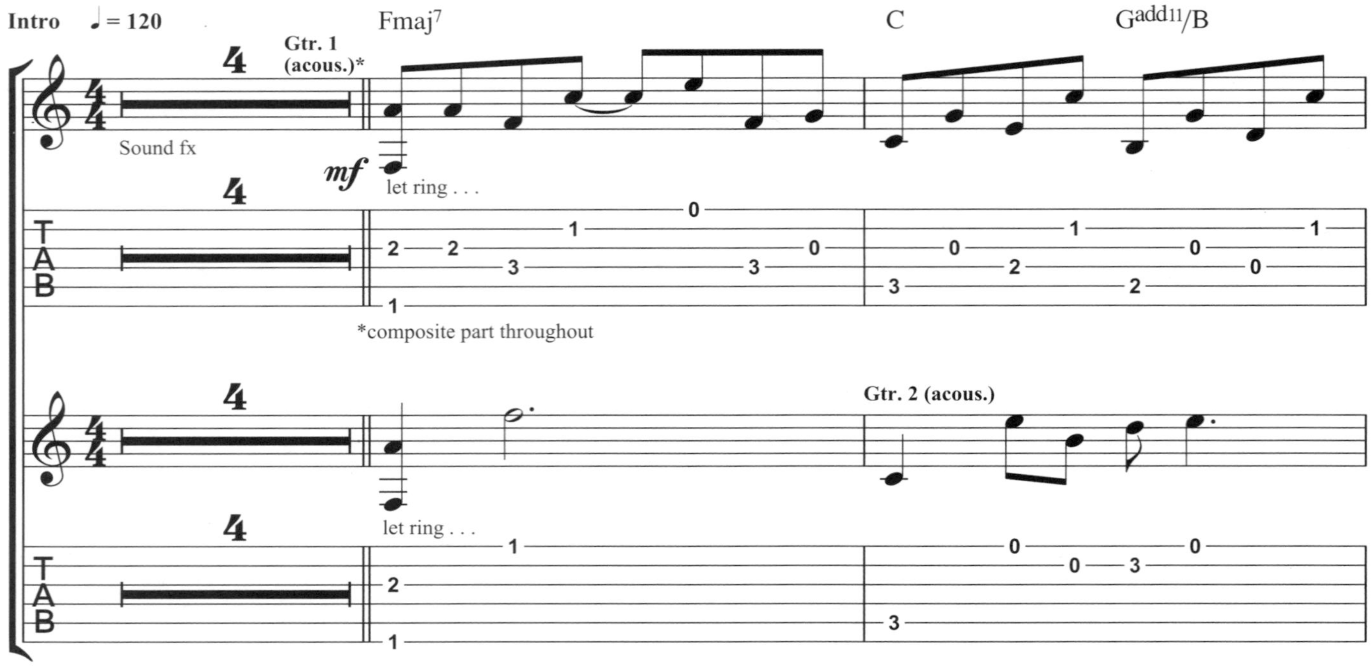

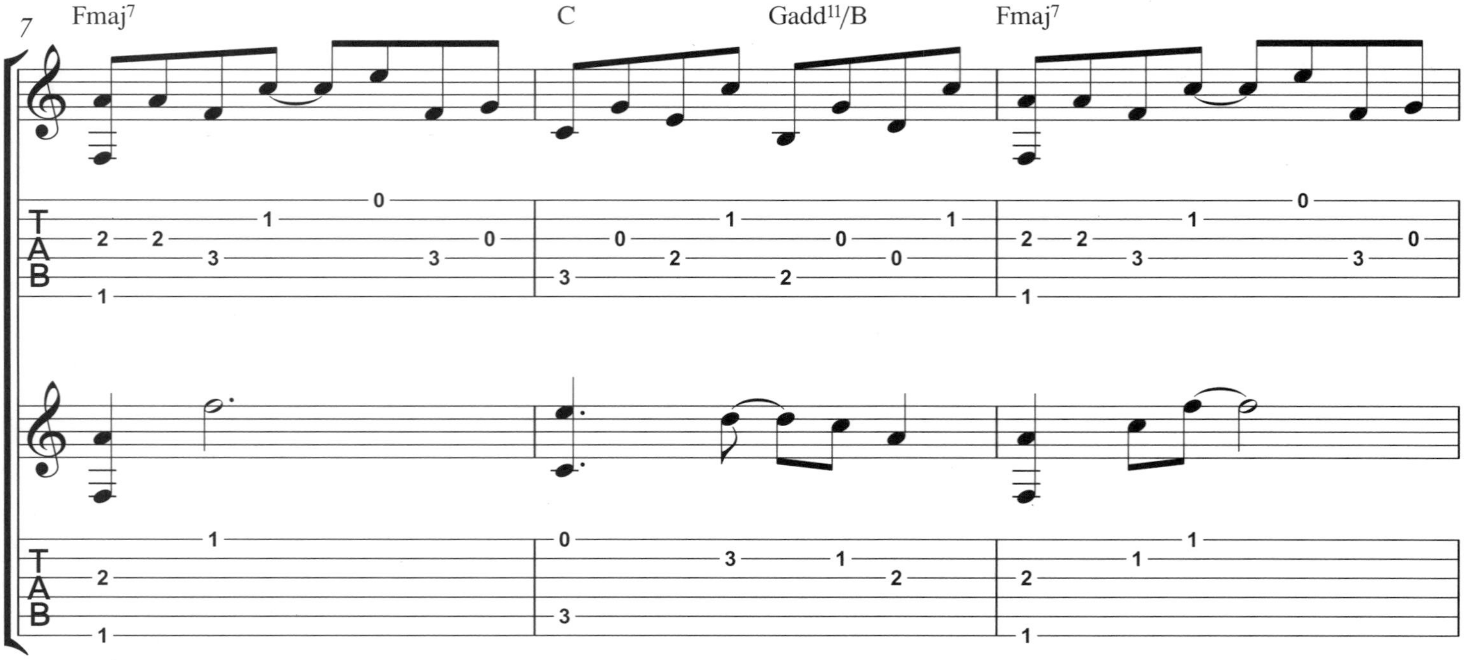

10
C
Gadd11/B
Fmaj7
C
Gadd11/B
TAB
Verse
13
Fmaj7
C
Gadd11/B
Fmaj7
1. They're sor - ry eyes, that cut through bone.
2. There's too ma - ny peo - ple, you used to know.
Fig. 1 . . .
Gtr. 2 w/sim. ad lib fills throughout
16
C
Gadd11/B
Fmaj7
C
Gadd11/B
That make it hard,
They see you com - ing,

19 Am E7 Fmaj7
to leave you a - lone. Leave you
they see you go. They know your
Gtr. 3
. . . end Fig. 1
22 C Gadd11/B Fmaj7 C Gadd11/B
here wear - ing your robes.
sec - rets, and you know theirs.
25 Fmaj7 C Gadd11/B Am E7
Wav - ing your guns, at some bo - dy new.
This town is cra - zy, no - bo - dy cares.
Chorus
29 Fmaj7 G6 Fmaj7
Ba - by you're a lost, ba - by you're a
TAB

32
G6
Fmaj7
G6
lost,
ba - by you're a lost
35
C
1.
2.
A7
cause.
38
Fmaj7
G6
Fmaj7
I'm tir - ed of fight - ing,
I'm tir - ed of fight-
41
G6
Fmaj7
G6
- ing.
Fight - ing for a lost

44
C
Middle
A
cause.
There's a place
47
Fmaj7
C
C/G
C
A
where you are going.
You ain't
51
Fmaj7
C
C/B
nev - er been be - fore.
54
A
Fmaj7
C
C
(G/B)
There's no - one laugh - ing at your back now.

58 Fmaj7 C
no one's standing at your door.
62 Fmaj7 C
Is that what you thought love was for?
65 Chorus Fmaj7 G6
Baby you're a lost,
68 Fmaj7 G6 Fmaj7
baby you're a lost,

71 G6 C A7
ba - by you're a lost cause.
74 Fmaj7 G6 Fmaj7
I'm tir - ed of fight - ing, I'm tir - ed of fight-
77 G6 Fmaj7 G6
- ing. Fight - ing for a lost
80 C
cause.

THE MIDDLE

WORDS & MUSIC BY JAMES ADKINS, THOMAS LINTON, RICHARD BURCH & ZACHARY LIND

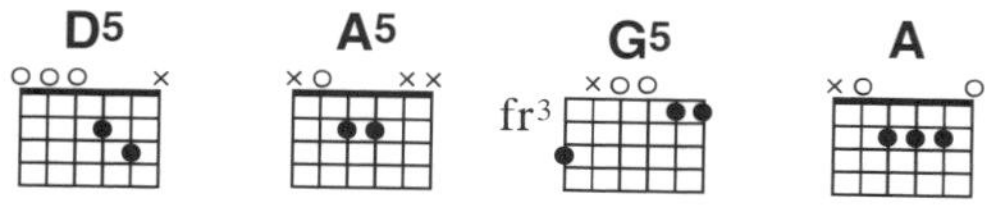

Drop D tuning

⑥ = D ③ = G

⑤ = A ② = B

④ = D ① = E

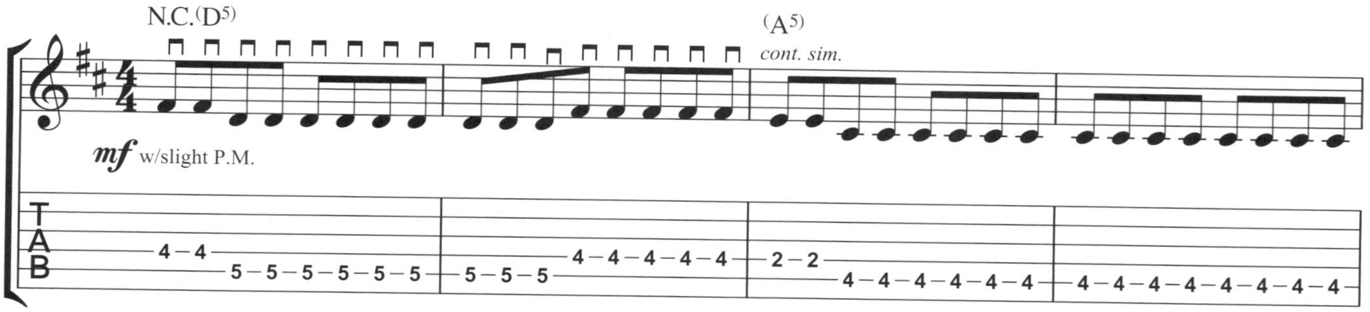

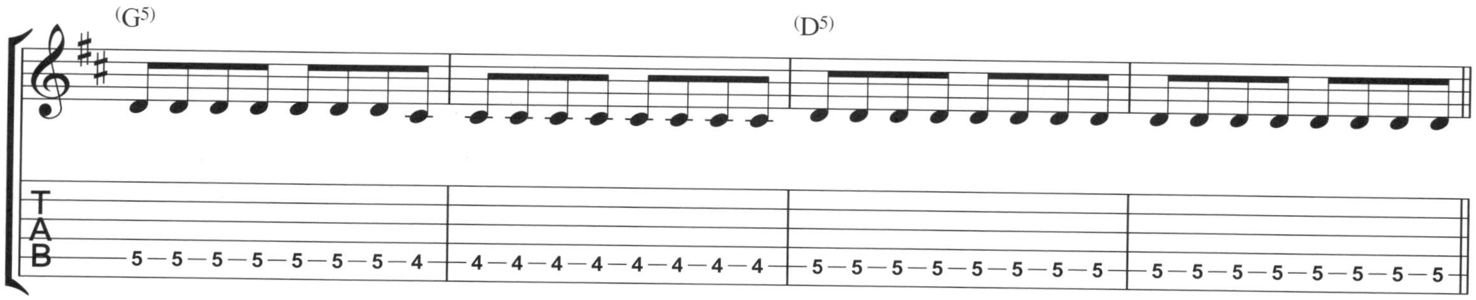

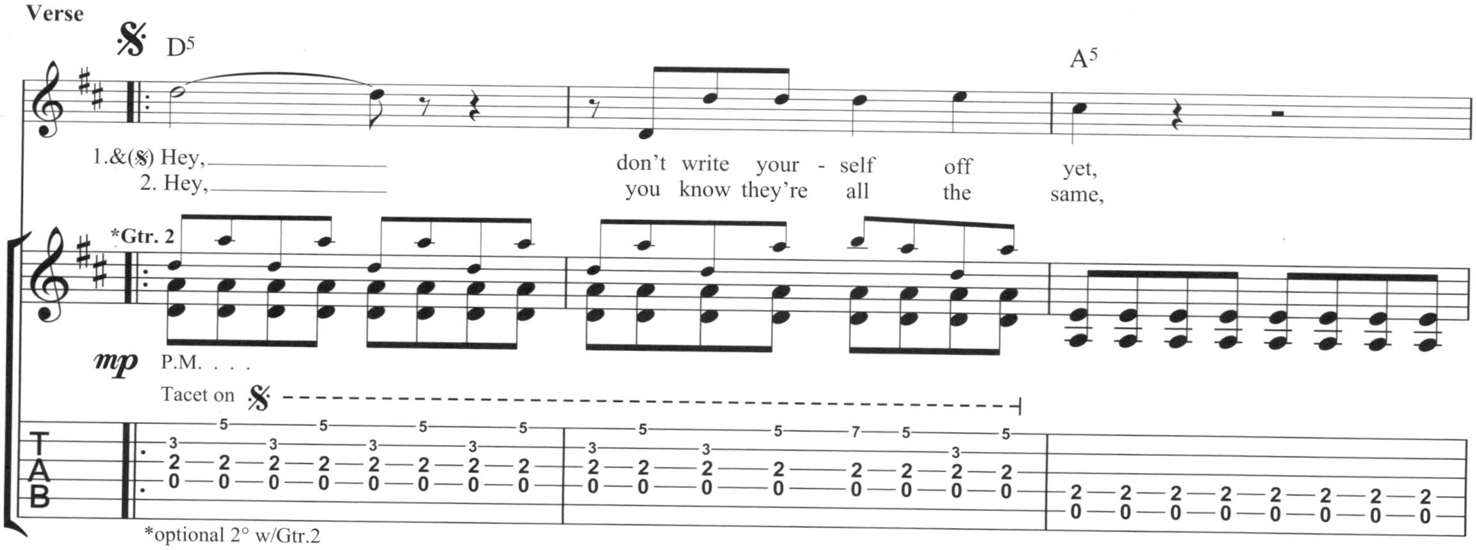

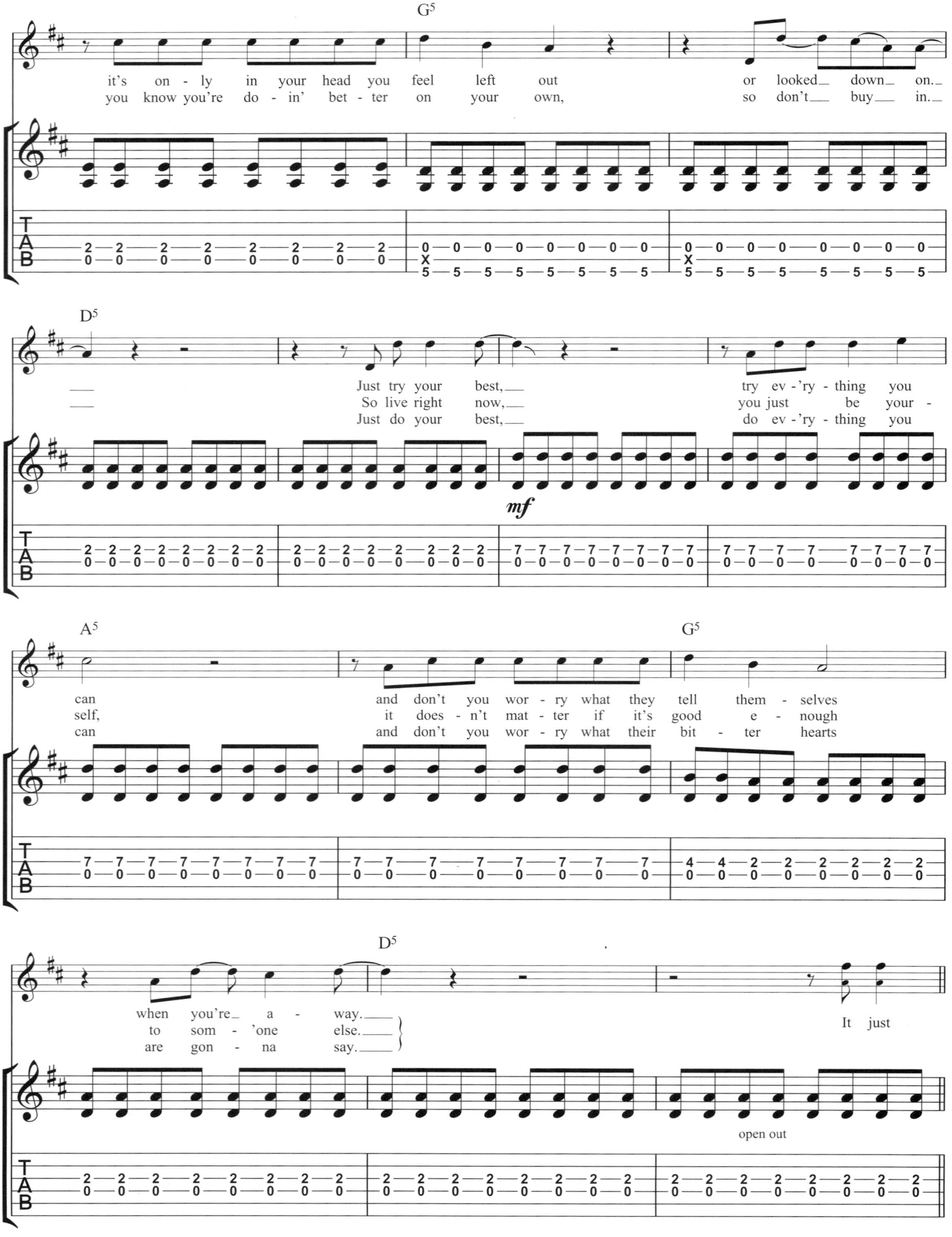
G5
it's on - ly in your head you feel left out or looked_ down_ on._
you know you're do - in' bet - ter on your own, so don't_ buy_ in._
D5
Just try your best,_ try ev - 'ry - thing you
So live right now,_ you just be your -
Just do your best,_ do ev - 'ry - thing you
mf
A5
G5
can and don't you wor - ry what they tell them - selves
self, it does - n't mat - ter if it's good e - nough
can and don't you wor - ry what their bit - ter hearts
D5
when you're a - way._
to som - 'one else._
are gon - na say._
It just
open out

Chorus
D5
A
takes some time lit - tle girl, you're in the mid - dle of the ride ev -
cont. sim.
let ring . . .
G5
- 'ry - thing, ev - 'ry - thing 'll be just fine, ev - 'ry - thing, ev - 'ry - thing 'll
let ring . . .
D
1.
2. & 𝄋
To Coda
be al - right, al - right.
- right.
It just
let ring . . .
Chorus
D5
A
takes some time lit - tle girl, you're in the mid - dle of the ride, ev -
cont. sim.
let ring . . .

G5
- 'ry - thing, ev - 'ry - thing 'll be just fine, ev - 'ry - thing, ev - 'ry - thing 'll
let ring . . .
Solo
A
Gtr. 2
cont. sim.
D
be al - right, al - right.
let ring . . .
ff
D
A
D
G5

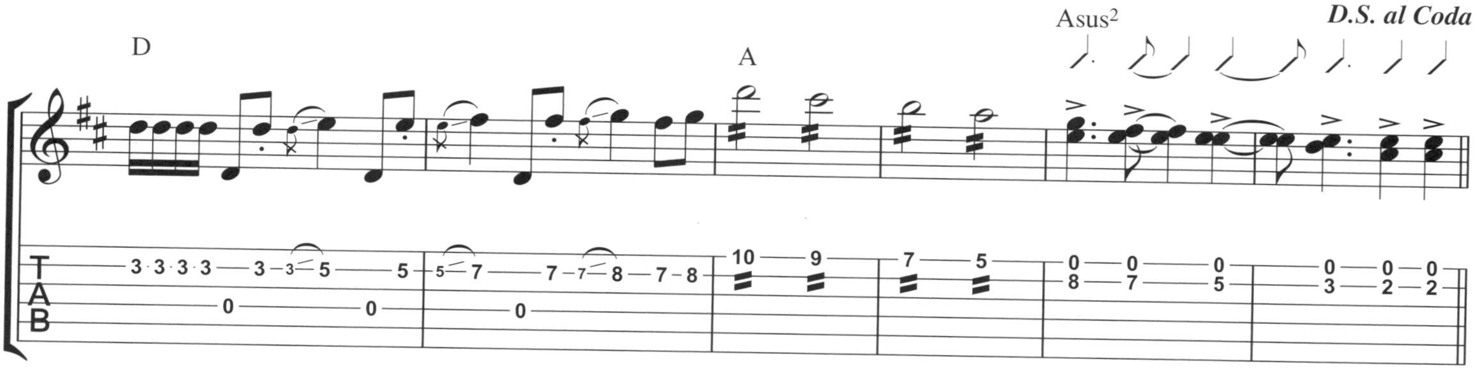

Coda

Outro chorus

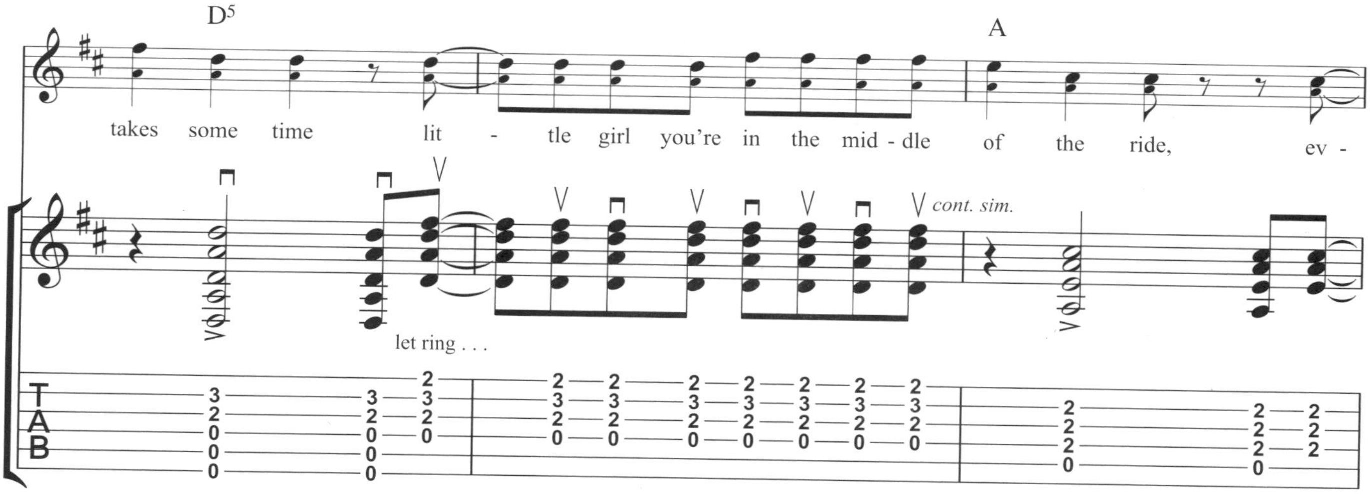

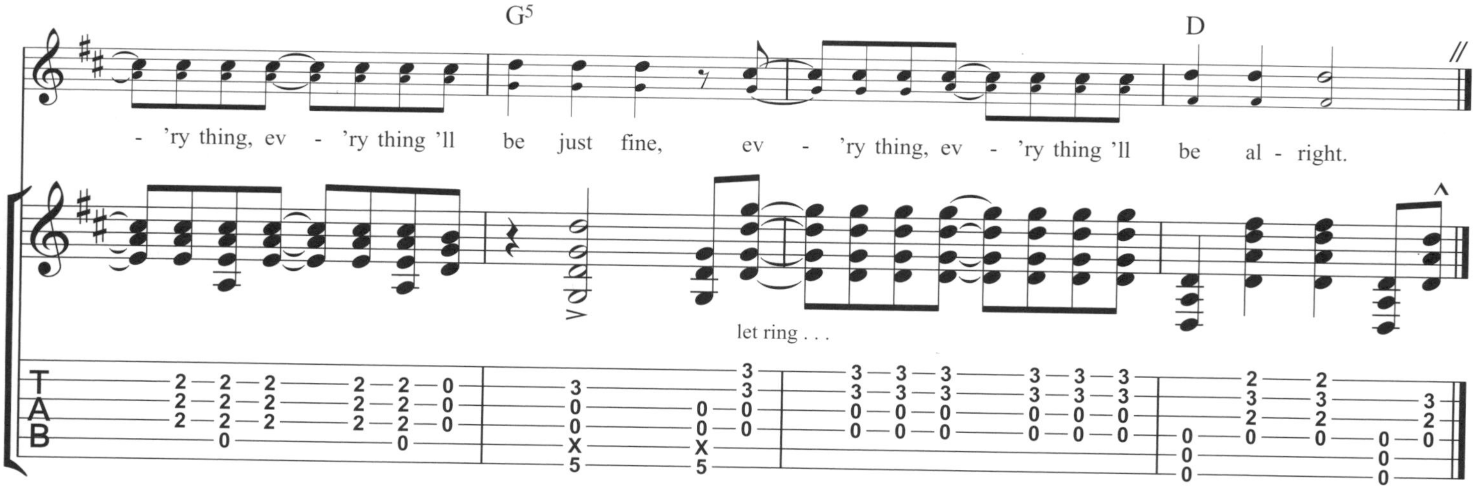

MUSCLE MUSEUM

LYRICS & MUSIC BY MATTHEW BELLAMY

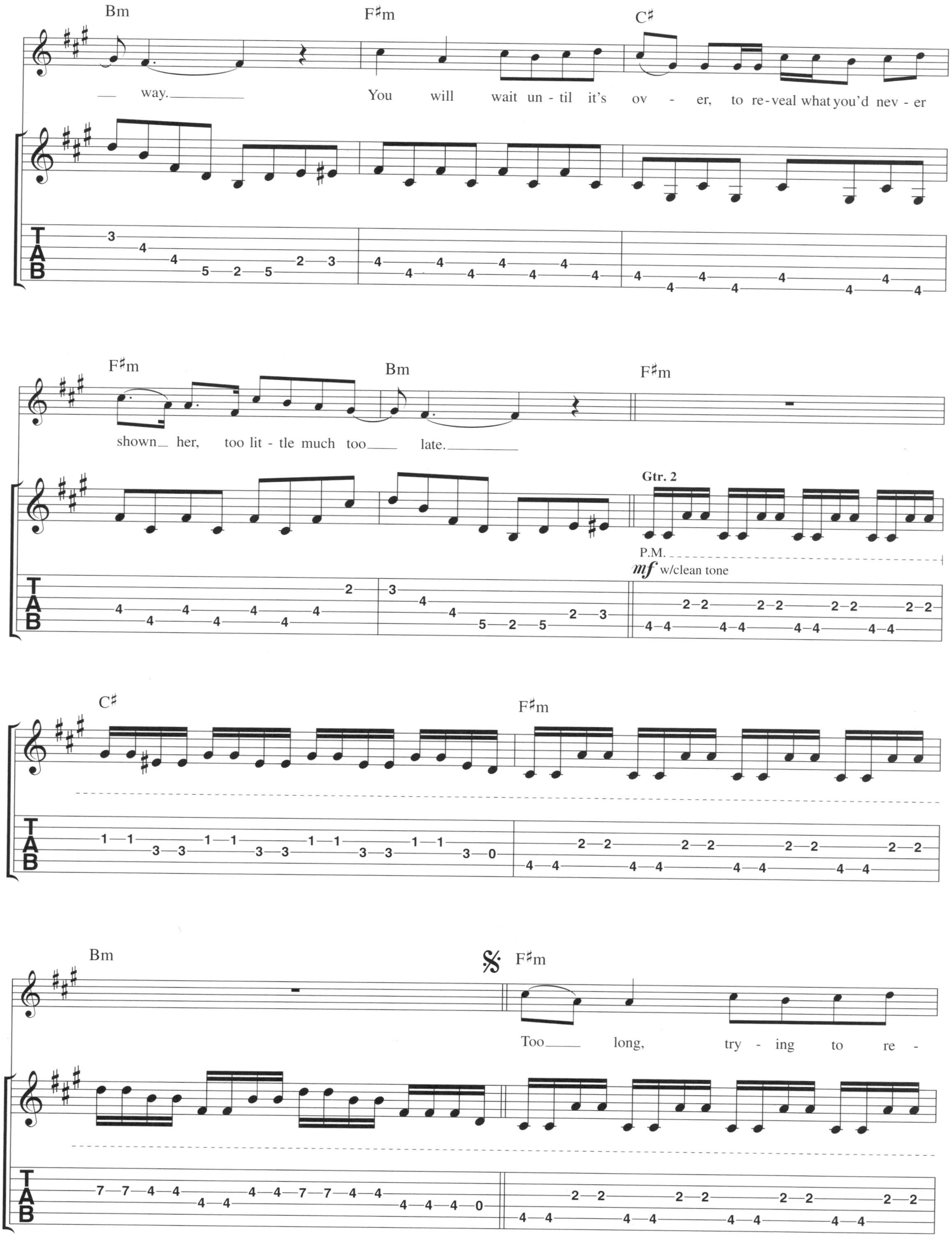
Bm
F♯m
C♯
— way.
You will wait un - til it's ov - er, to re - veal what you'd nev - er
F♯m
Bm
F♯m
shown her, too lit - tle much too late.
Gtr. 2
P.M.
mf w/clean tone
C♯
F♯m
Bm
F♯m
Too long, try - ing to re -

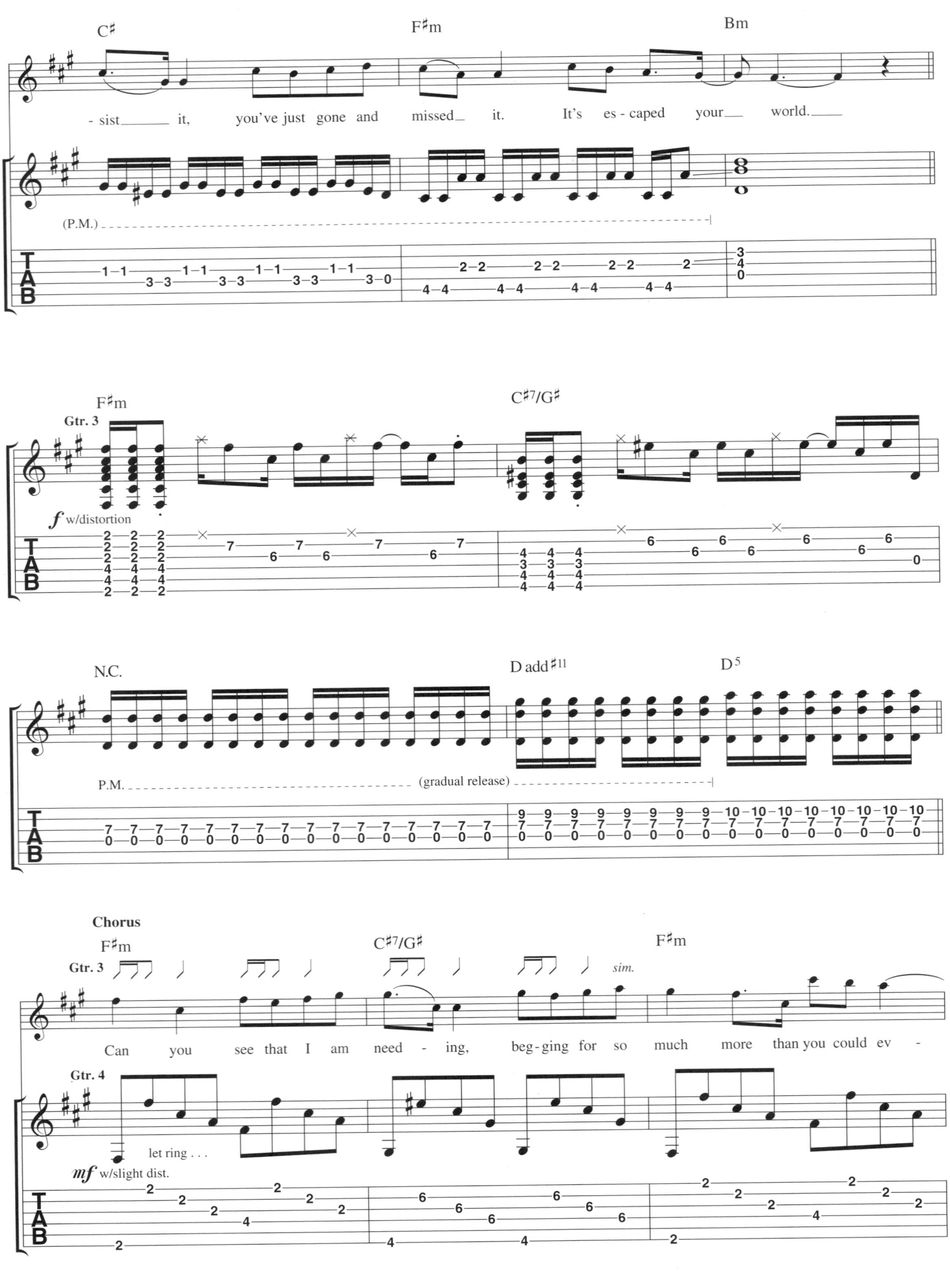
C♯
F♯m
Bm
- sist ___ it, you've just gone and missed _ it. It's es - caped your __ world. ___
(P.M.)
F♯m
Gtr. 3
f w/distortion
C♯7/G♯
N.C.
D add♯11
D5
P.M.
(gradual release)
Chorus
F♯m
Gtr. 3
C♯7/G♯
sim.
F♯m
Can you see that I am need - ing, beg-ging for so much more than you could ev -
Gtr. 4
let ring . . .
mf w/slight dist.

Bm
F♯m
C♯7/G♯
- er give. And I don't want you to a - dore me, don't want you to ig -
F♯m
Bm
E
To Coda
- nore me, when it pleas - es you. Yeah and I'll do
C♯/E♯
F♯m
Gtr. 3
it on my own.
Bass arr. for gtr.
F♯m
C♯
Gtr. 1
Gtr. 3 tacet

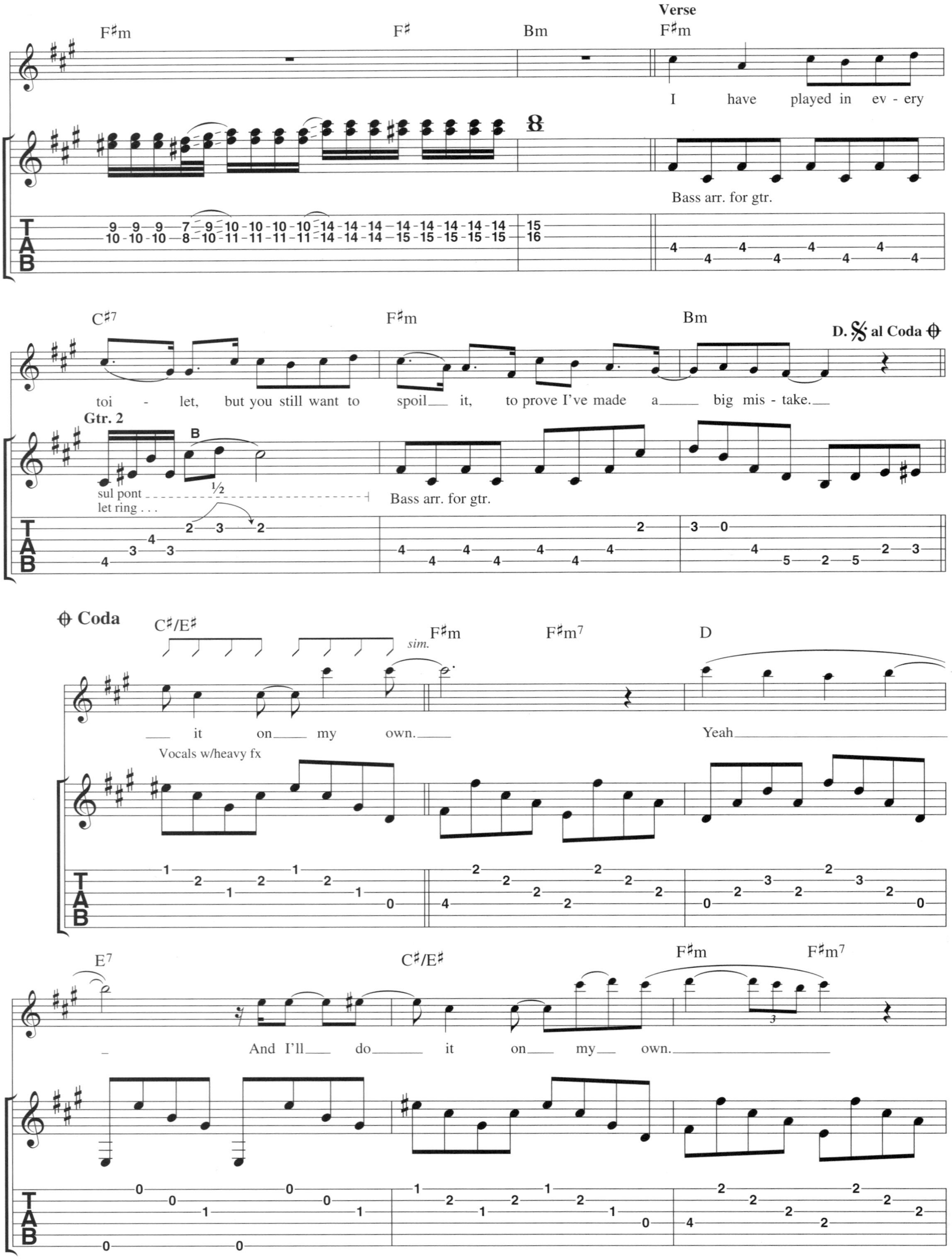
Verse
F♯m F♯ Bm F♯m
I have played in ev - ery
8
Bass arr. for gtr.
C♯7 F♯m Bm
D.S. al Coda
toi - let, but you still want to spoil it, to prove I've made a big mis - take.
Gtr. 2
B
sul pont
let ring . . .
Bass arr. for gtr.
Coda
C♯/E♯ sim. F♯m F♯m7 D
it on my own. Yeah
Vocals w/heavy fx
E7 C♯/E♯ F♯m F♯m7
And I'll do it on my own.

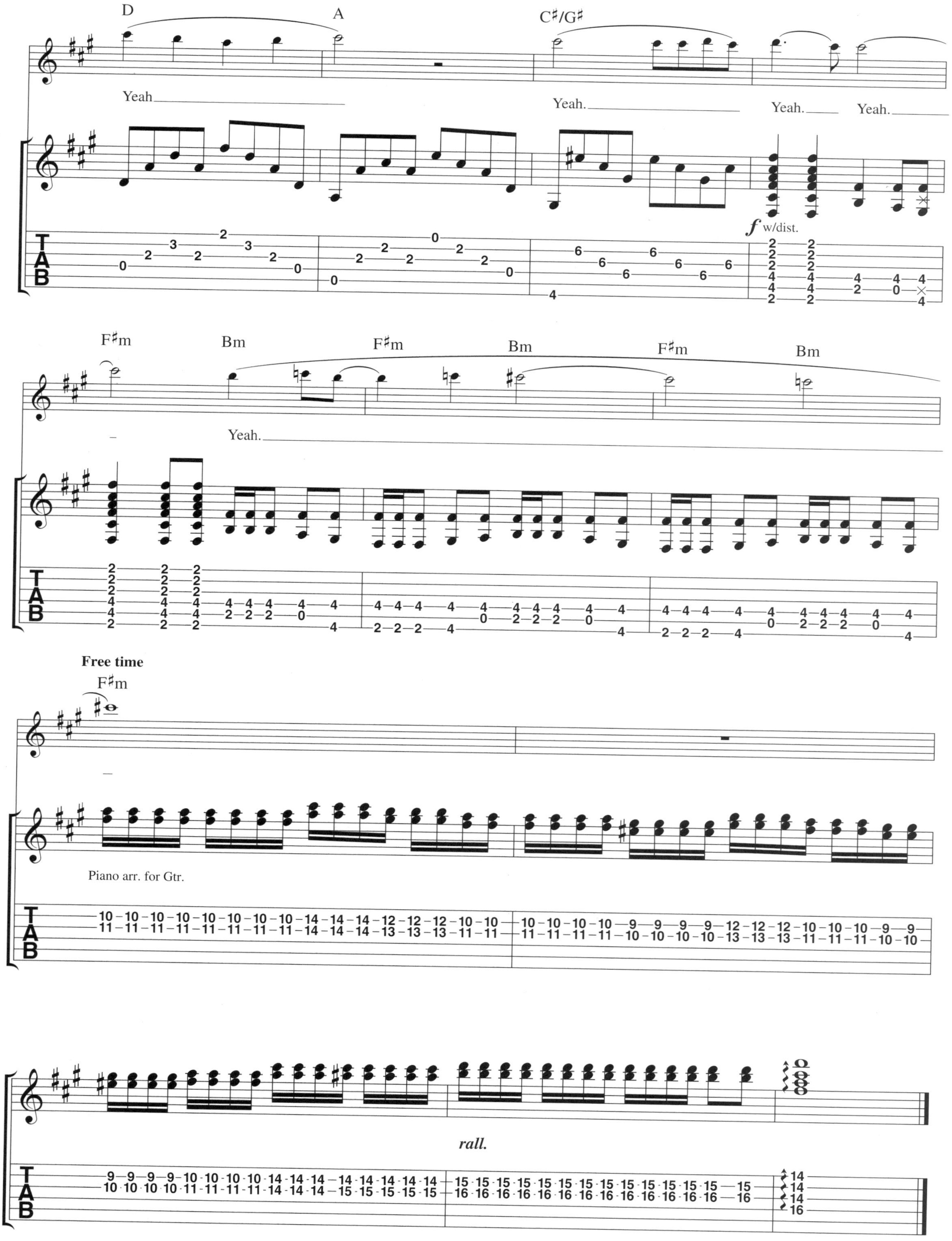
D
A
C♯/G♯
Yeah
Yeah.
Yeah.
Yeah.
f w/dist.
F♯m
Bm
F♯m
Bm
F♯m
Bm
Yeah.
Free time
F♯m
Piano arr. for Gtr.
rall.

NUCLEAR

WORDS & MUSIC BY RYAN ADAMS

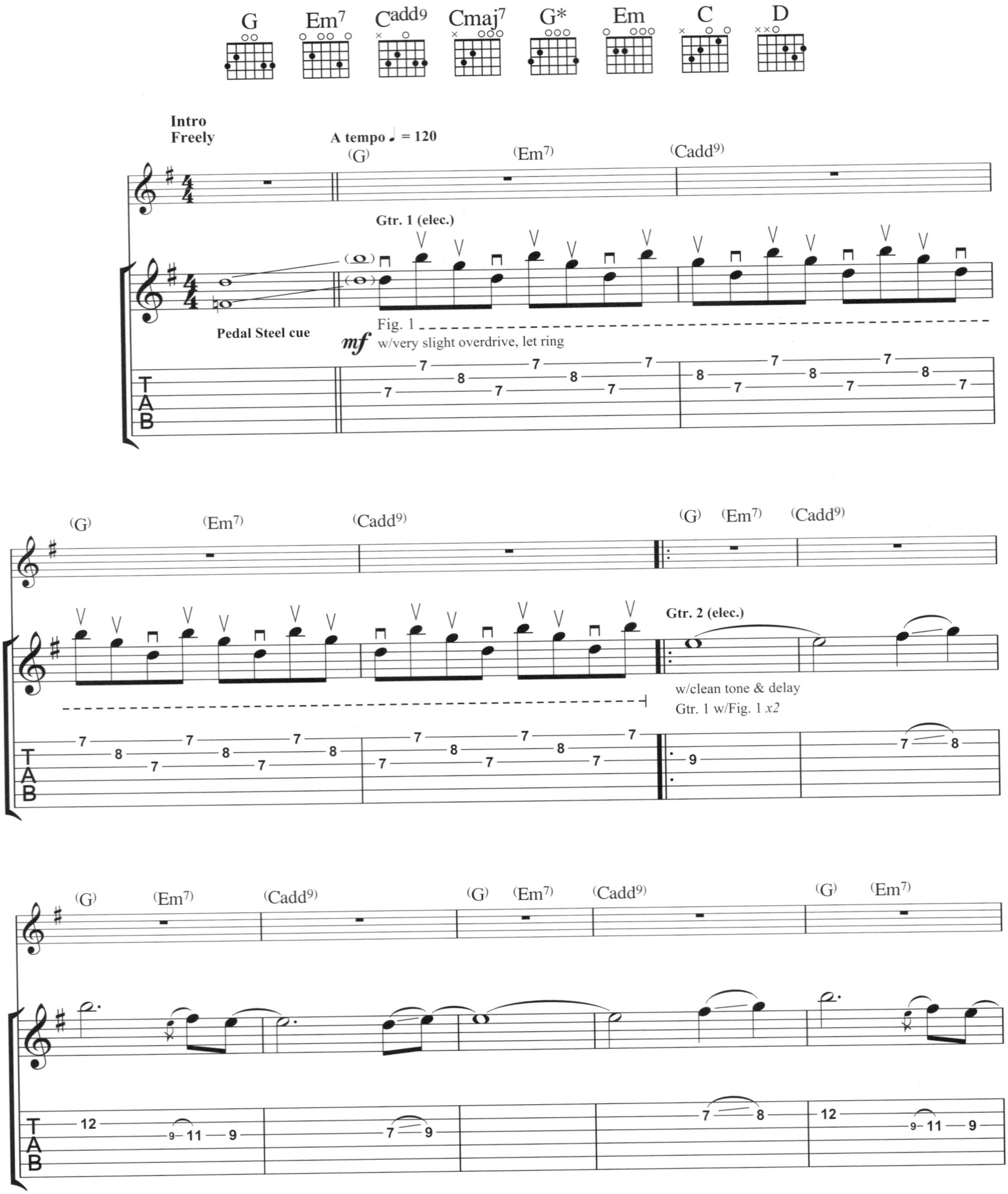

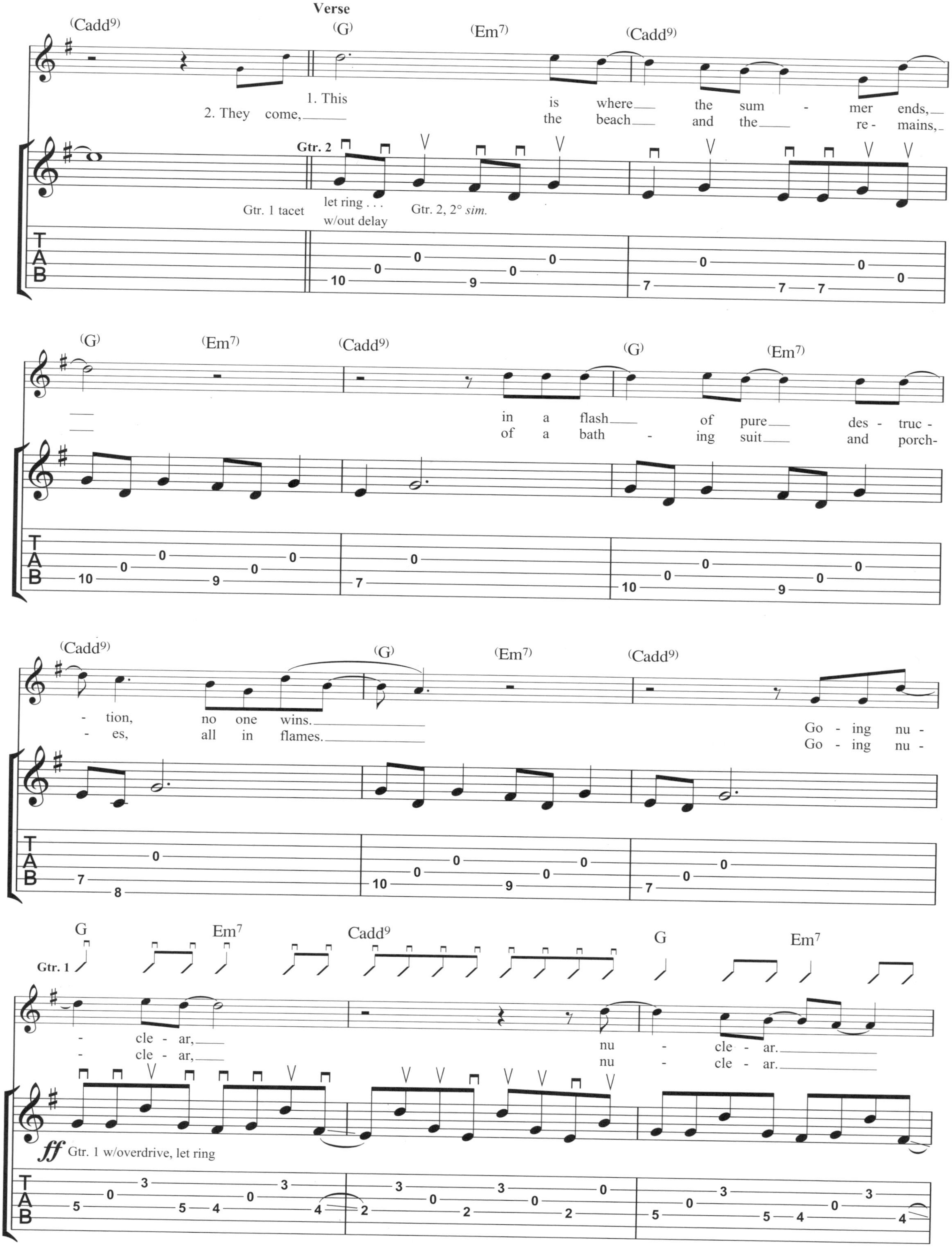
Verse
(Cadd9) (G) (Em7) (Cadd9)
1. This is where the sum - mer ends,
2. They come, the beach and the re - mains,
Gtr. 2
Gtr. 1 tacet
let ring . . .
w/out delay
Gtr. 2, 2° sim.
(G) (Em7) (Cadd9) (G) (Em7)
in a flash of pure des - truc -
of a bath - ing suit and porch -
(Cadd9) (G) (Em7) (Cadd9)
- tion, no one wins.
- es, all in flames.
Go - ing nu -
Go - ing nu -
G Em7 Cadd9 G Em7
Gtr. 1
- cle - ar, nu - cle - ar.
- cle - ar, nu - cle - ar.
ff Gtr. 1 w/overdrive, let ring

Cadd9
(G)
(Em7)
(Cadd9)
Vio - lets in my eye - lids go - ing red.
Oh and I saw how the yank - ees lost to the braves.
mf Gtr. 1 tacet
Chorus
1.
Cmaj7
Gtr. 1 & 2*
ff Gtrs. 1 & 2 w/overdrive
*composite part
G*
Sen - ti - men - tal geek,
Cmaj7
cont. sim.
shut up and go to sleep,

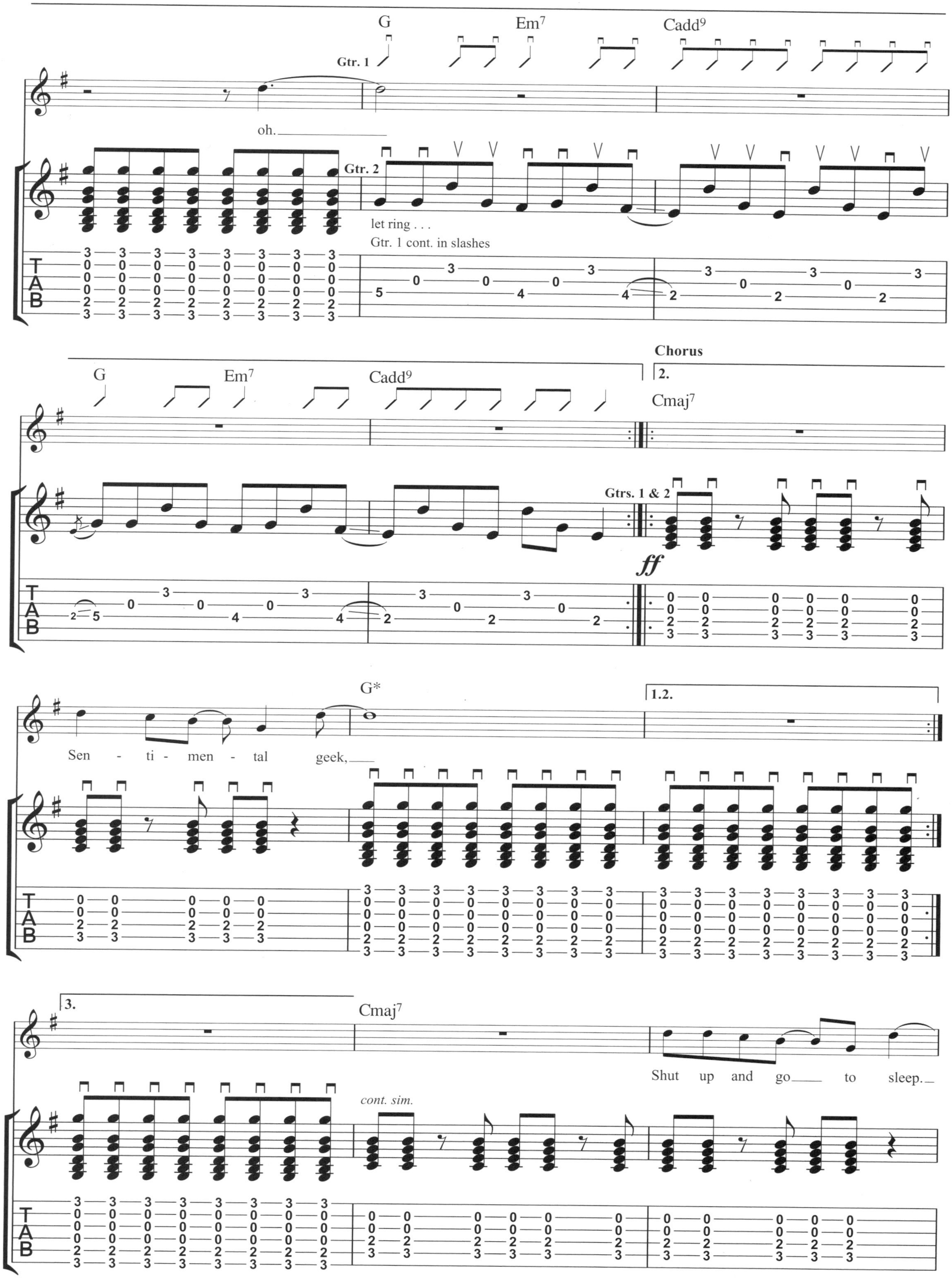
G
Em7
Cadd9
Gtr. 1
oh.
Gtr. 2
let ring . . .
Gtr. 1 cont. in slashes
Chorus
2.
Cmaj7
Gtrs. 1 & 2
ff
G*
1.2.
Sen - ti - men - tal geek,
3.
cont. sim.
Shut up and go to sleep.

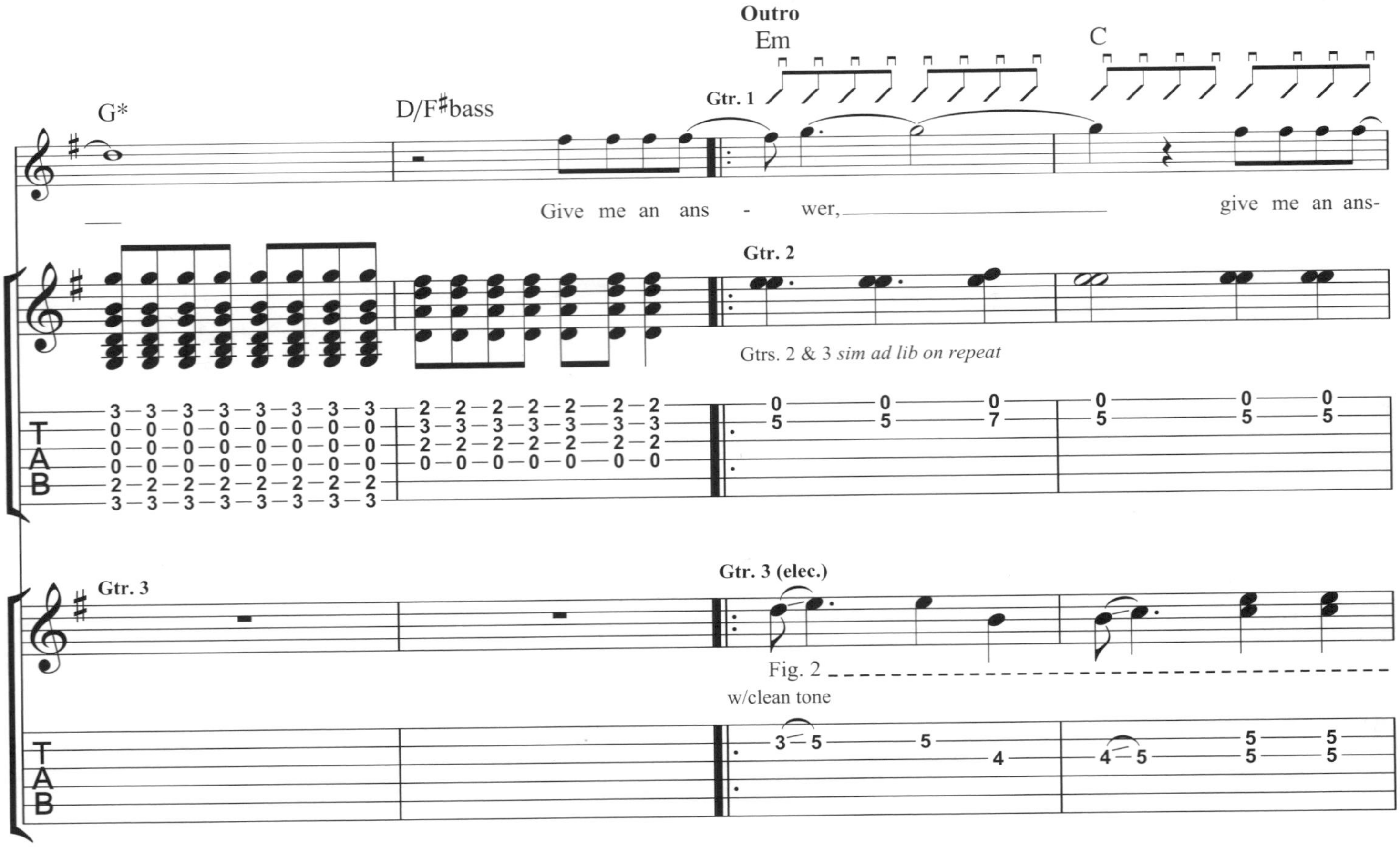

Outro
Em
C
G*
D/F♯bass
Gtr. 1
Give me an ans - wer, give me an ans-
Gtr. 2
Gtrs. 2 & 3 sim ad lib on repeat
Gtr. 3
Gtr. 3 (elec.)
Fig. 2
w/clean tone

G
1.
2.
Gtr. 1 cont. sim.
D
D
- wer, give me an ans - Give me an ans
full
full
full
full
full

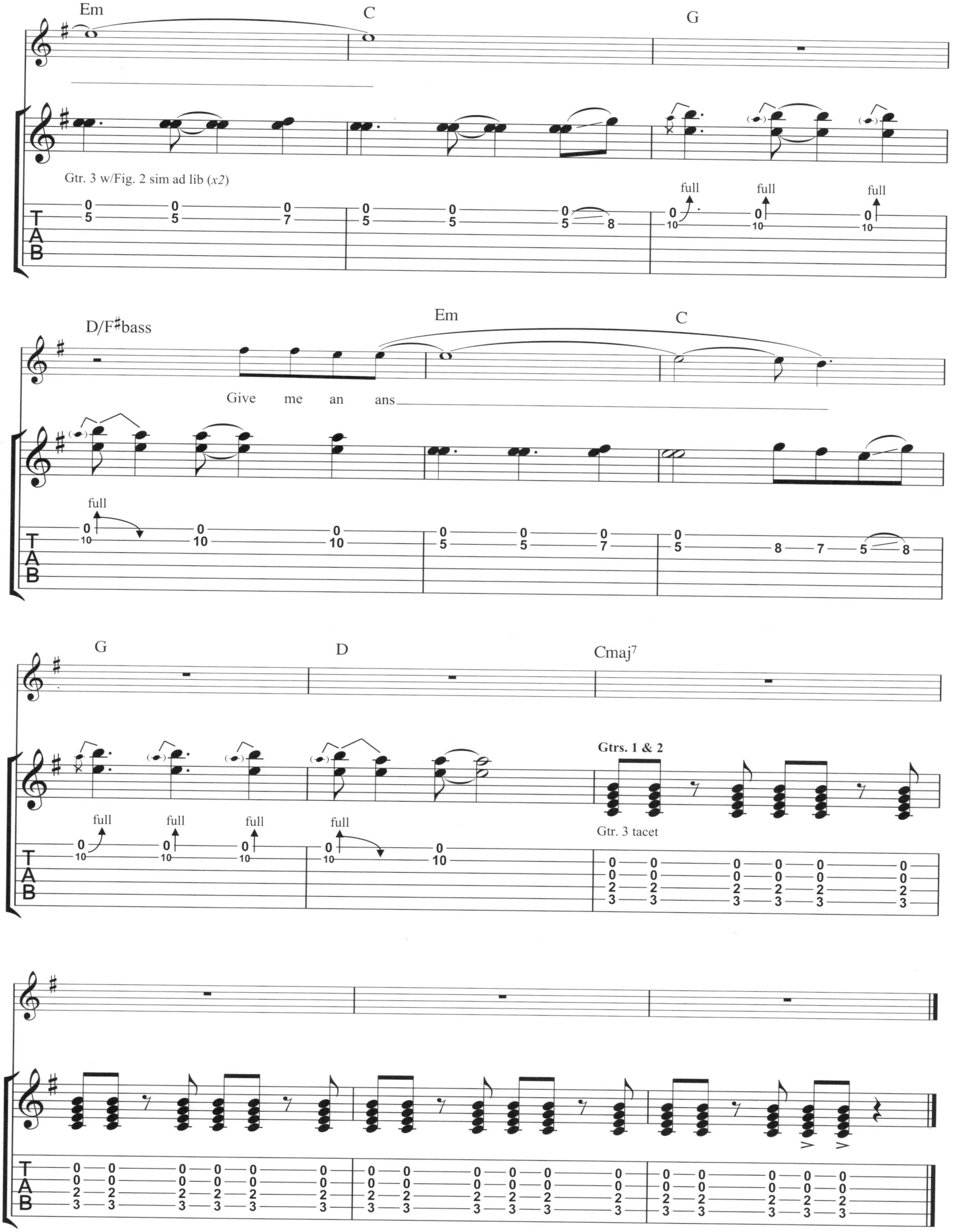
Em
C
G
Gtr. 3 w/Fig. 2 sim ad lib (x2)
full
full
full
D/F♯bass
Em
C
Give me an ans
full
G
D
Cmaj7
Gtrs. 1 & 2
full
full
full
full
Gtr. 3 tacet

Outtathaway

WORDS & MUSIC BY CRAIG NICHOLLS

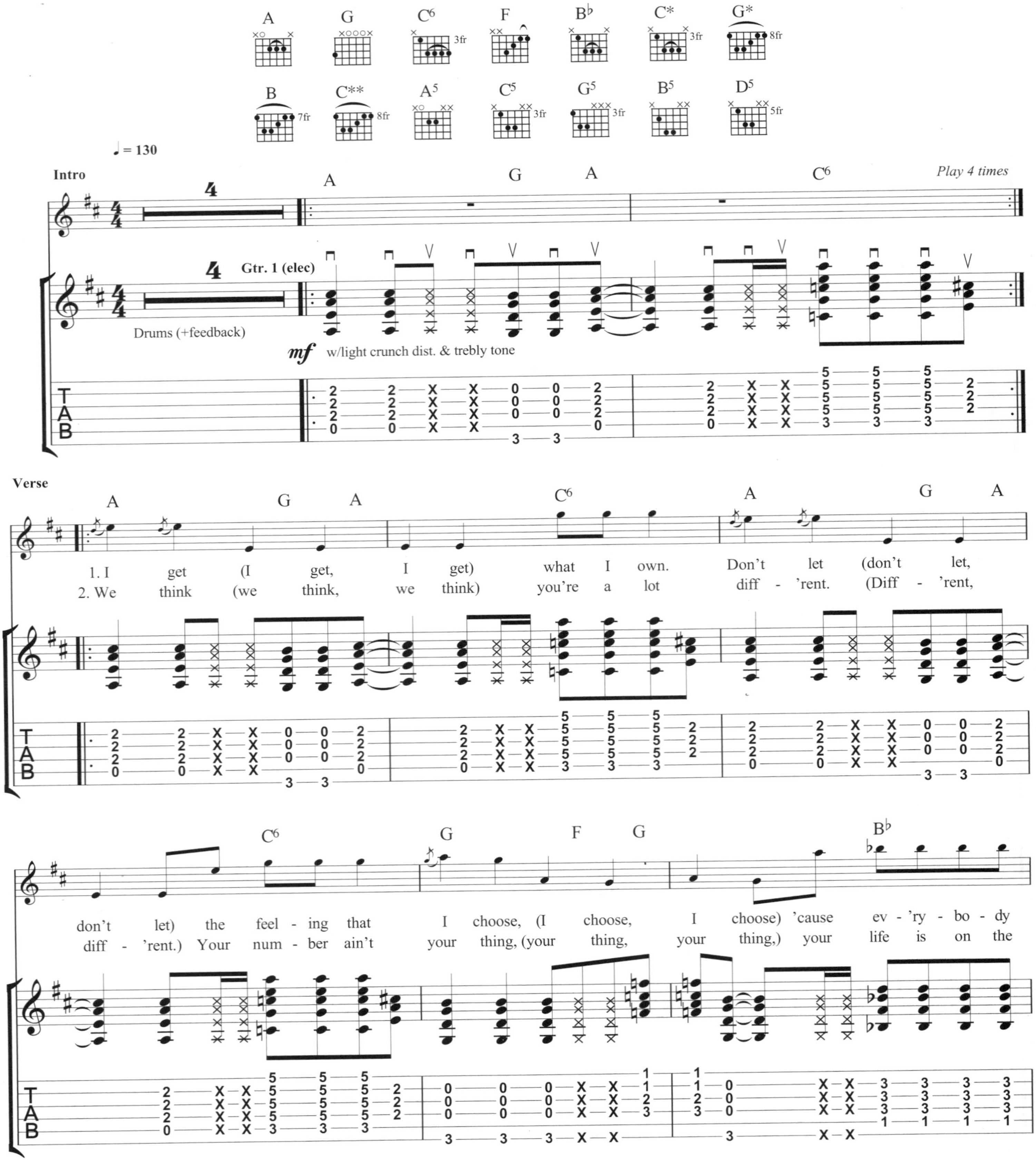

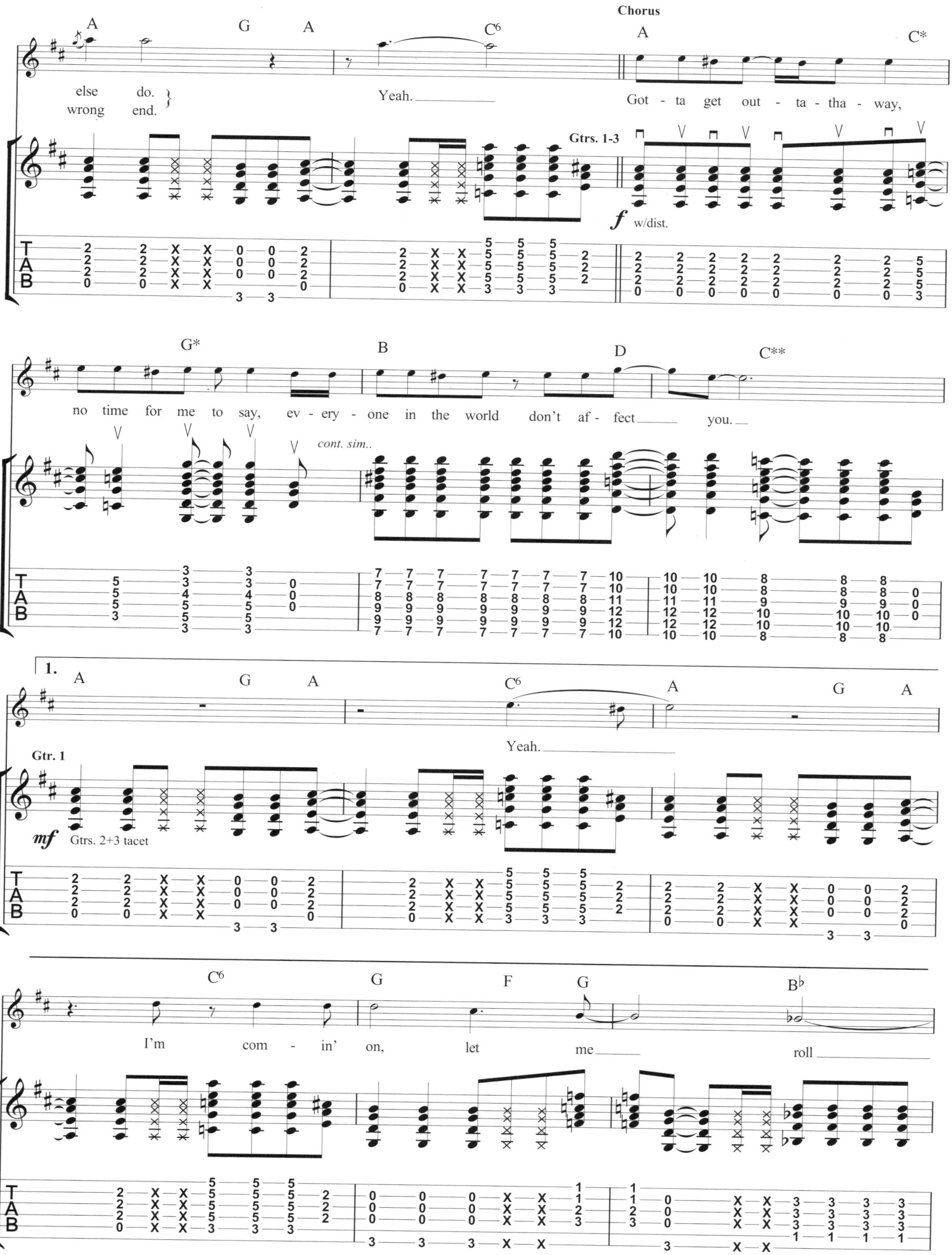
Chorus
A G A C6 A C*
else do. wrong end.
Yeah.
Got - ta get out - ta - tha - way,
Gtrs. 1-3
w/dist.
G* B D C**
no time for me to say, ev - ery - one in the world don't af - fect you.
cont. sim..
1.
A G A C6 A G A
Yeah.
Gtr. 1
Gtrs. 2+3 tacet
C6 G F G B♭
I'm com - in' on, let me roll

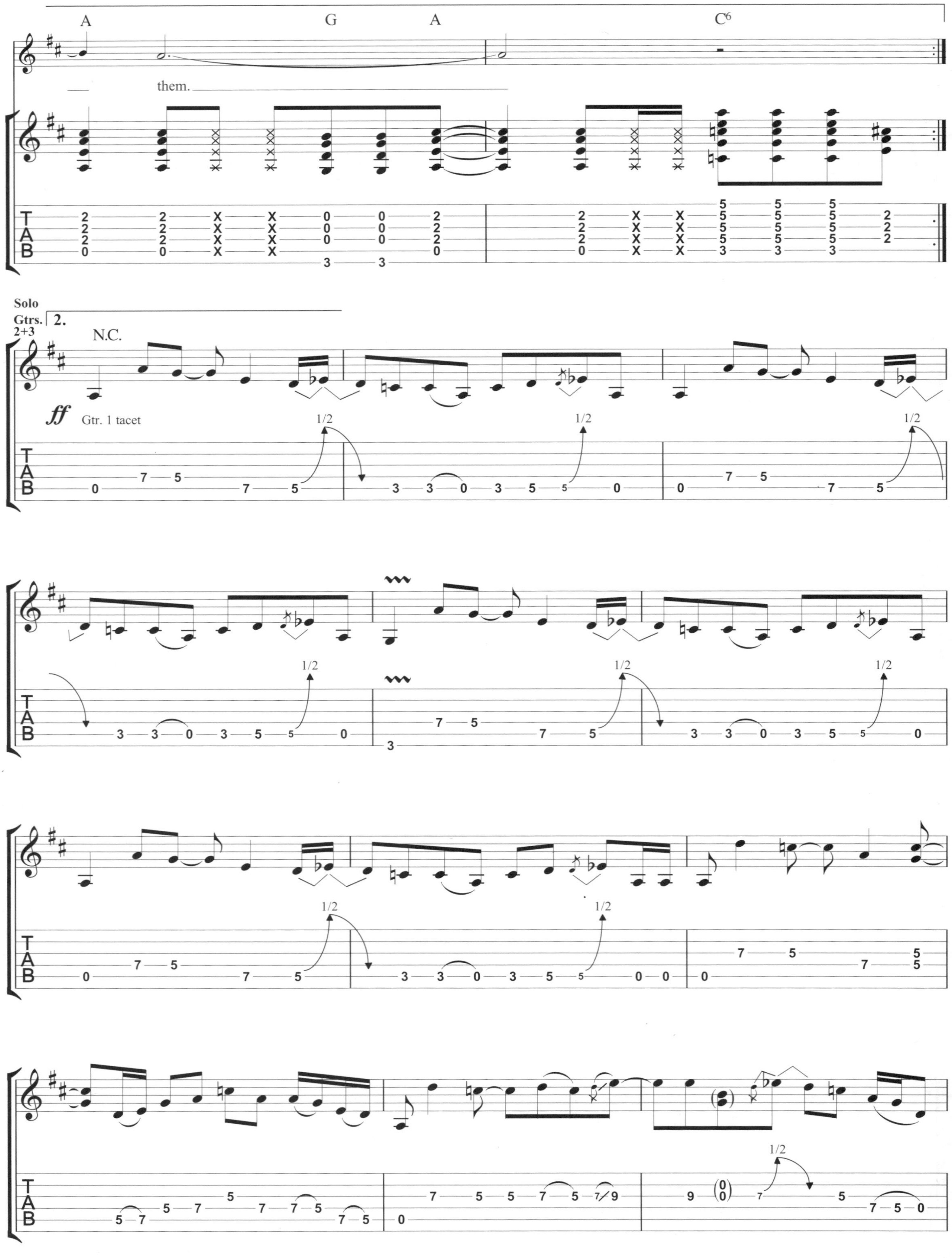
A
G
A
C6
them.
Solo Gtrs. 2+3
2.
N.C.
ff
Gtr. 1 tacet
1/2

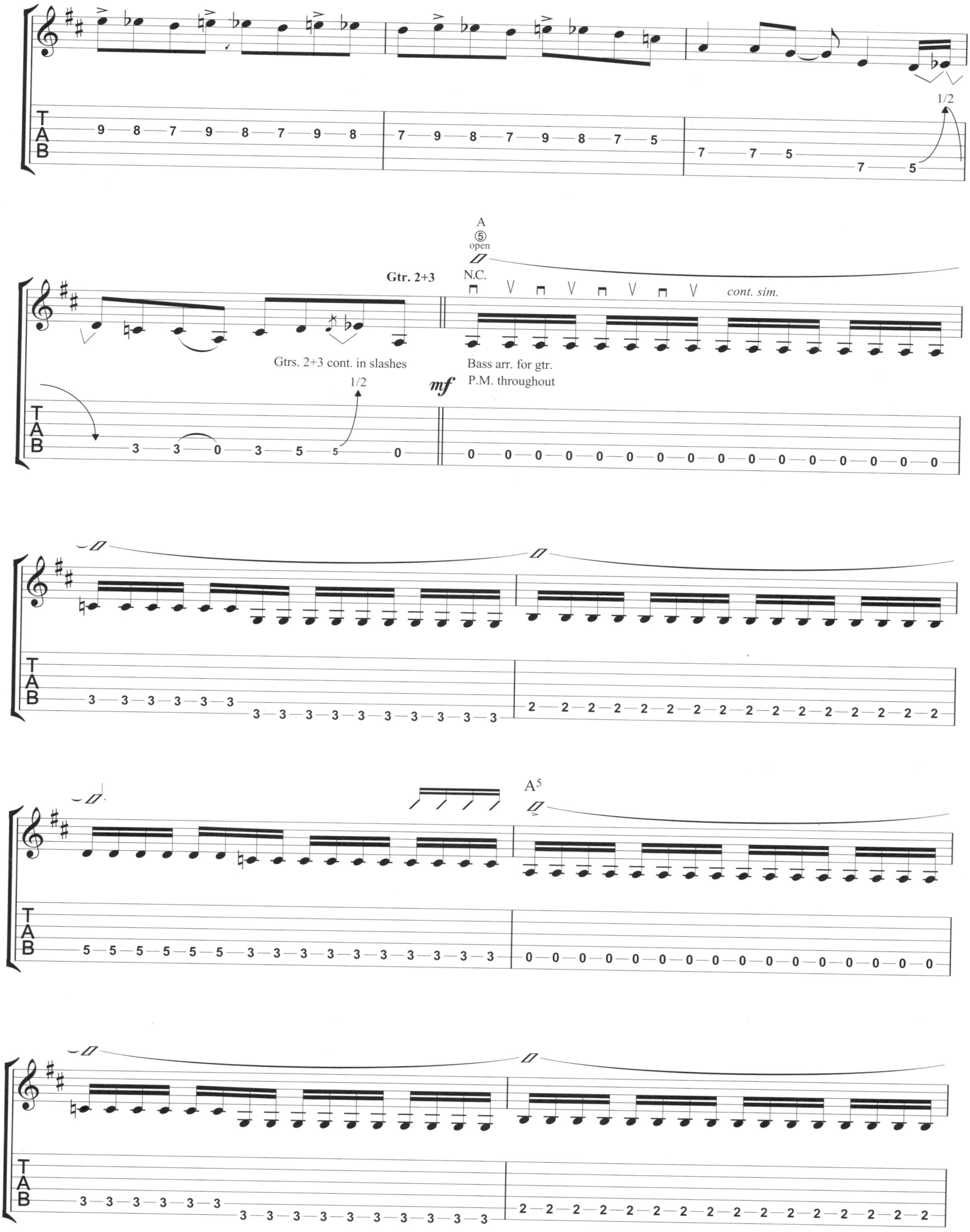

1/2
A
⑤
open
Gtr. 2+3
N.C.
cont. sim.
Gtrs. 2+3 cont. in slashes
Bass arr. for gtr.
P.M. throughout
mf
A5

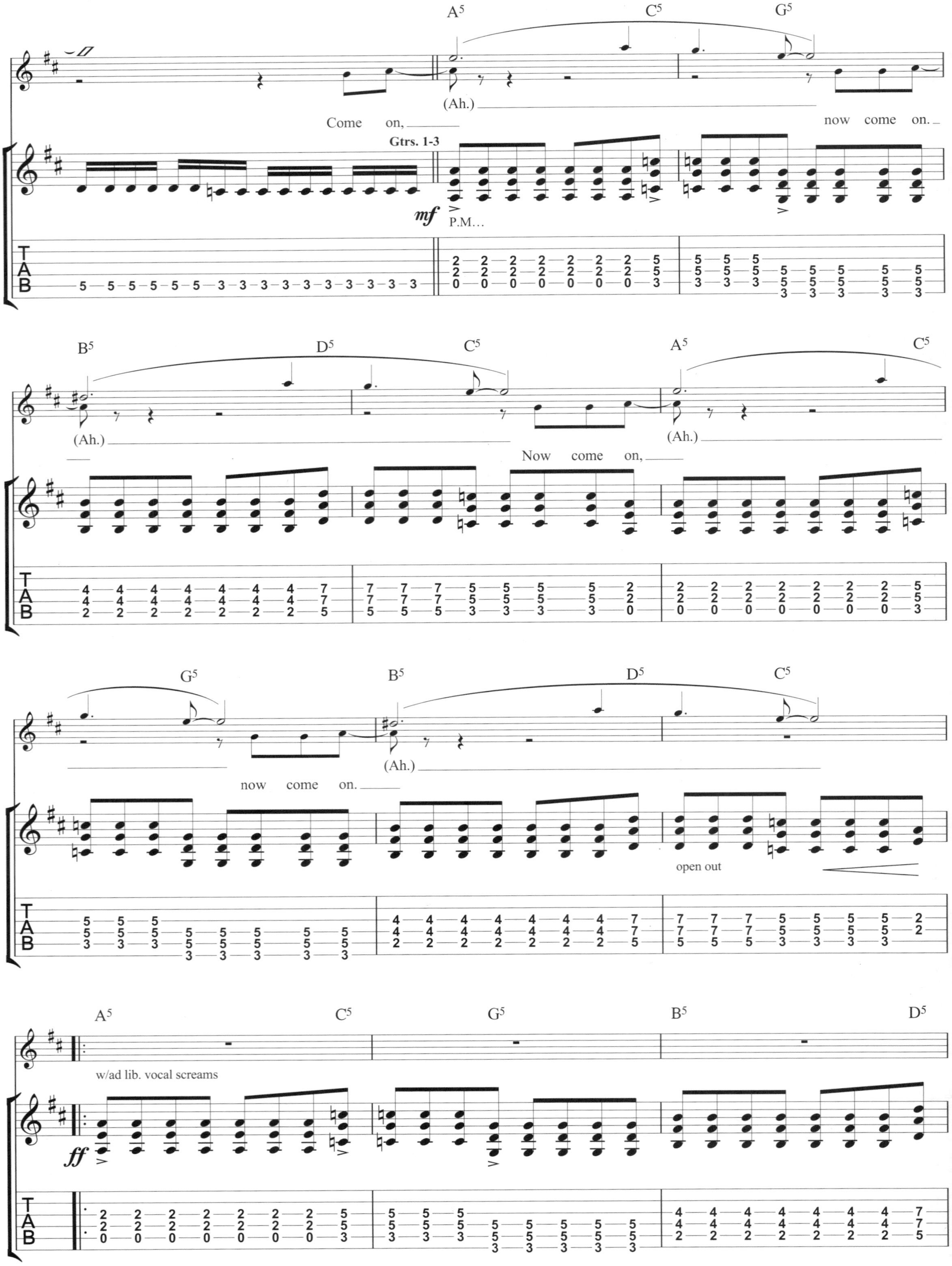
A5 C5 G5
Come on,
(Ah.)
now come on.
Gtrs. 1-3
mf
P.M...
T A B
B5 D5 C5 A5 C5
(Ah.)
Now come on,
(Ah.)
G5 B5 D5 C5
now come on.
(Ah.)
open out
A5 C5 G5 B5 D5
w/ad lib. vocal screams
ff

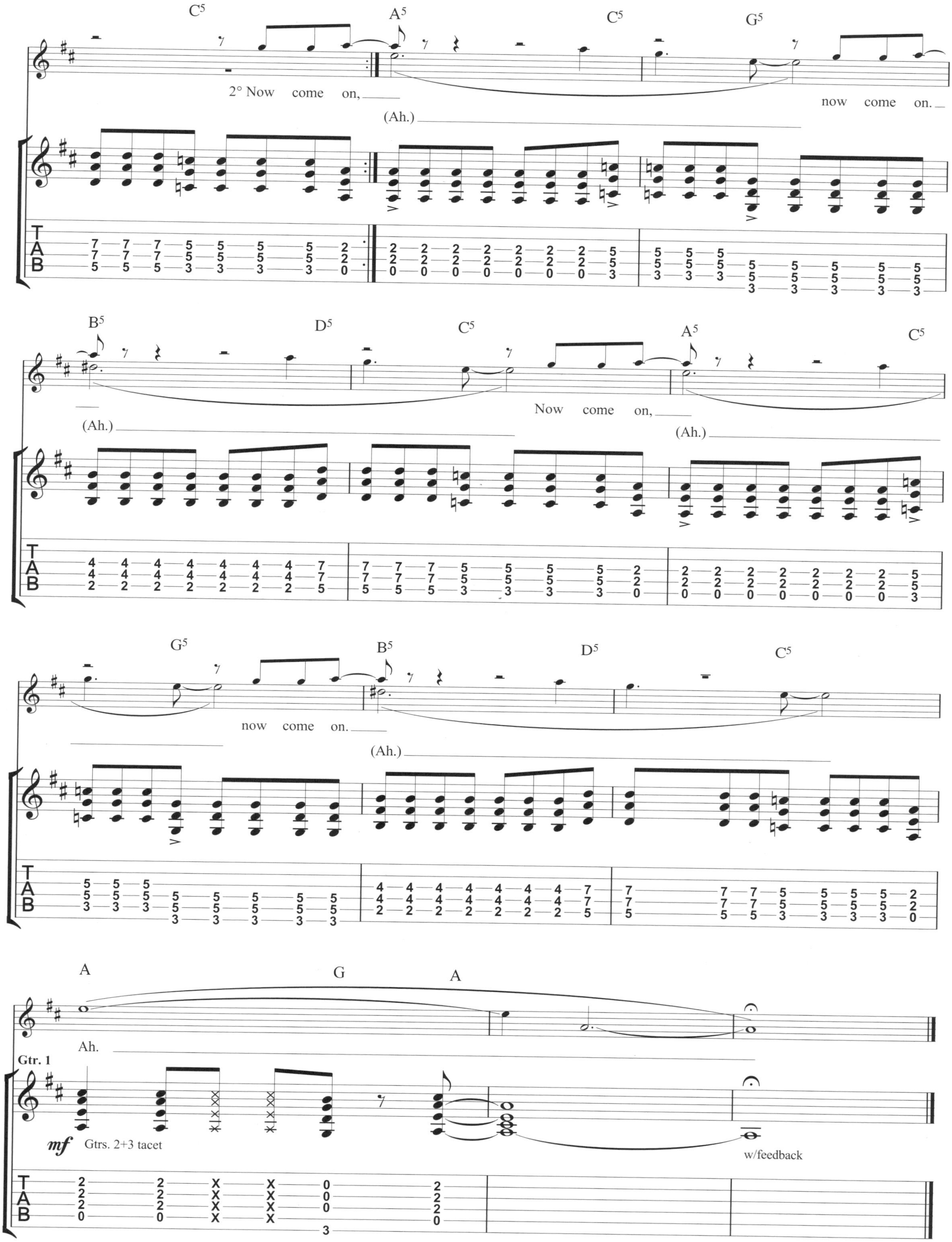
C5 A5 C5 G5
2° Now come on,
(Ah.)
now come on.
B5 D5 C5 A5 C5
(Ah.)
Now come on,
(Ah.)
G5 B5 D5 C5
now come on.
(Ah.)
A G A
Ah.
Gtr. 1
mf
Gtrs. 2+3 tacet
w/feedback

OBSESSIONS

WORDS & MUSIC BY BRETT ANDERSON & RICHARD OAKES

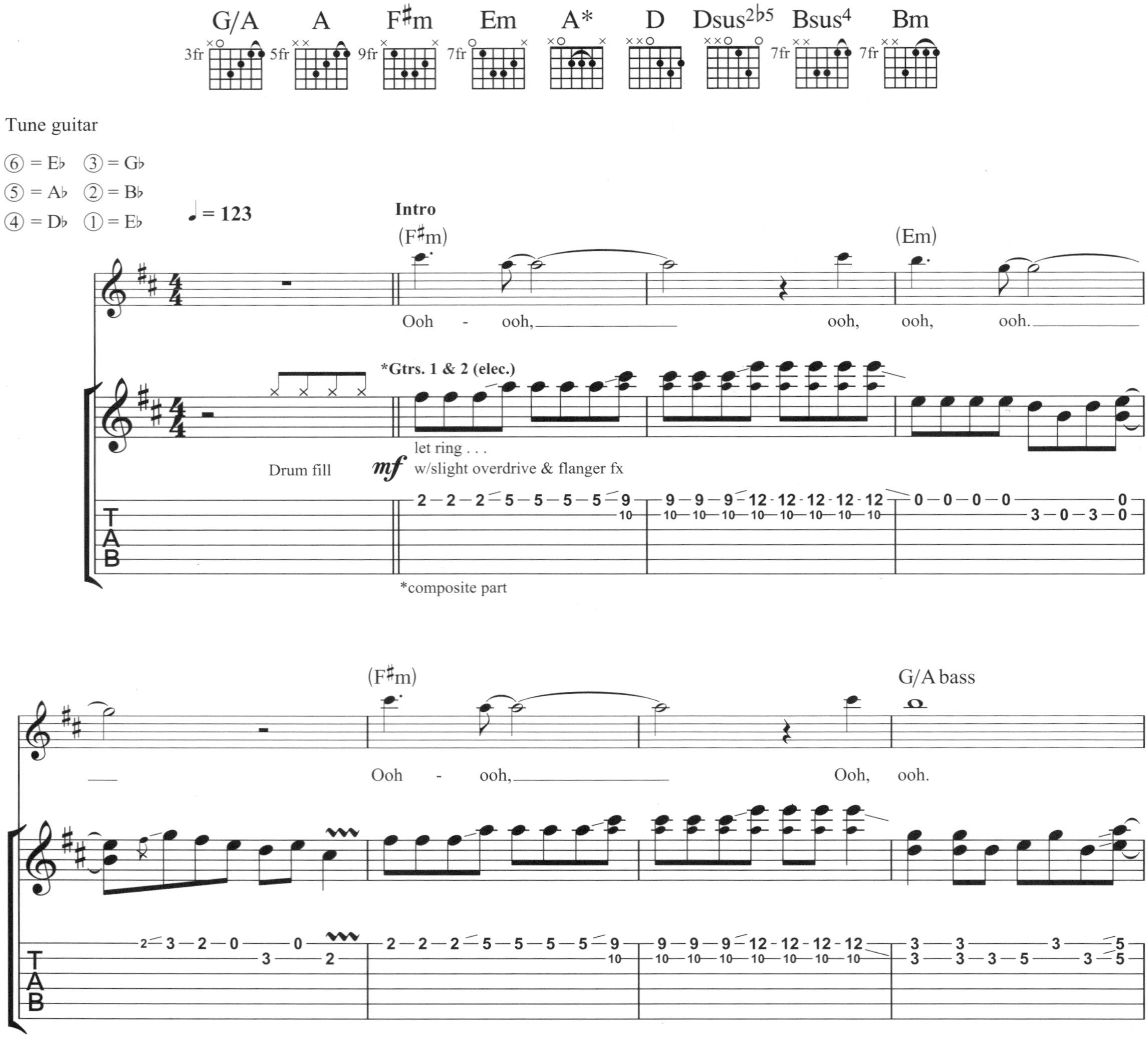

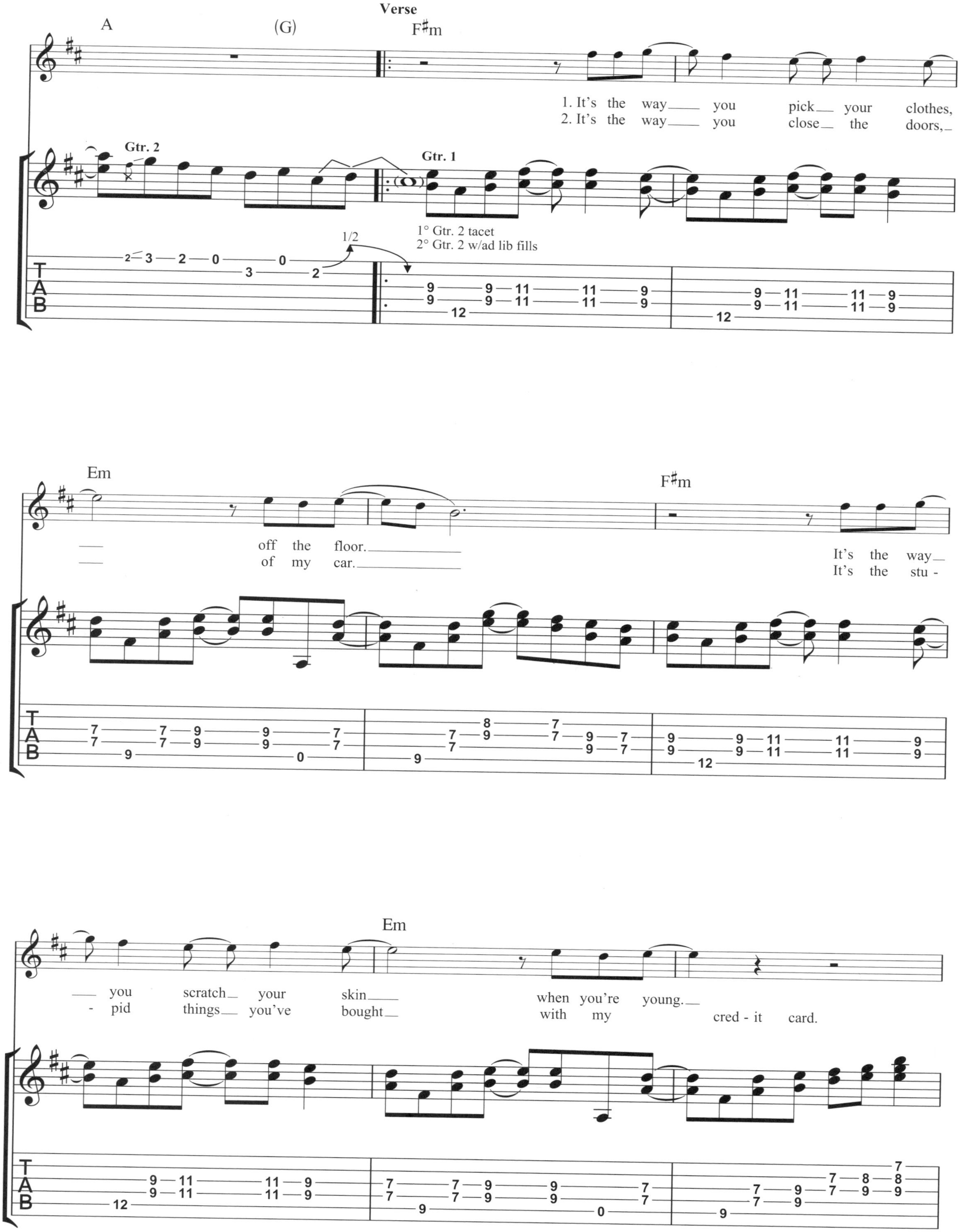
Verse
A (G) F♯m
1. It's the way you pick your clothes,
2. It's the way you close the doors,
Gtr. 2
Gtr. 1
1/2
1° Gtr. 2 tacet
2° Gtr. 2 w/ad lib fills
Em F♯m
off the floor. It's the way
of my car. It's the stu -
Em
you scratch your skin when you're young.
- pid things you've bought with my cred - it card.

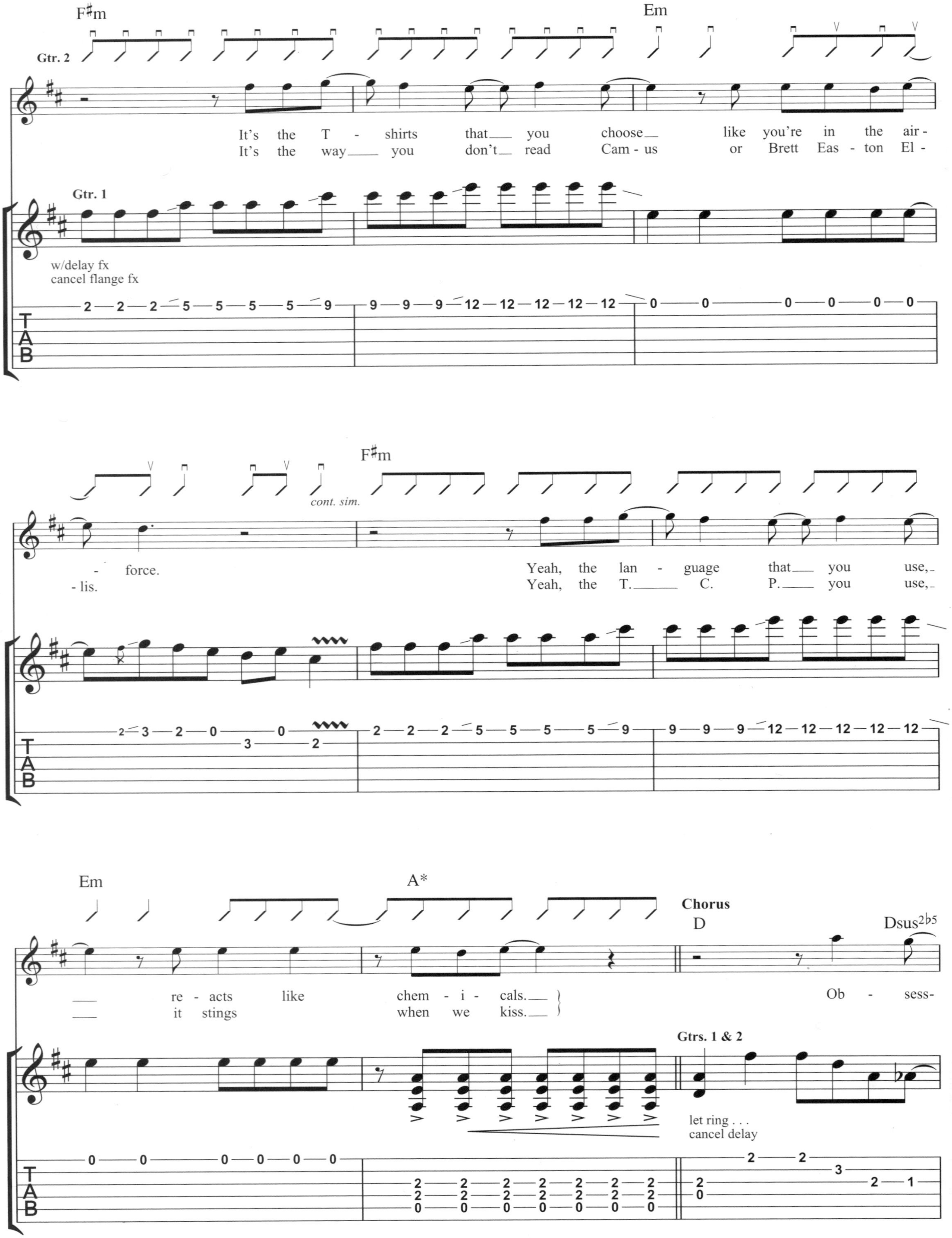
F♯m
Em
Gtr. 2
It's the T - shirts that you choose like you're in the air -
It's the way you don't read Cam - us or Brett Eas - ton El -
Gtr. 1
w/delay fx
cancel flange fx
cont. sim.
F♯m
- force.
- lis.
Yeah, the lan - guage that you use,
Yeah, the T. C. P. you use,
Em
A*
Chorus
D
Dsus2♭5
re - acts like chem - i - cals.
it stings when we kiss.
Ob - sess-
Gtrs. 1 & 2
let ring . . .
cancel delay

Bsus4 Bm F♯m
-ions in my head don't con-nect with my in-tel-lect,
Em G/A
it's called ob-ses-sion, can you han-dle it?
A D Dsus2♭5
It's con-nect-ed to the hip
Bsus4 Bm F♯m Em
sound and it moves with the un-der-ground. It's called ob-ses-
T
A
B

G/A
1. A
2. A
- sion, when you're a - round.
Instrumental
Bm
F♯m
(Harmonica & Gtr.)
f w/clean tone & delay fx
Bm
Em
A
D
Dsus2♭5
Bm
F♯m
let ring . . .
w/dist.
Em
G/A bass
A
w/bar
TAB

Chorus

D Dsus2♭5 Bsus4 Bm F♯m
Ob - sess - ions, it's like sex, it's sim -
Gtrs. 1 & 2
let ring . . .
Gtr. 3 tacet
Em
- ple and com - plex. It's called ob - ses - sion,
G/A A D Dsus2♭5
can you han - dle it? It's con - nect
Bsus4 Bm F♯m
- ed to the hip sound and it moves with the un - der - ground.

Em
It's called ob - ses - sion,
G/A bass
when you're a - round.
A
Ooh,
Outro solo
D
ooh.
Gtr. 1
Gtr. 2 cont. sim.
Dsus2♭5
Ooh,
Bm
ooh.
F♯m
Ooh,
Em
ooh.
Ooh,
G/A bass
ooh.
A
repeat to fade
Oo.

Something To Talk About

WORDS & MUSIC BY DAMON GOUGH

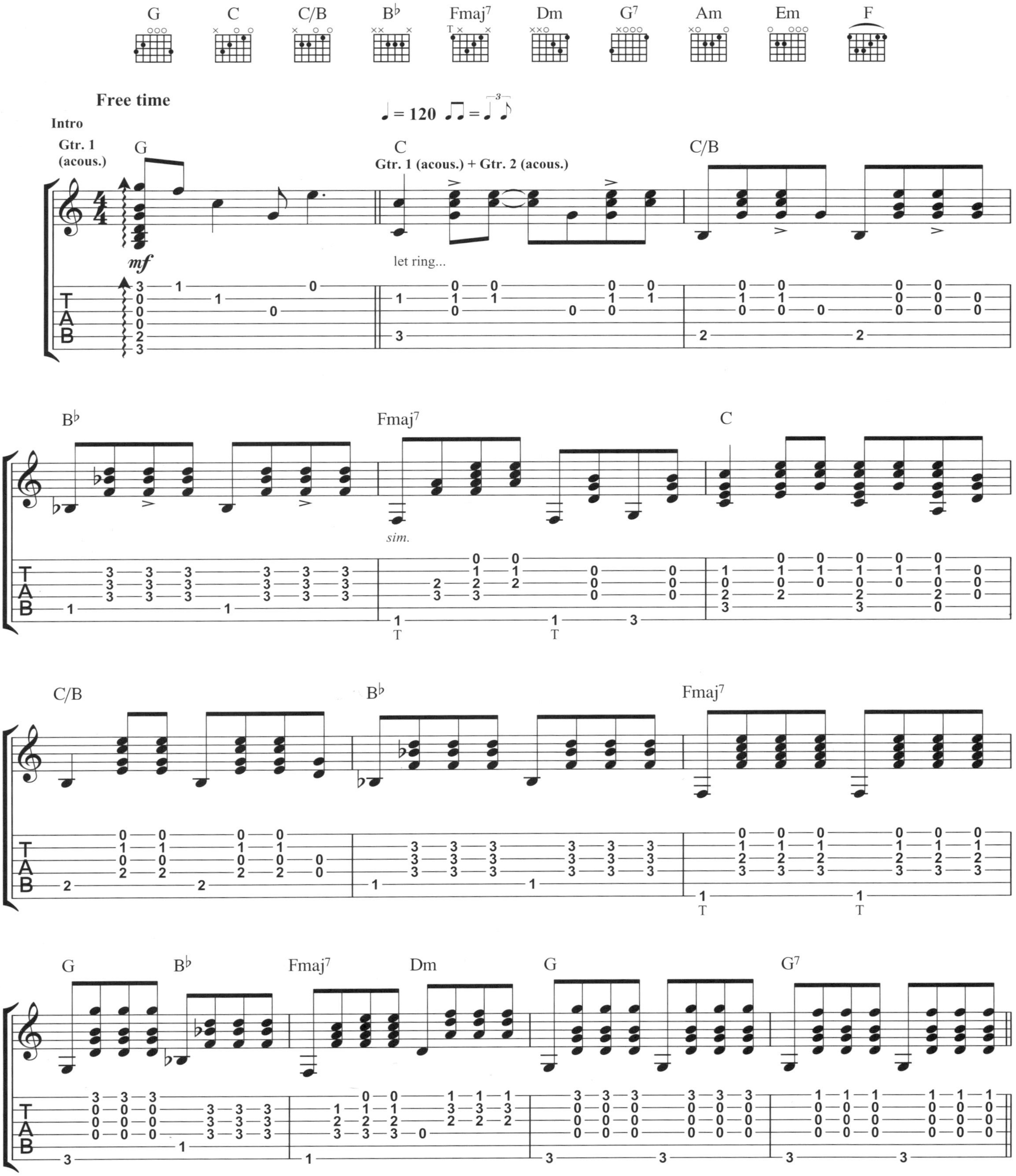

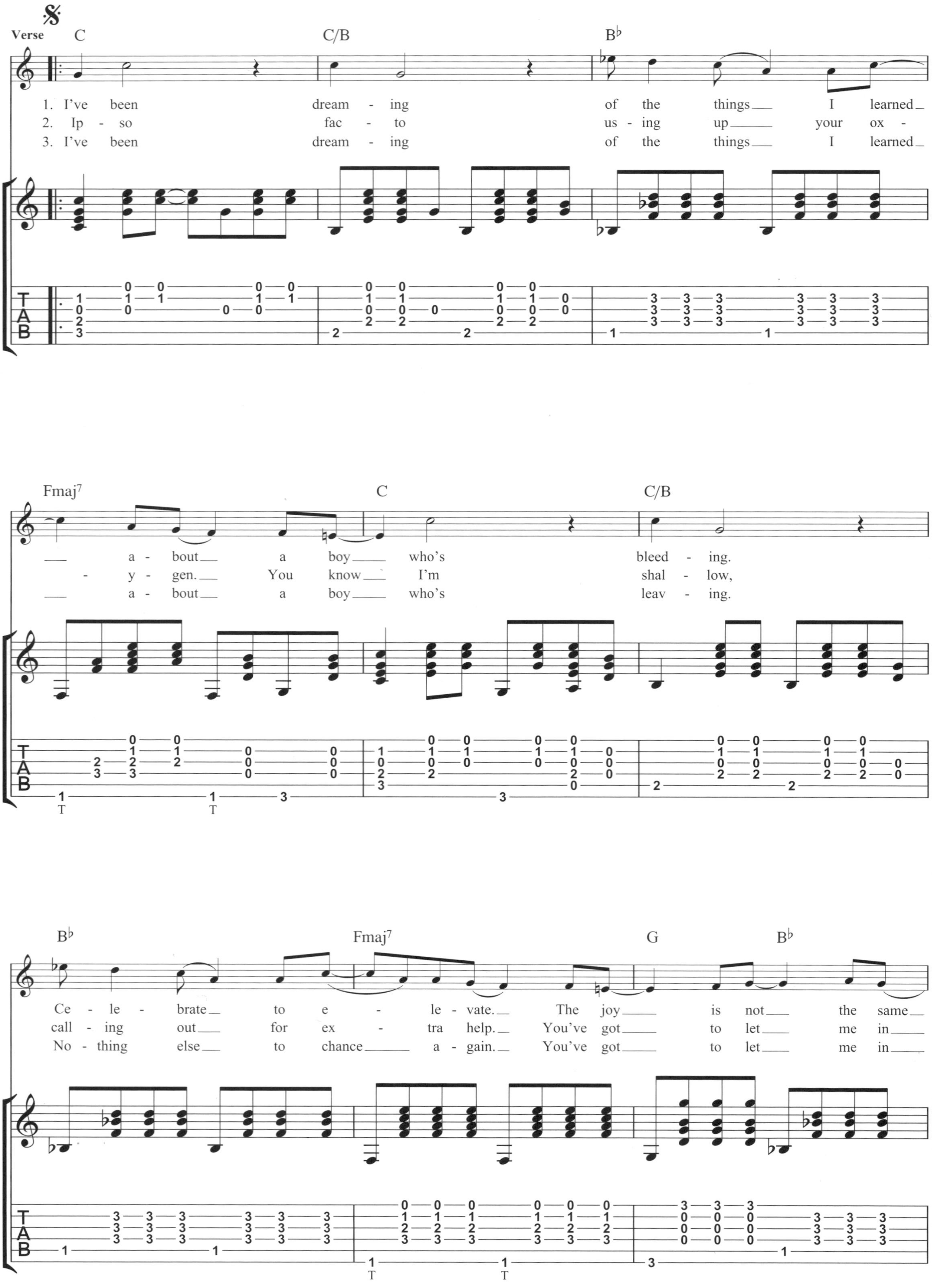
Verse
C
C/B
B♭
1. I've been dream - ing of the things I learned
2. Ip - so fac - to us - ing up your ox -
3. I've been dream - ing of the things I learned
TAB
Fmaj7
C
C/B
a - bout a boy who's bleed - ing.
- y - gen. You know I'm shal - low,
a - bout a boy who's leav - ing.
B♭
Fmaj7
G
B♭
Ce - le - brate to e - le - vate. The joy is not the same
call - ing out for ex - tra help. You've got to let me in
No - thing else to chance a - gain. You've got to let me in

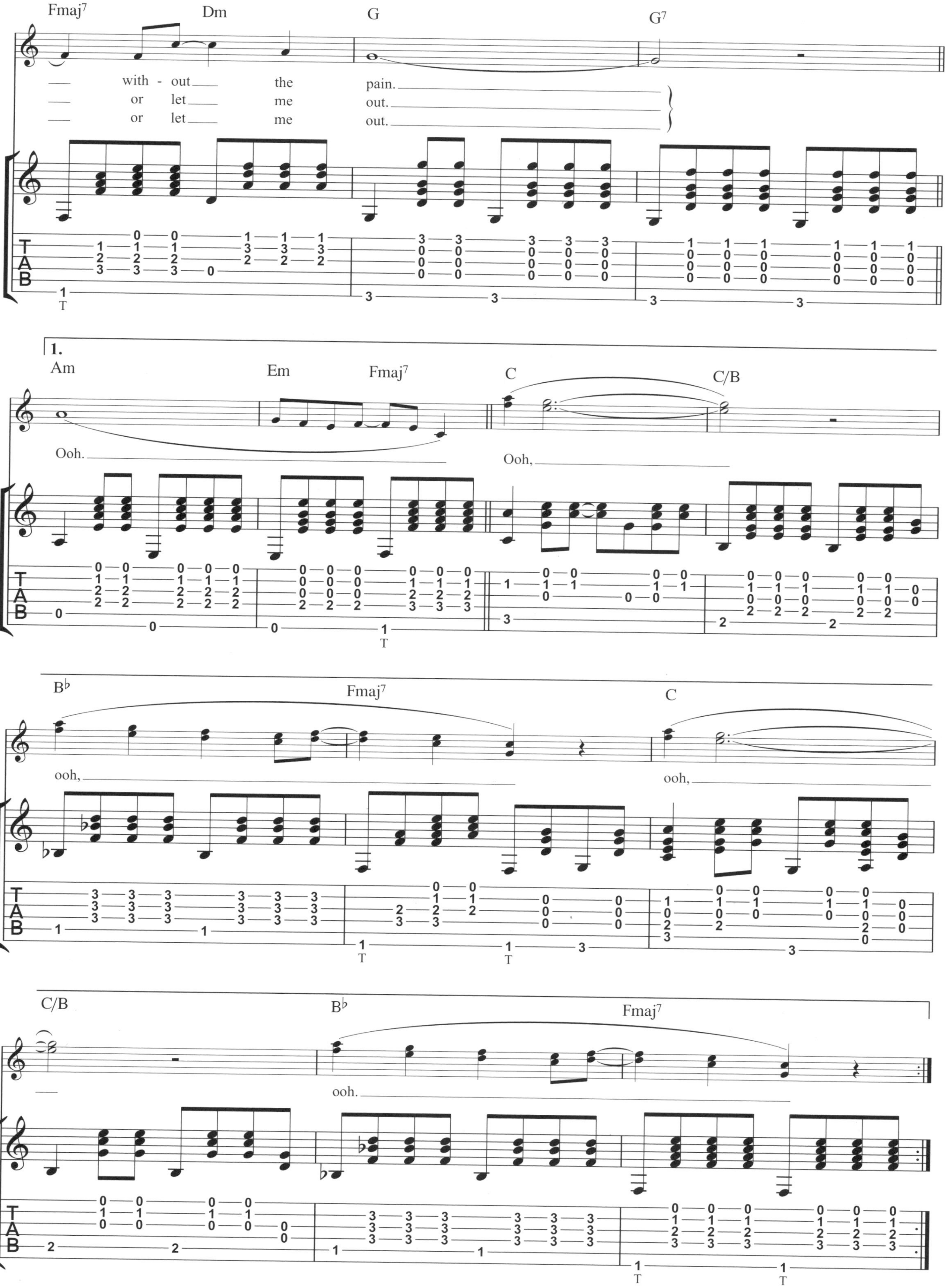
Fmaj7 Dm G G7
with - out the pain.
or let me out.
or let me out.
1.
Am Em Fmaj7 C C/B
Ooh.
Ooh,
B♭ Fmaj7 C
ooh,
ooh,
C/B B♭ Fmaj7
ooh.
TAB

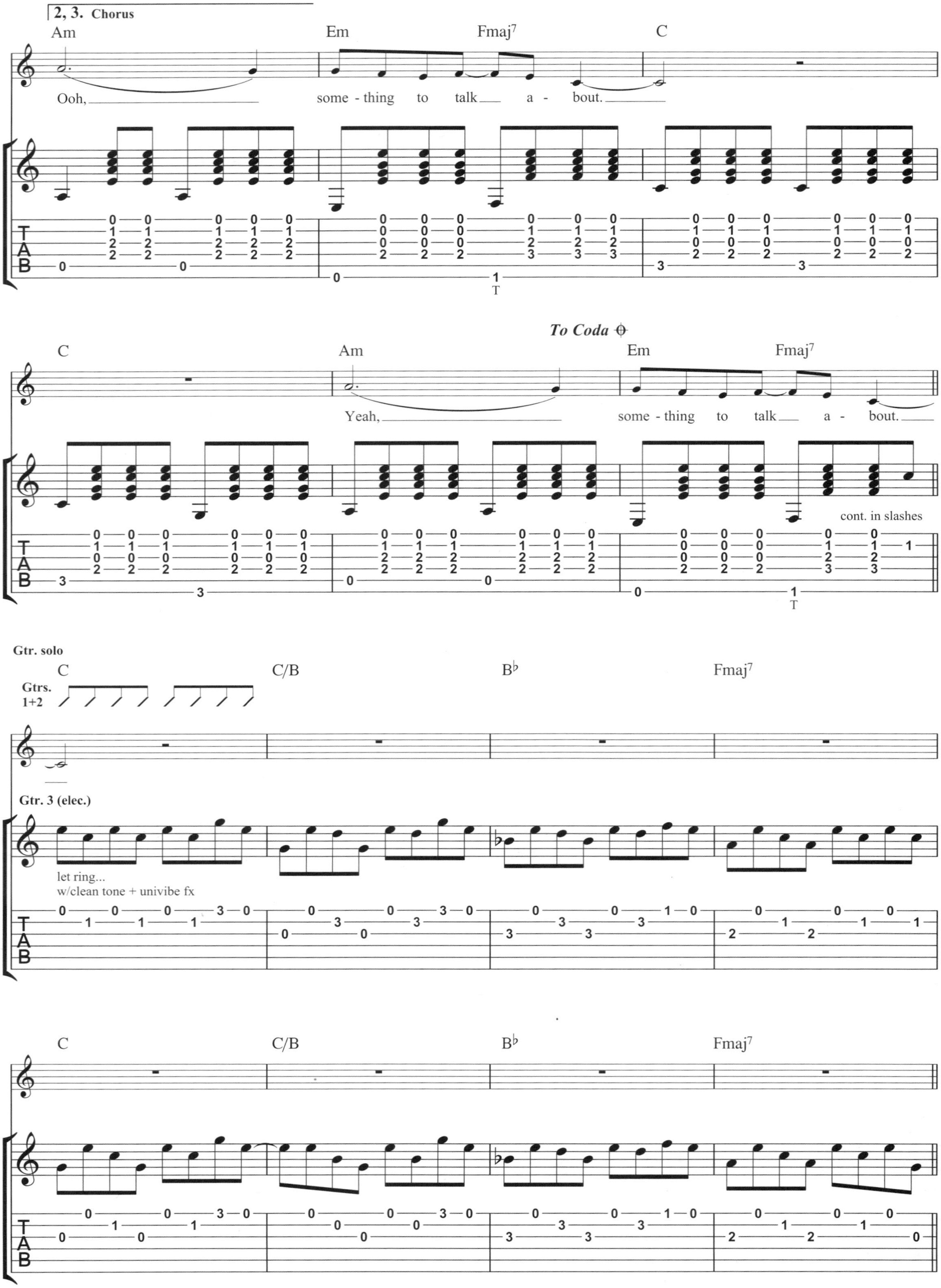
2, 3. Chorus
Am Em Fmaj7 C
Ooh, some - thing to talk a - bout.
C Am Em Fmaj7
To Coda
Yeah, some - thing to talk a - bout.
cont. in slashes
Gtr. solo
C C/B B♭ Fmaj7
Gtrs. 1+2
Gtr. 3 (elec.)
let ring...
w/clean tone + univibe fx
C C/B B♭ Fmaj7

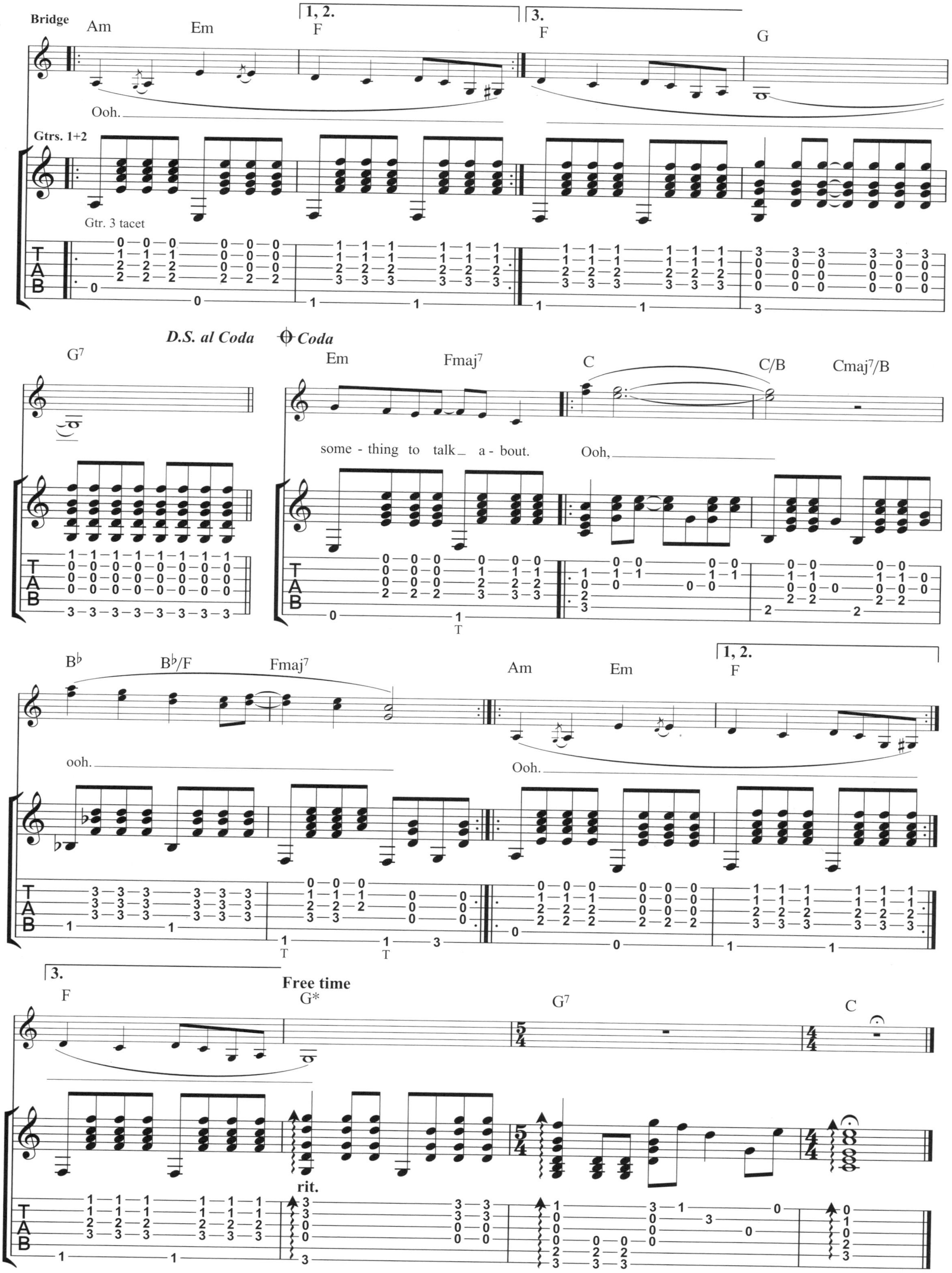
Bridge
Am
Em
1, 2.
F
3.
F
G
Ooh.
Gtrs. 1+2
Gtr. 3 tacet
G7
D.S. al Coda
Coda
Em
Fmaj7
C
C/B
Cmaj7/B
some - thing to talk _ a - bout.
Ooh,
B♭
B♭/F
Fmaj7
ooh.
Am
Em
1, 2.
F
Ooh.
3.
F
Free time
G*
G7
C
rit.

SIDE

WORDS & MUSIC BY FRAN HEALY

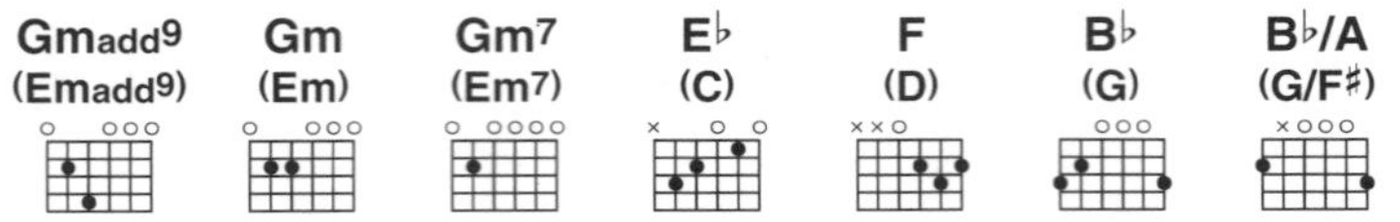

All Gtrs.: Capo 3rd fret

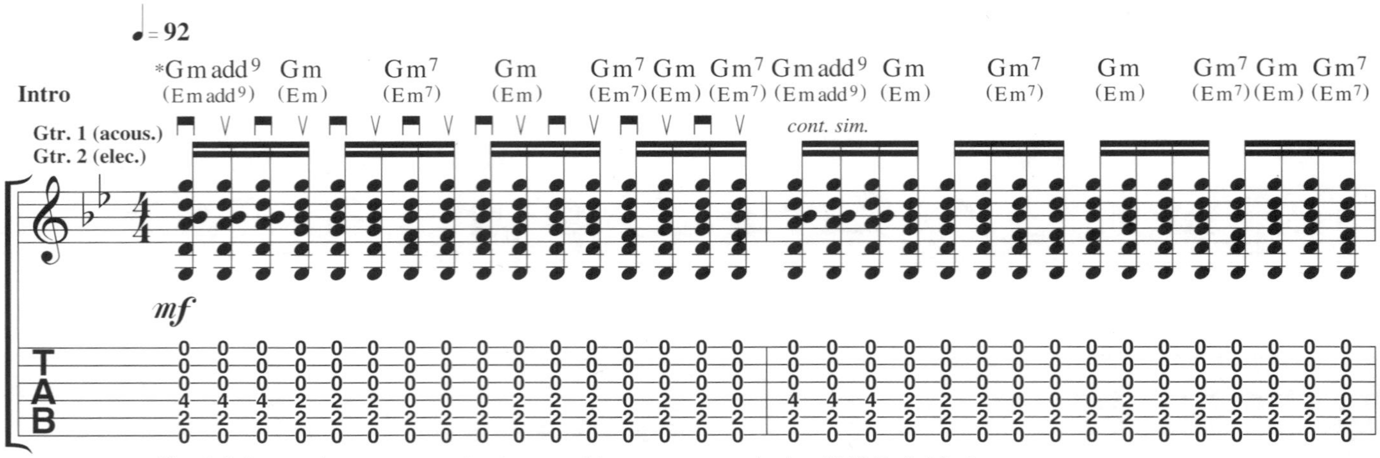

*Symbols in parentheses represent chord names with respect to capoed guitar (TAB 0= 3rd fret). Symbols above represent actual sounding chords.

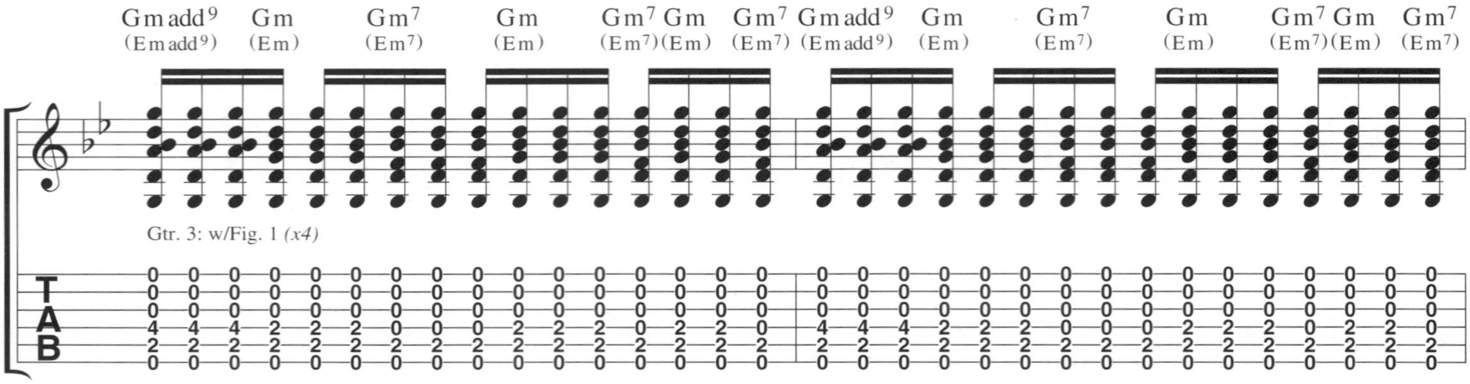

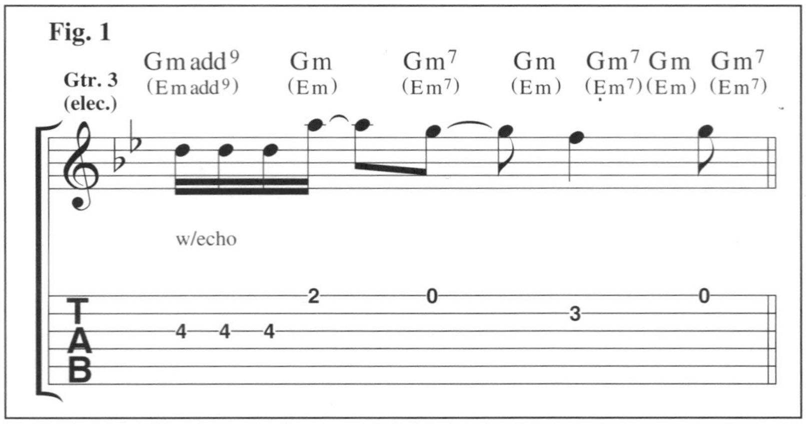

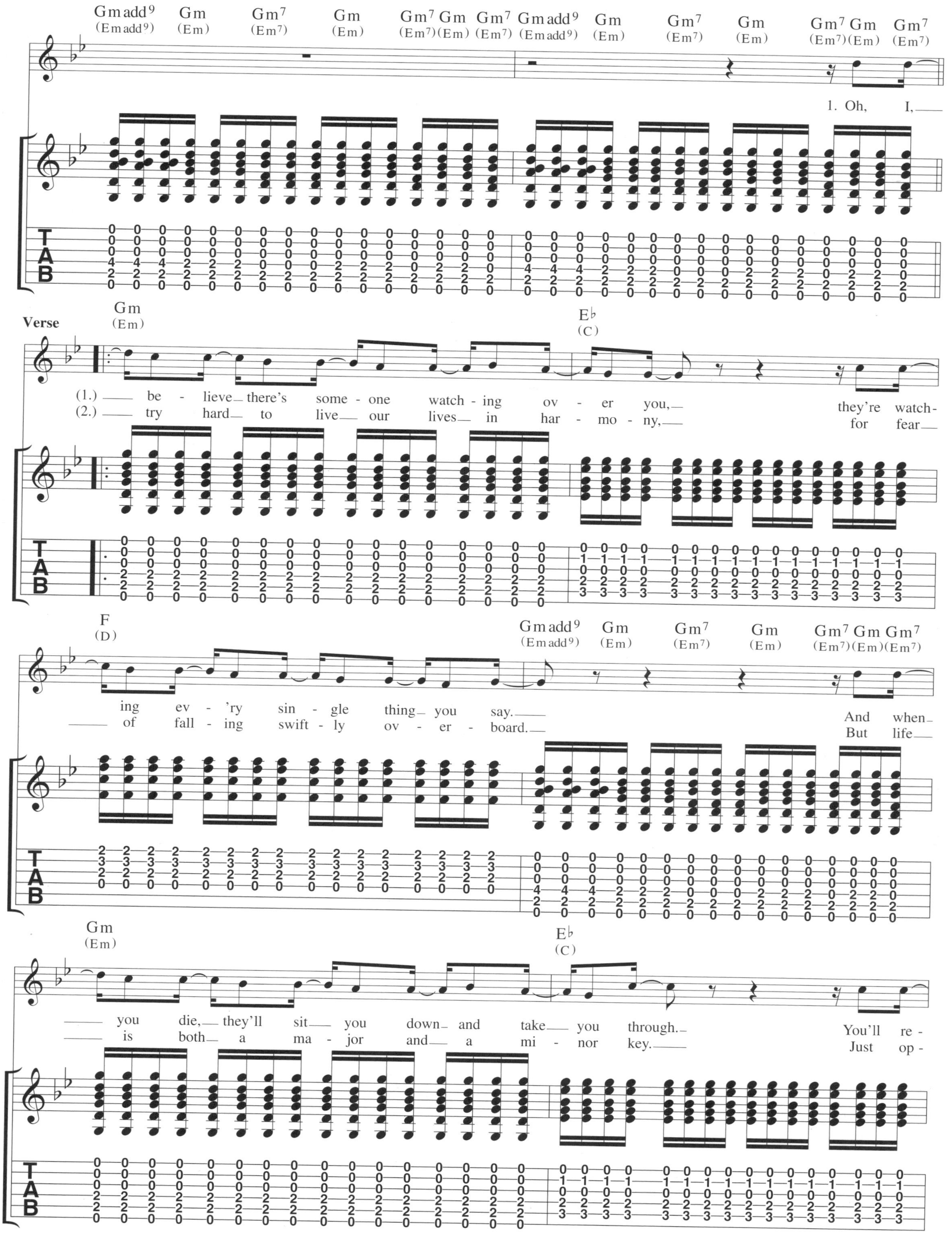
Gmadd9 (Emadd9) Gm (Em) Gm7 (Em7) Gm (Em) Gm7 Gm (Em7)(Em) Gm7 (Em7) Gmadd9 (Emadd9) Gm (Em) Gm7 (Em7) Gm (Em) Gm7 Gm (Em7)(Em) Gm7 (Em7)
1. Oh, I,
Verse
Gm (Em)
Eb (C)
(1.) be - lieve there's some - one watch - ing ov - er you, they're watch-
(2.) try hard to live our lives in har - mo - ny, for fear
F (D)
Gmadd9 (Emadd9) Gm (Em) Gm7 (Em7) Gm (Em) Gm7 Gm Gm7 (Em7)(Em)(Em7)
ing ev - 'ry sin - gle thing you say. And when
of fall - ing swift - ly ov - er - board. But life
Gm (Em)
Eb (C)
you die, they'll sit you down and take you through. You'll re -
is both a ma - jor and a mi - nor key. Just op -
TAB

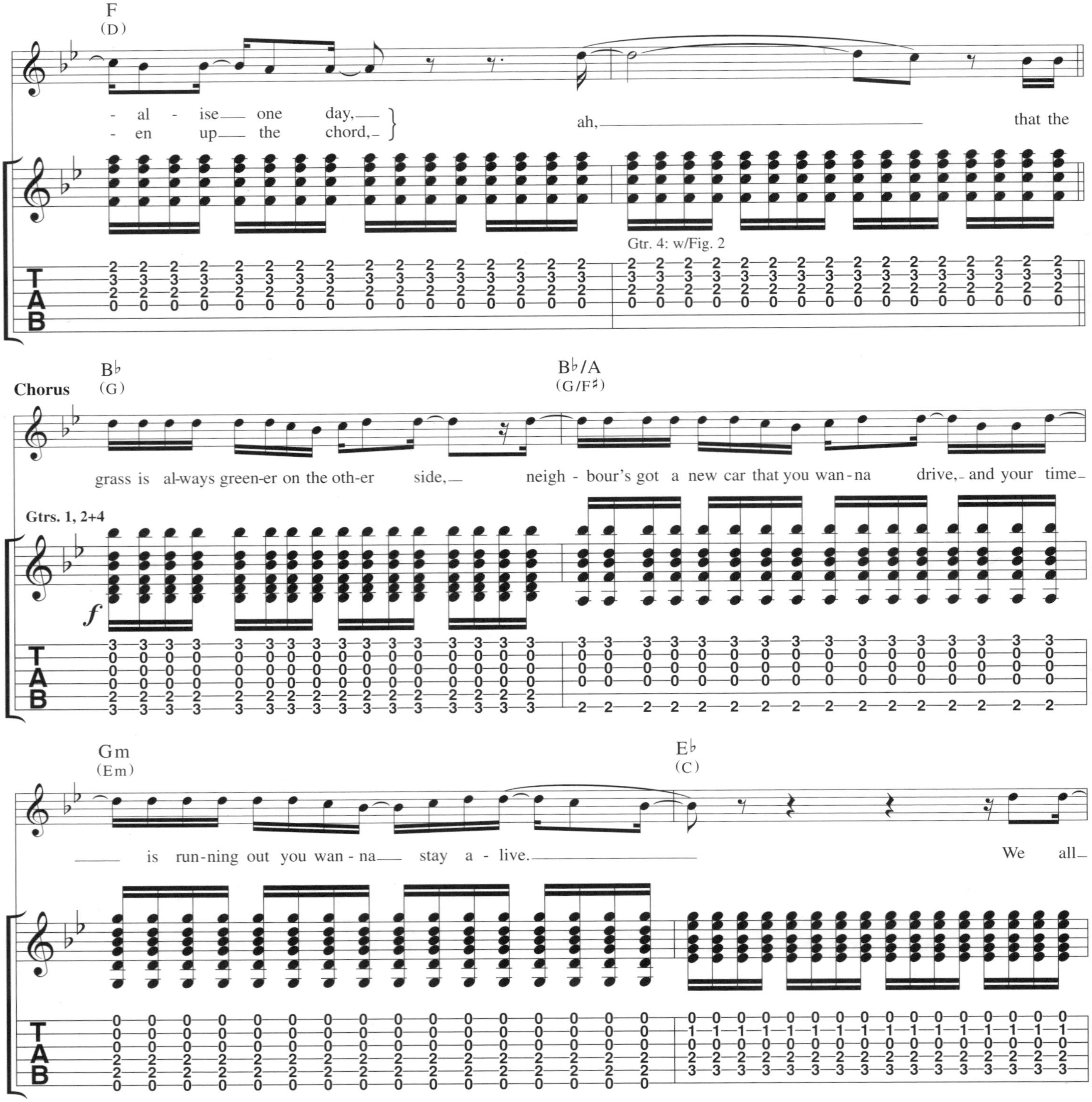
F
(D)
- al - ise one day,
- en up the chord,
ah, that the
Gtr. 4: w/Fig. 2
Chorus
B♭
(G)
B♭/A
(G/F♯)
grass is al-ways green-er on the oth-er side, neigh - bour's got a new car that you wan-na drive, and your time
Gtrs. 1, 2+4
f
Gm
(Em)
E♭
(C)
is run-ning out you wan - na stay a - live. We all
TAB

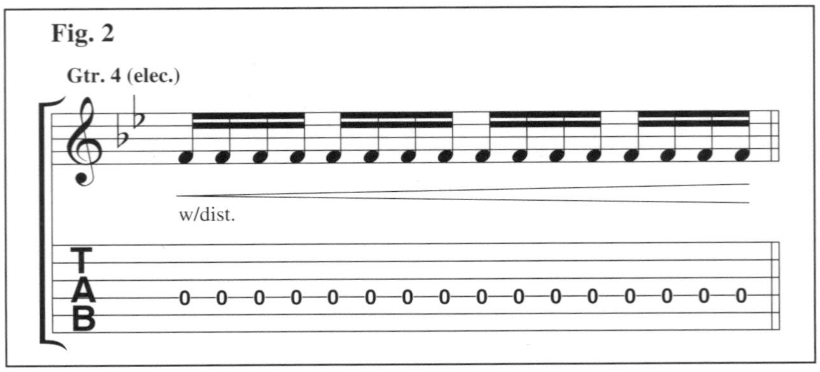
Fig. 2
Gtr. 4 (elec.)
w/dist.
TAB

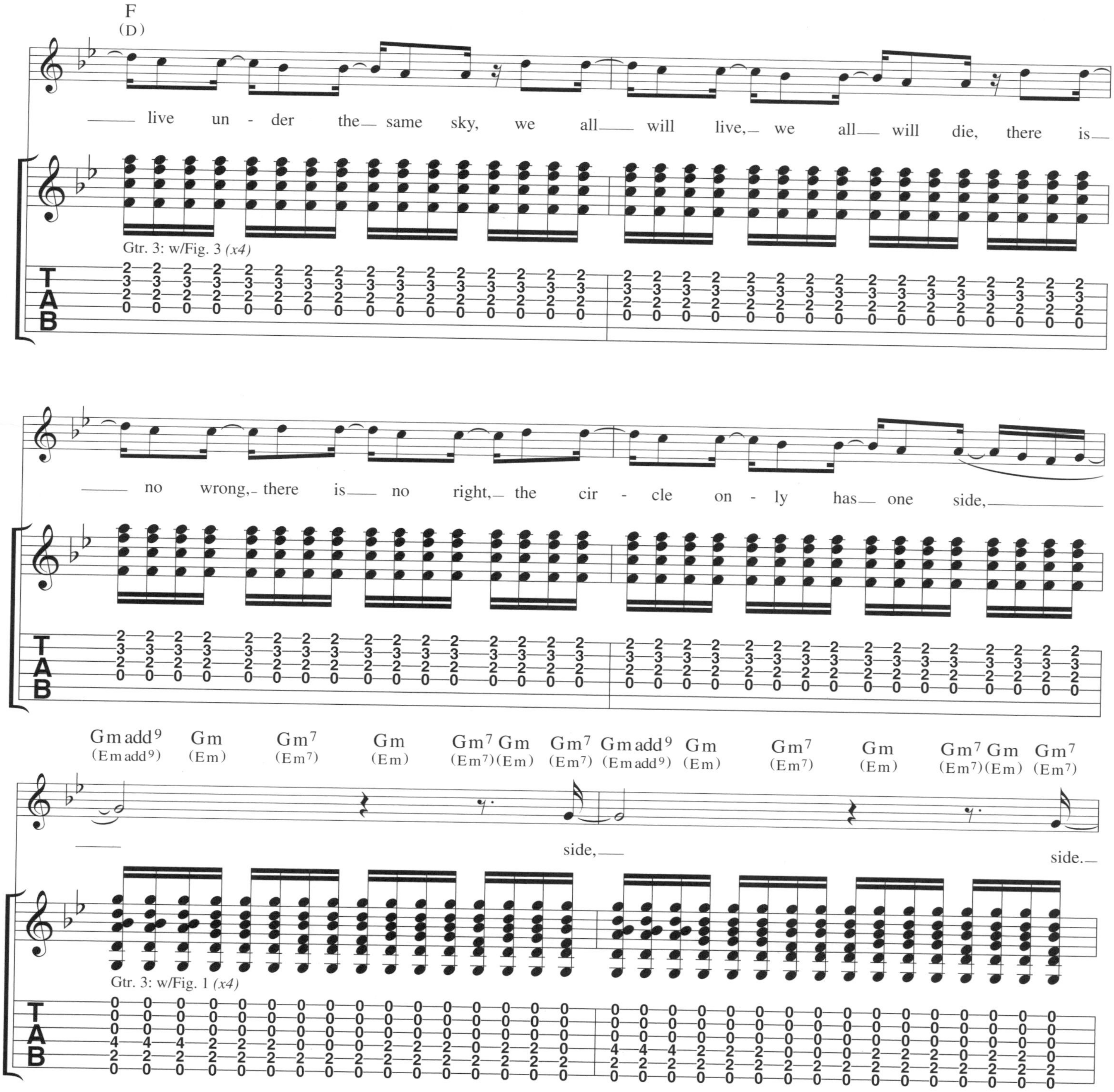
F
(D)
live under the same sky, we all will live, we all will die, there is
Gtr. 3: w/Fig. 3 (x4)
no wrong, there is no right, the circle only has one side,
Gmadd9 (Emadd9) Gm (Em) Gm7 (Em7) Gm (Em) Gm7 (Em7) Gm (Em) Gm7 (Em7) Gmadd9 (Emadd9) Gm (Em) Gm7 (Em7) Gm (Em) Gm7 (Em7) Gm (Em) Gm7 (Em7)
side, side.
Gtr. 3: w/Fig. 1 (x4)

Fig. 3
Gtr. 3
F
(D)

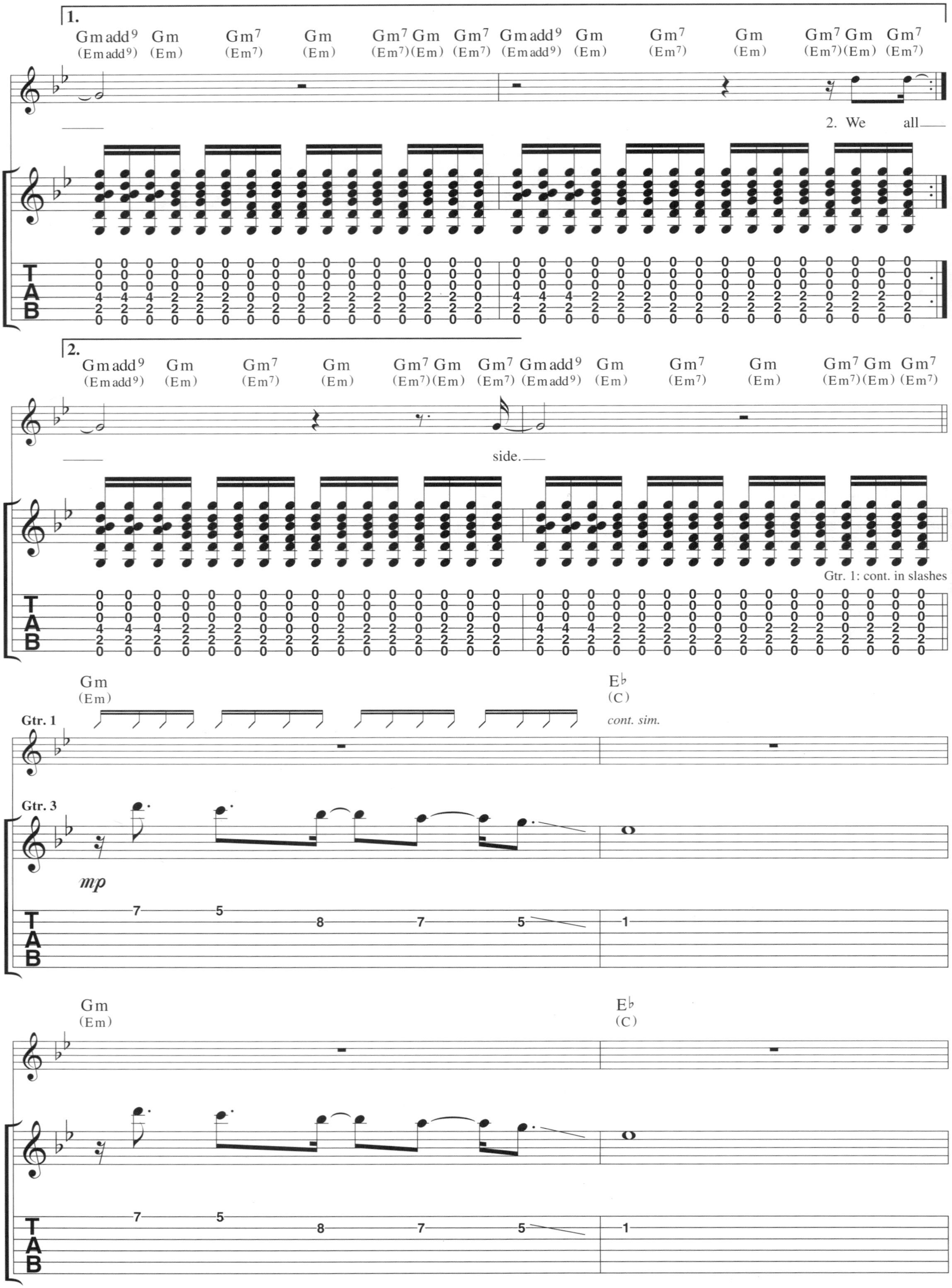
1.
Gmadd9 (Emadd9) Gm (Em) Gm7 (Em7) Gm (Em) Gm7 (Em7) Gm (Em) Gm7 (Em7) Gmadd9 (Emadd9) Gm (Em) Gm7 (Em7) Gm (Em) Gm7 (Em7) Gm (Em) Gm7 (Em7)
2. We all
2.
Gmadd9 (Emadd9) Gm (Em) Gm7 (Em7) Gm (Em) Gm7 (Em7) Gm (Em) Gm7 (Em7) Gmadd9 (Emadd9) Gm (Em) Gm7 (Em7) Gm (Em) Gm7 (Em7) Gm (Em) Gm7 (Em7)
side.
Gtr. 1: cont. in slashes
Gm (Em)
E♭ (C)
Gtr. 1
cont. sim.
Gtr. 3
mp
Gm (Em)
E♭ (C)
TAB

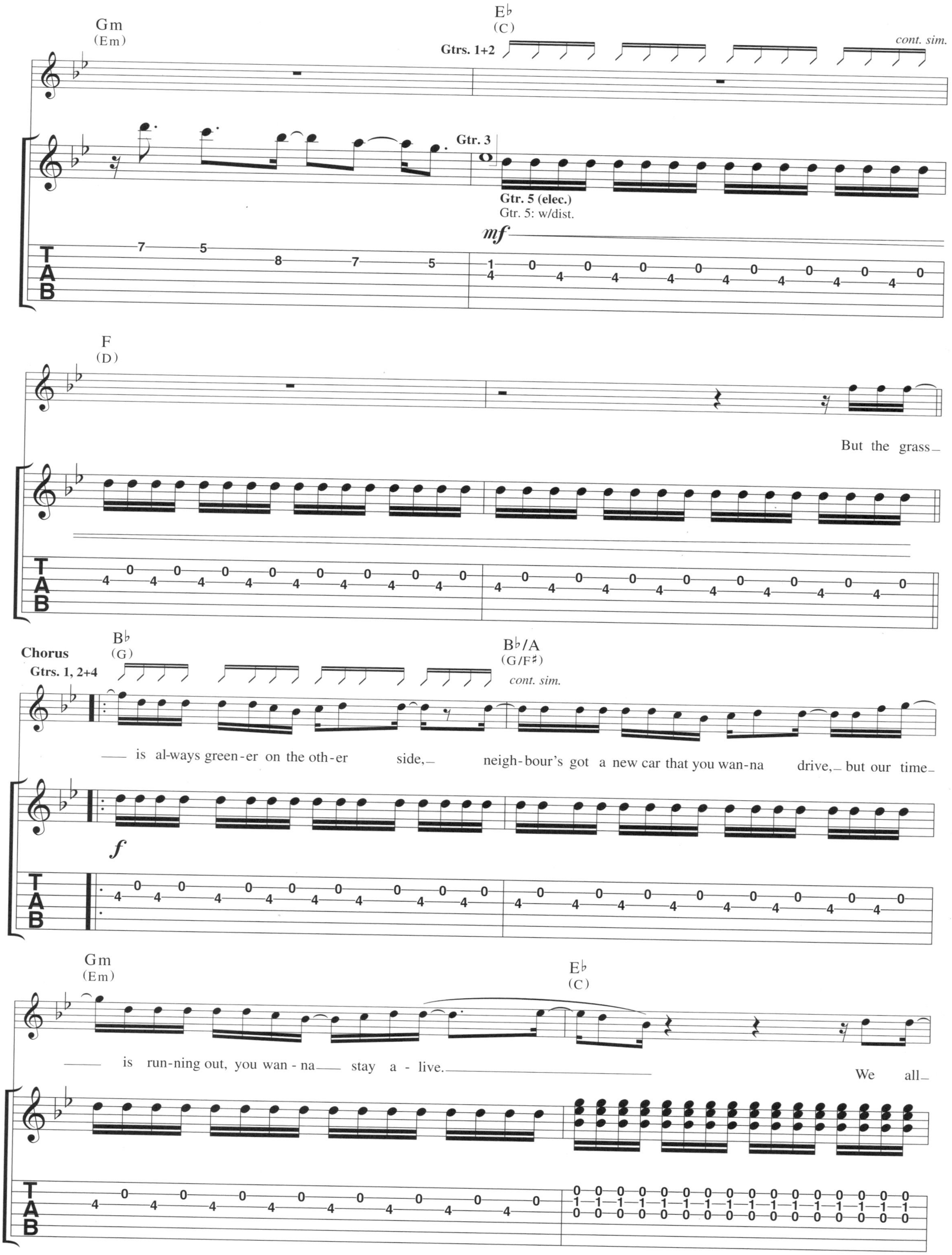
Gm (Em)
E♭ (C)
Gtrs. 1+2
cont. sim.
Gtr. 3
Gtr. 5 (elec.)
Gtr. 5: w/dist.
mf
F (D)
But the grass
Chorus
Gtrs. 1, 2+4
B♭ (G)
B♭/A (G/F♯)
cont. sim.
is al-ways green-er on the oth-er side,
neigh-bour's got a new car that you wan-na drive, but our time
f
Gm (Em)
E♭ (C)
is run-ning out, you wan-na stay a-live.
We all

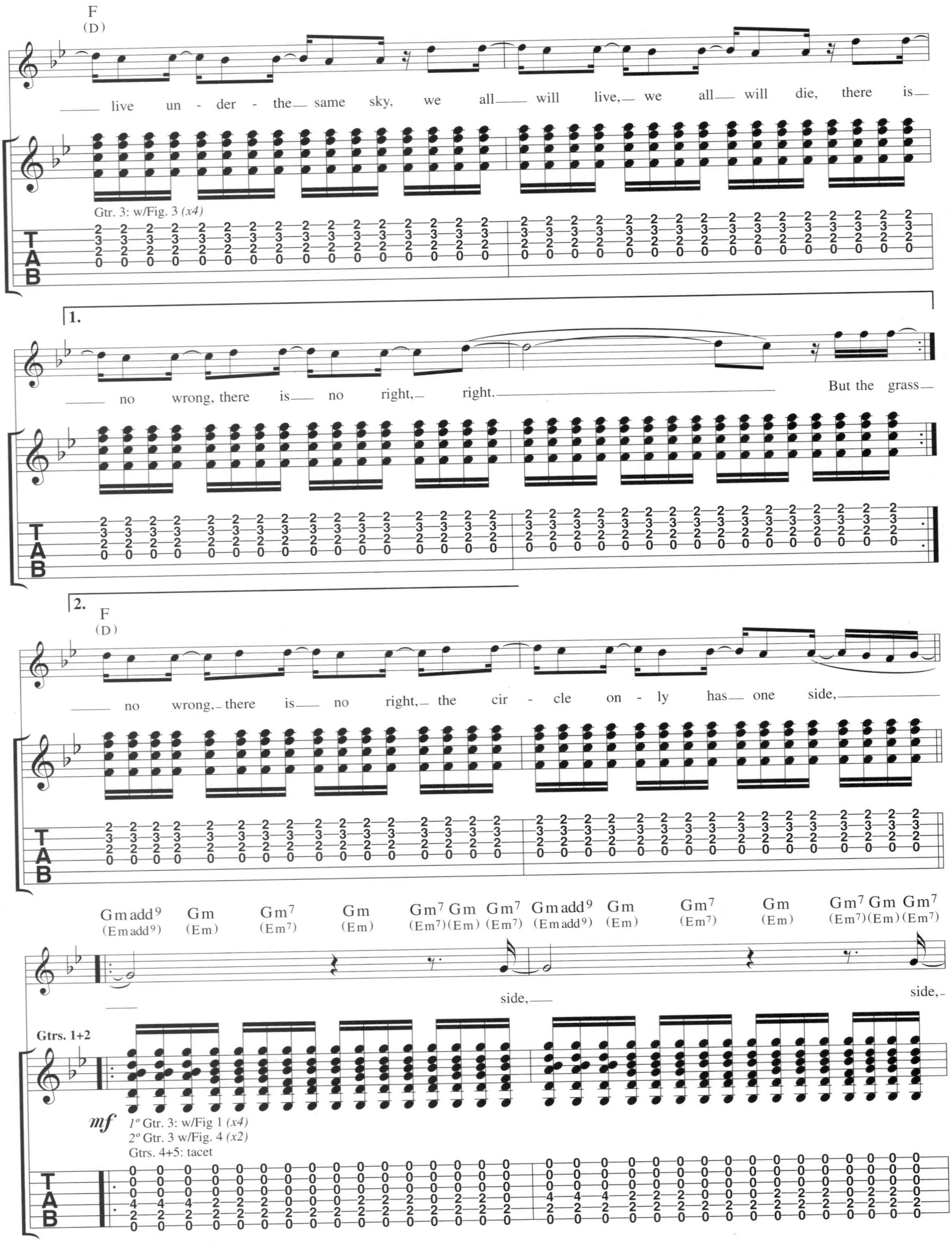
F (D)
live un - der - the same sky, we all will live, we all will die, there is
Gtr. 3: w/Fig. 3 (x4)
1.
no wrong, there is no right, right. But the grass
2.
F (D)
no wrong, there is no right, the cir - cle on - ly has one side,
Gmadd9 (Emadd9) Gm (Em) Gm7 (Em7) Gm (Em) Gm7 (Em7) Gm (Em) Gm7 (Em7) Gmadd9 (Emadd9) Gm (Em) Gm7 (Em7) Gm (Em) Gm7 (Em7) Gm (Em) Gm7 (Em7)
side, side,
Gtrs. 1+2
mf
1º Gtr. 3: w/Fig 1 (x4)
2º Gtr. 3 w/Fig. 4 (x2)
Gtrs. 4+5: tacet

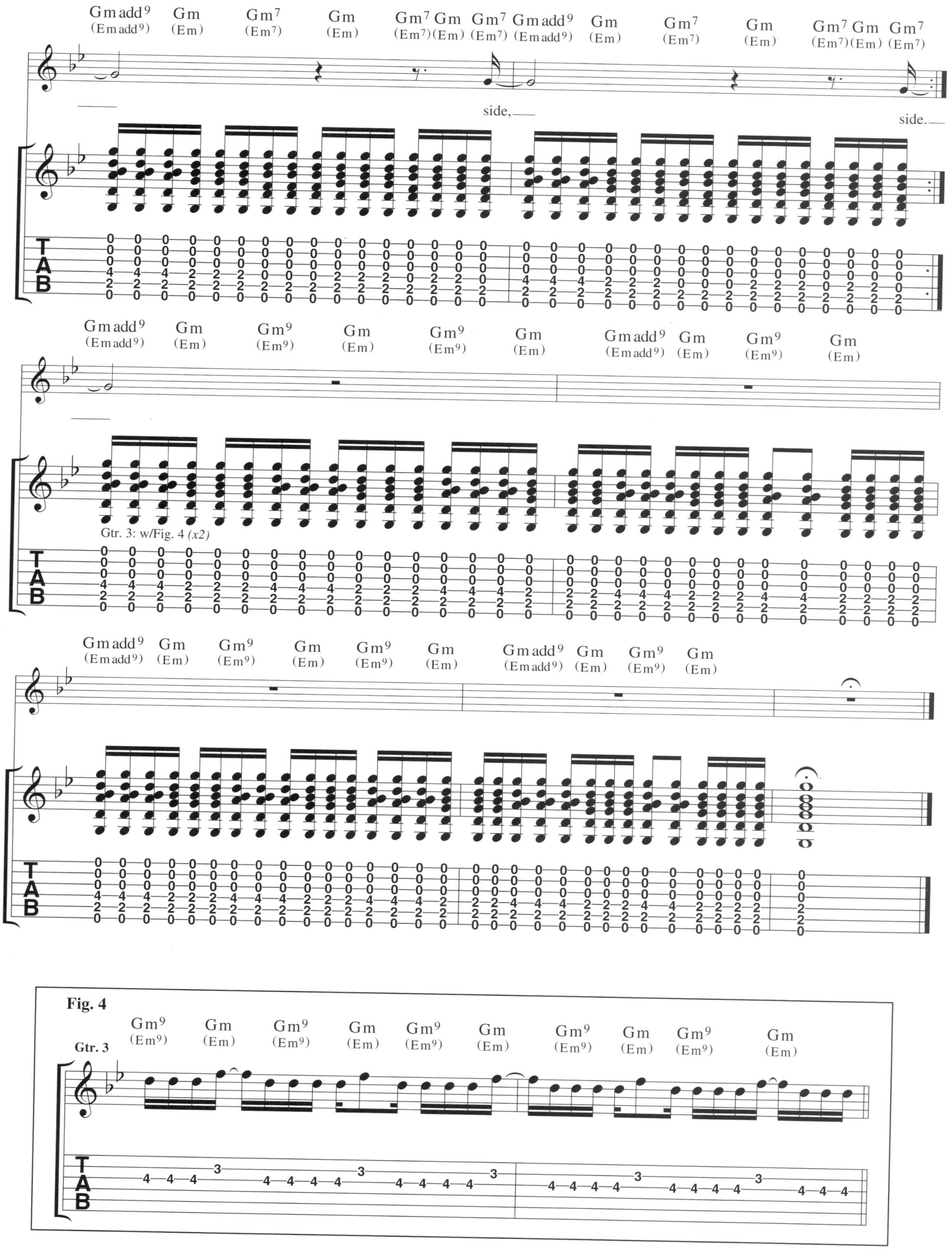
Gm add9 (Em add9) Gm (Em) Gm7 (Em7) Gm (Em) Gm7 (Em7) Gm (Em) Gm7 (Em7) Gm add9 (Em add9) Gm (Em) Gm7 (Em7) Gm (Em) Gm7 (Em7) Gm (Em) Gm7 (Em7)
side,
side.
TAB
Gm add9 (Em add9) Gm (Em) Gm9 (Em9) Gm (Em) Gm9 (Em9) Gm (Em) Gm add9 (Em add9) Gm (Em) Gm9 (Em9) Gm (Em)
Gtr. 3: w/Fig. 4 (x2)
TAB
Gm add9 (Em add9) Gm (Em) Gm9 (Em9) Gm (Em) Gm9 (Em9) Gm (Em) Gm add9 (Em add9) Gm (Em) Gm9 (Em9) Gm (Em)
TAB
Fig. 4
Gm9 (Em9) Gm (Em) Gm9 (Em9) Gm (Em) Gm9 (Em9) Gm (Em) Gm9 (Em9) Gm (Em) Gm9 (Em9) Gm (Em)
Gtr. 3
TAB

STILL WAITING

WORDS & MUSIC BY GREIG NORI, DERYCK WHIBLEY, STEVE JOCZ & DAVE BAKSH

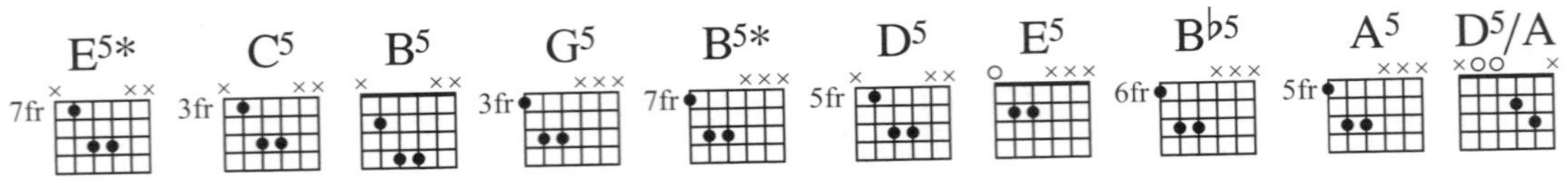

Gtrs. 3 & 4 (elec.)
*Gtrs. 1 & 2
E5 C5 E5 C5 B5
ff All gtrs. w/heavy overdrive
Fig. 2
*composite part
Verse
E5 B♭5 A5 B♭5 A5 G5 A5 E5
(shouted) 1. Drop dead a bullet to my head, your words are like a
2. Ignorance and understanding, were the first ones to
Gtrs. 1 & 2
Gtr. 3 tacet
P.M.
G5 E5 B♭5 A5 B♭5 A5 G5 A5
gun in hand. You can't change, the state of the nation,
jump in line. Out of step for what we believe in,
G5 A5 B5* D5 E5
we just need some motivation. Since I have
but who's left to start the pleading? How far

B♭5 A5 G5 B♭5 A5 G5 A5 E5 G5
seen no con - vic - tion, just lies and more con - tra - dic - tions.
will we take this, it's not hard to see through the thick - ness.
P.M. P.M. P.M. P.M. P.M.
E5 B♭5 A5 B♭5 A5 G5 A5 G5 A5
So tell me, what would you say? I'd say it's
P.M. P.M. P.M.
Chorus
B5* E5* C5
Gtrs. 3 & 4 pick scrape
time to lis - ten.
So am I, still wait - ing,
P.M. open out

G5 B5 E5* C5
for this world to stop hat - ing. Can't find a good rea - son,
1.
Interlude
G5 B5 E5 C5
can't find hope to be - lieve in.
*Gtrs. 1 & 2 (elec.)
ff All gtrs. w/heavy overdrive
*composite part
2.
Bridge
E5 C5 B5 B5 E5*
to be - lieve. This

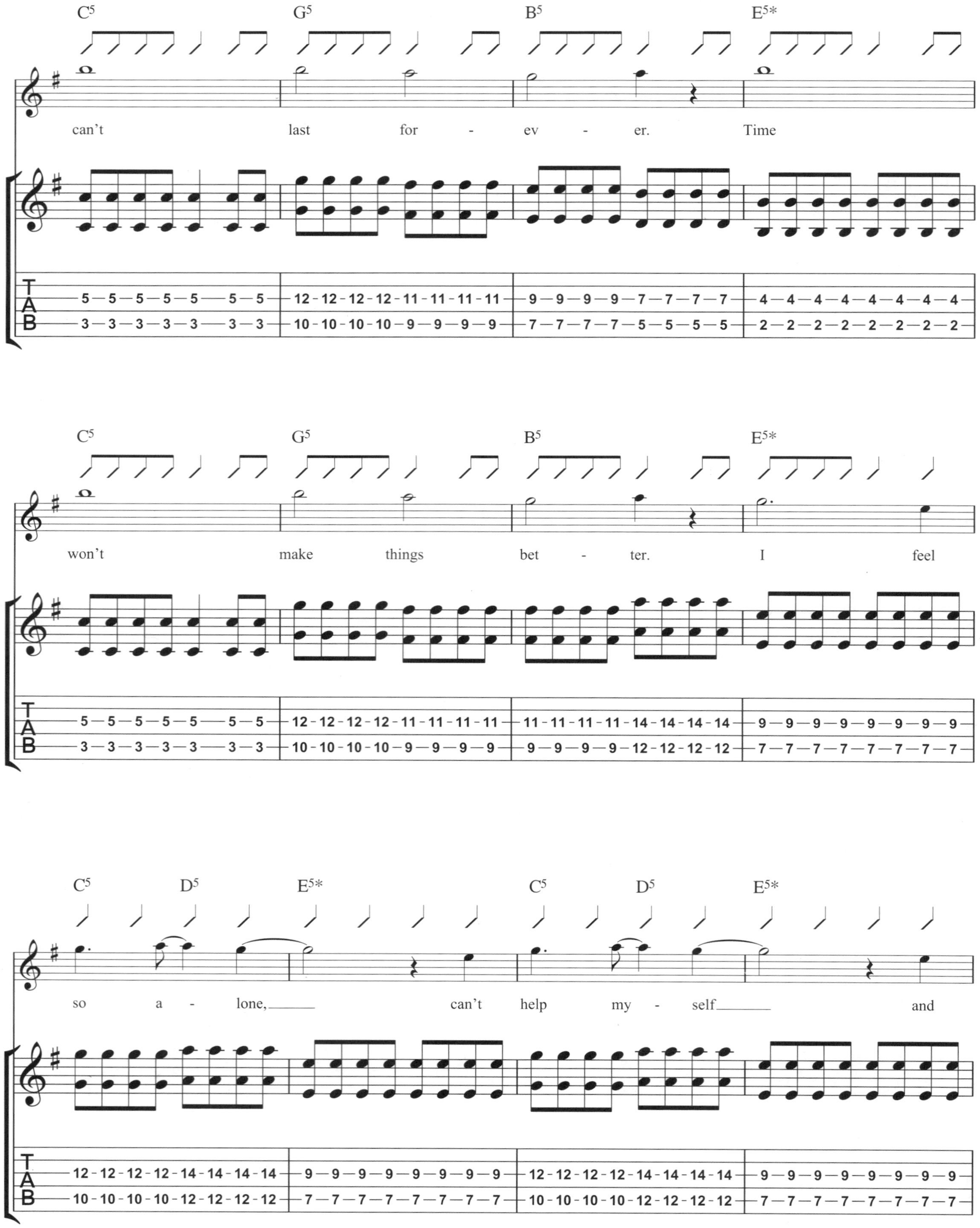
C5 G5 B5 E5*
can't last for - ev - er. Time
C5 G5 B5 E5*
won't make things bet - ter. I feel
C5 D5 E5* C5 D5 E5*
so a - lone, can't help my - self and

C5 D5 E5* C5/Gbass D5 E5
no - one knows if this is worth - less tell me.
Fig. 1
C5 G5 B5
So!
E5 C5 G5 B5 D5/A
1.
Gtr. 2
Gtrs. 3 & 4 (elec.)
Gtr. 1 w/Fig. 1
Gtr. 4 w/heavy overdrive

2.
B5 E5 C5 G5
What harm we done? We're in a war that
Gtr. 3
Gtr. 1 w/Fig. 1 (x2)
B5 E5 C5 G5
can't be won. This can't be real, 'cause I don't know
B5
what to feel.
+ pick scrape
Chorus
E5*
So am I,
Gtrs. 1 & 2 w/Fig. 2

C5 G5 B5*
still wait - ing, for this world to stop hat - ing.
E5* C5 G5
Can't find a good rea - son, can't find hope
1. 2.
B5* B5* E5*
to be - lieve. to be - lieve.
All Gtrs.
T
A
B

Sunrise

Words & Music by Jarvis Cocker, Nick Banks, Candida Doyle, Stephen Mackey & Mark Webber

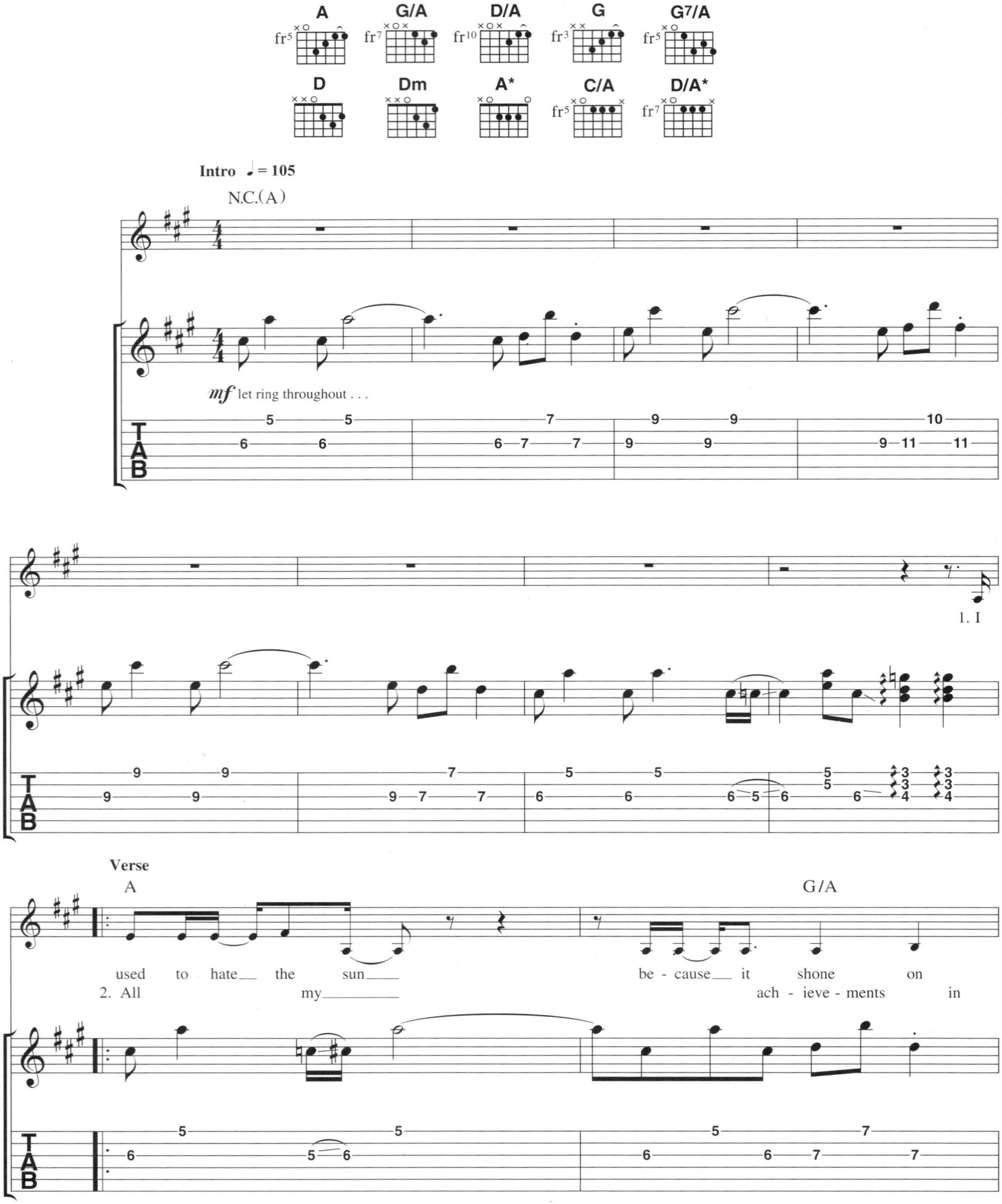

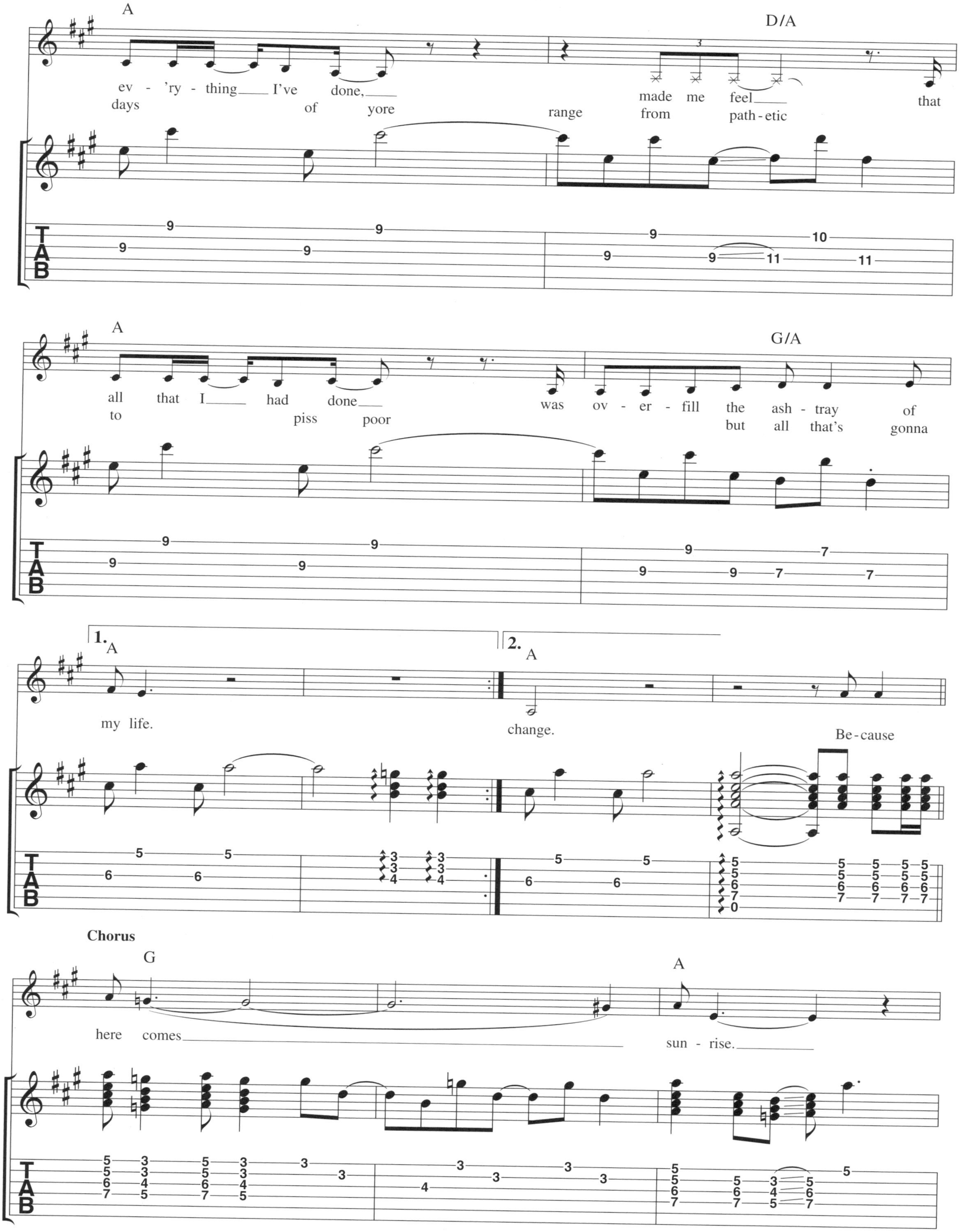
A
D/A
ev - 'ry - thing___ I've done,___ made me feel___ that
days of yore range from path - etic
A
G/A
all that I___ had done___ was ov - er - fill the ash - tray of
to piss poor but all that's gonna
1. A
2. A
my life.
change.
Be-cause
Chorus
G
A
here comes___ sun - rise.___

G
Yeah, it's your
A
sun - rise.
I used to hide from the sun,
mp
G7/A
A
tried to live my whole life un - der - ground. Mm,
cont. sim.
D/A
A
why d'ya have to rise and ru - in all my fun? Just turn ov -
slowly cresc.
TAB

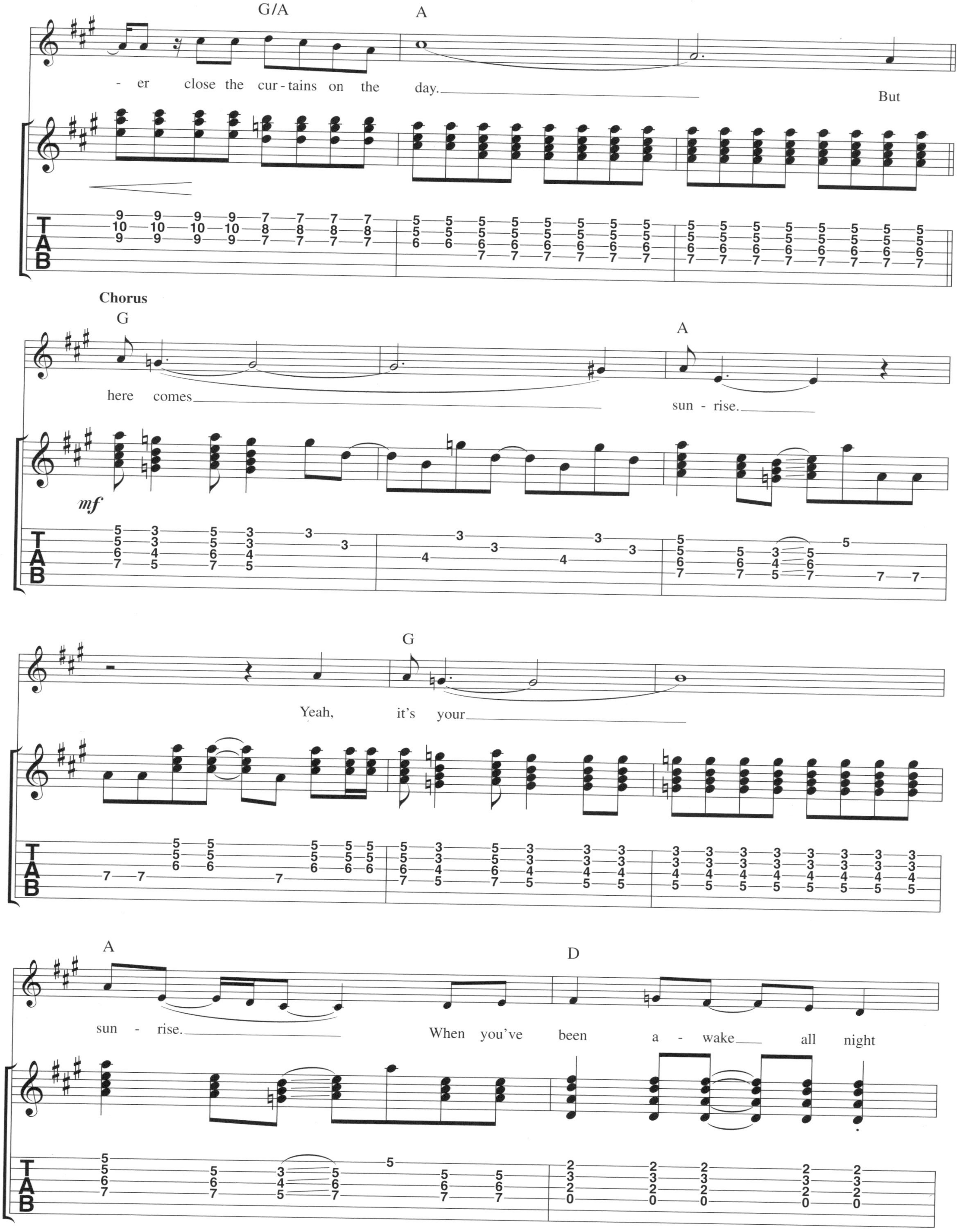
G/A
A
-er close the cur-tains on the day.
But
Chorus
G
A
here comes sun-rise.
mf
G
Yeah, it's your
A
D
sun-rise.
When you've been a-wake all night

A
Dm
A
long and you feel like crash - ing out at dawn. But you've
Dm
been a - wake all night so why should you crash out at dawn?
New tempo ♩= 132
A
A*
C/A
mp optional w/acoustic
D/A*
A*
TAB

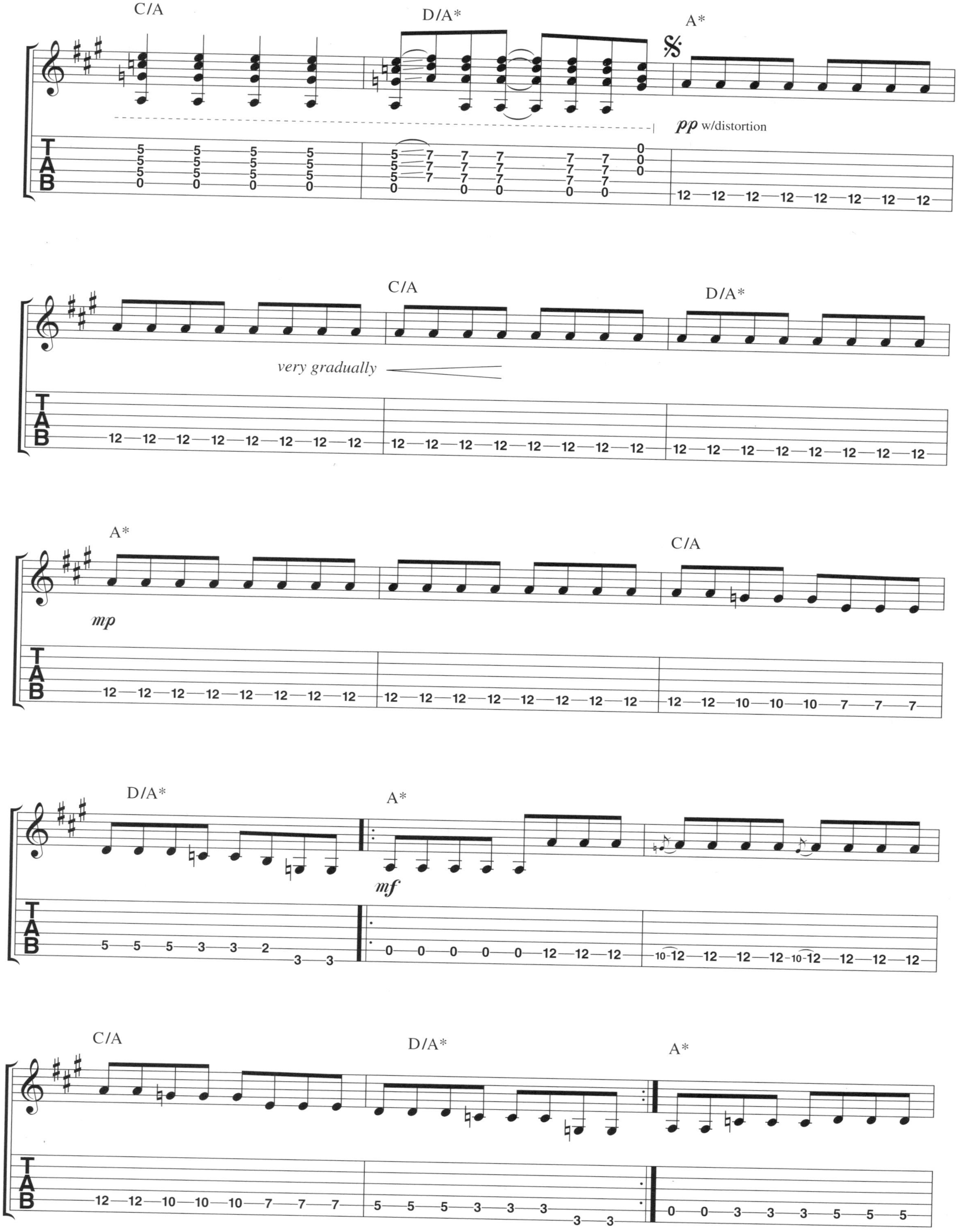
C/A
D/A*
A*
pp w/distortion
C/A
D/A*
very gradually
A*
mp
C/A
D/A*
A*
mf
C/A
D/A*
A*

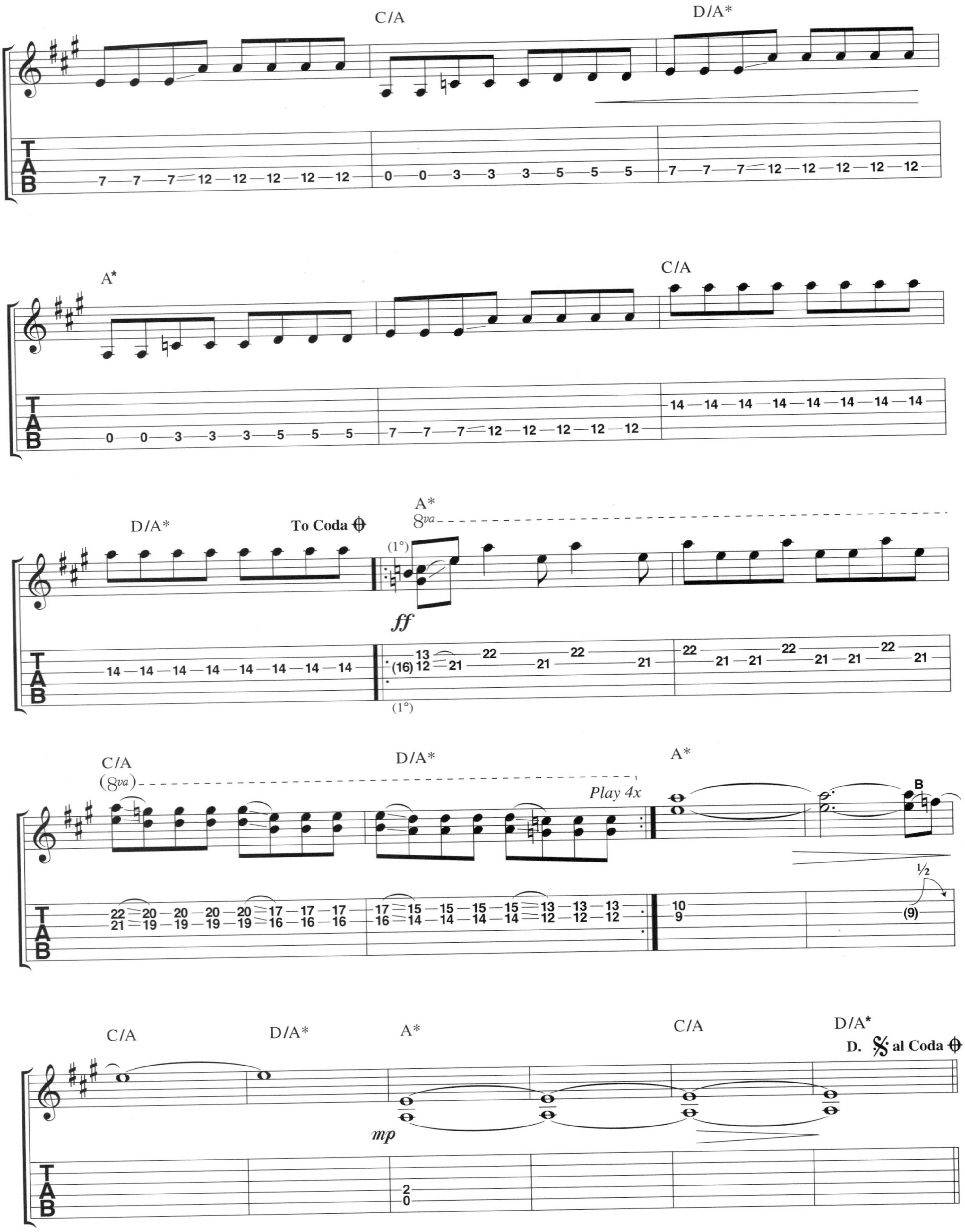
C/A
D/A*
A*
C/A
D/A*
To Coda
8va
(1°)
ff
C/A
(8va)
D/A*
Play 4x
A*
B
½
C/A
D/A*
A*
C/A
D/A*
mp
D. al Coda

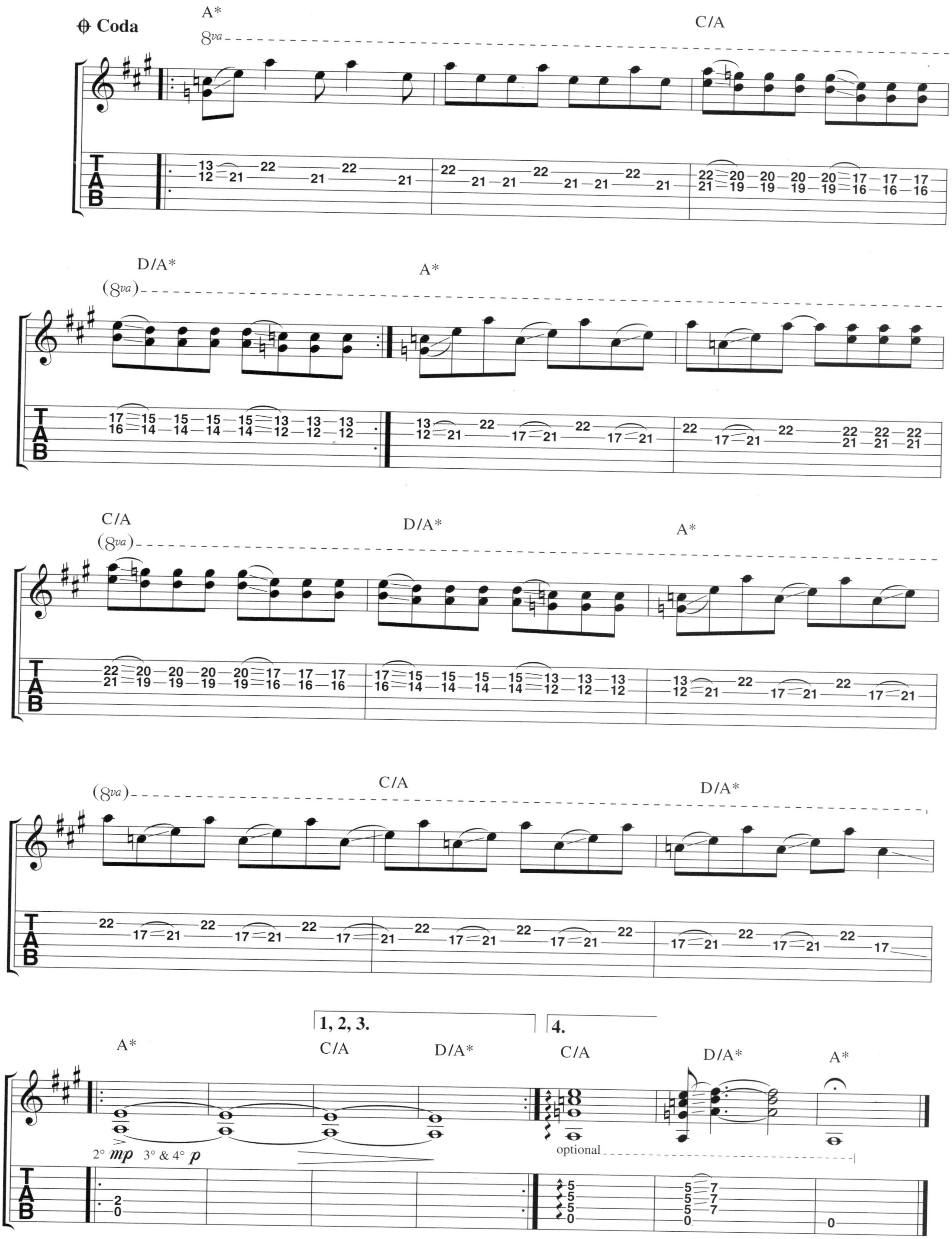
Coda
A*
8va
C/A
D/A*
(8va)
A*
C/A
(8va)
D/A*
A*
(8va)
C/A
D/A*
1, 2, 3.
4.
A*
C/A
D/A*
C/A
D/A*
A*
2° mp 3° & 4° p
optional

Stop Crying Your Heart Out

Words & Music by Noel Gallagher

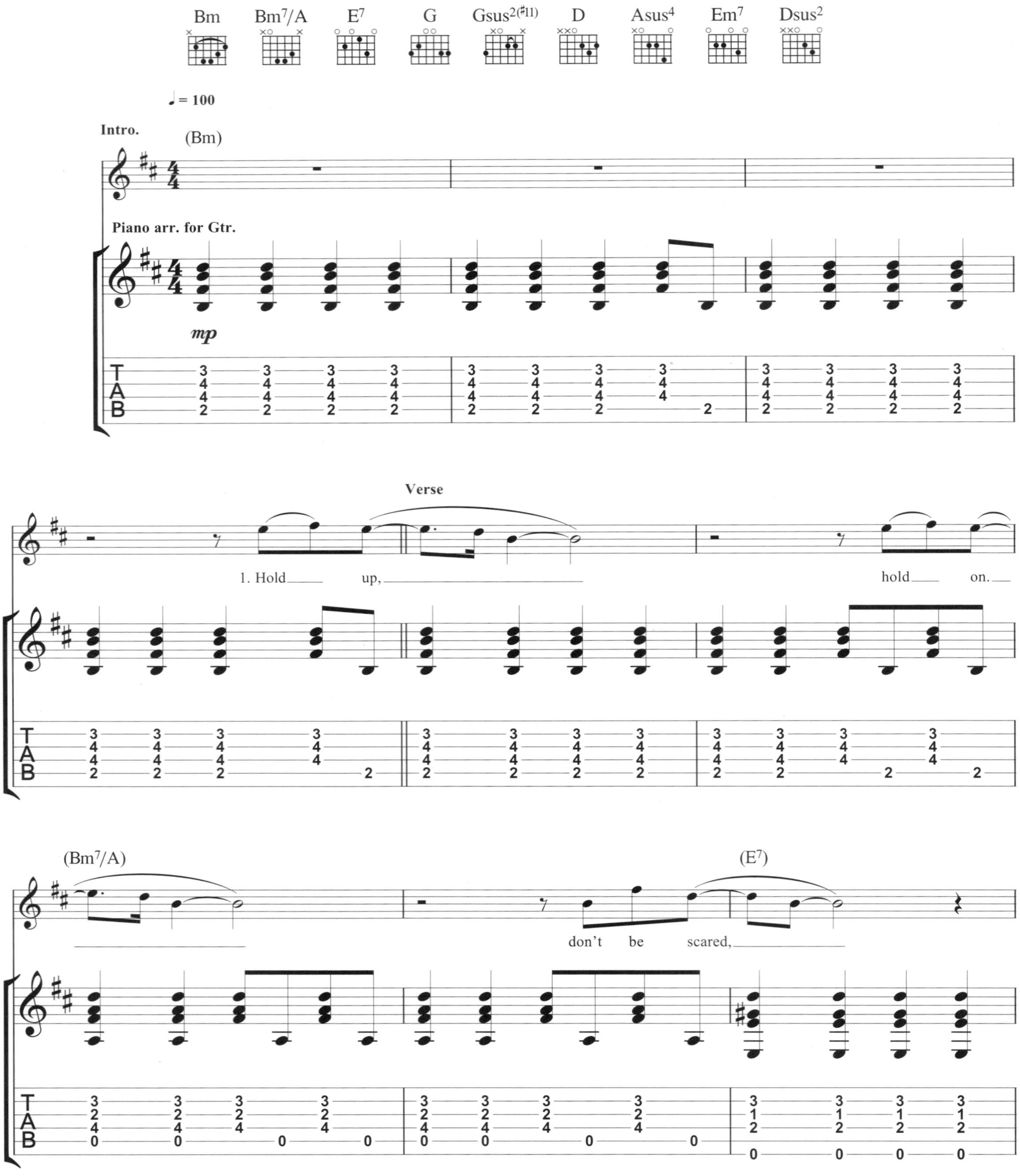

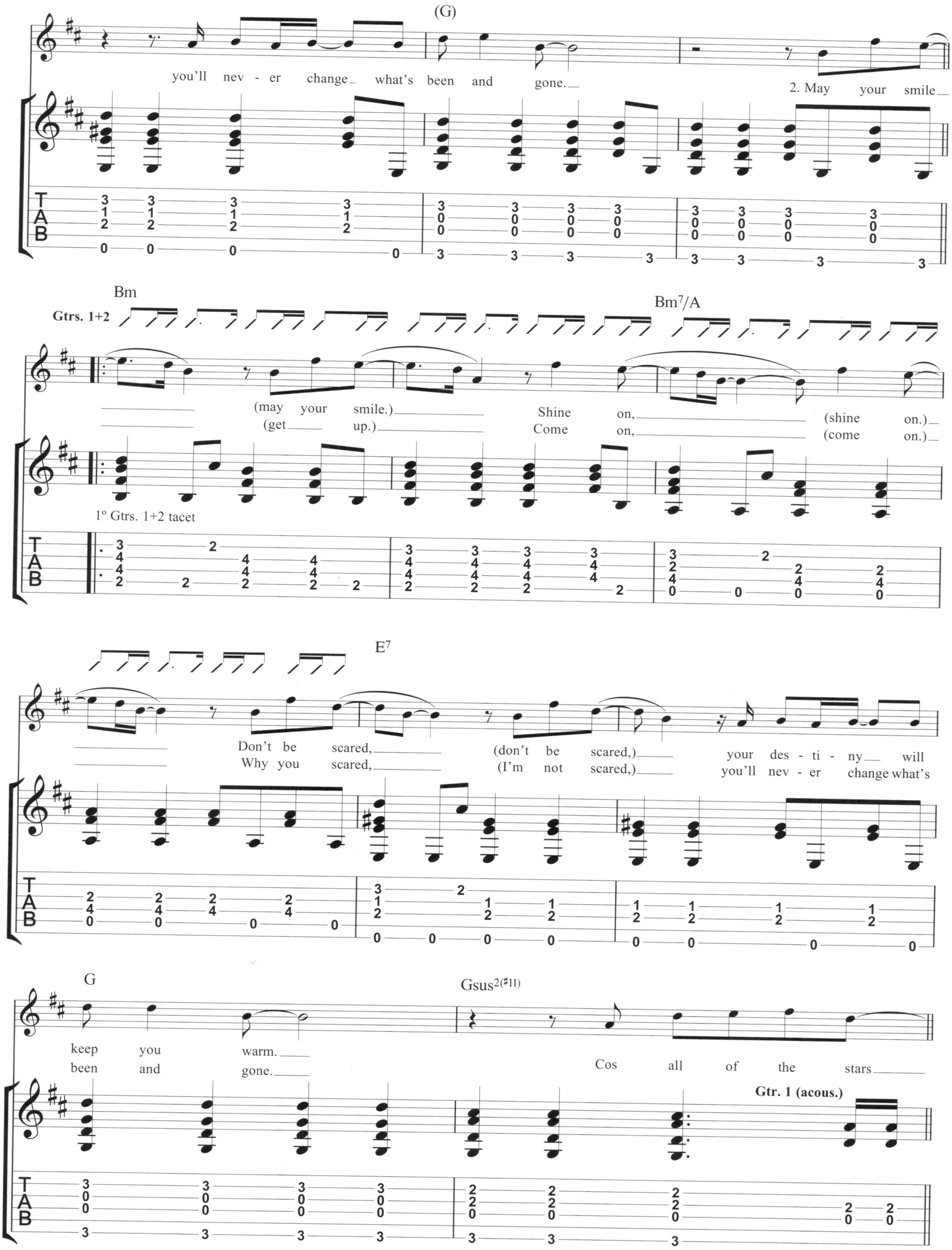
(G)
you'll nev - er change what's been and gone.
2. May your smile
Bm
Gtrs. 1+2
Bm7/A
(may your smile.) Shine on, (shine on.)
(get up.) Come on, (come on.)
1º Gtrs. 1+2 tacet
E7
Don't be scared, (don't be scared,) your des - ti - ny will
Why you scared, (I'm not scared,) you'll nev - er change what's
G
Gsus2(♯11)
keep you warm.
been and gone.
Cos all of the stars
Gtr. 1 (acous.)

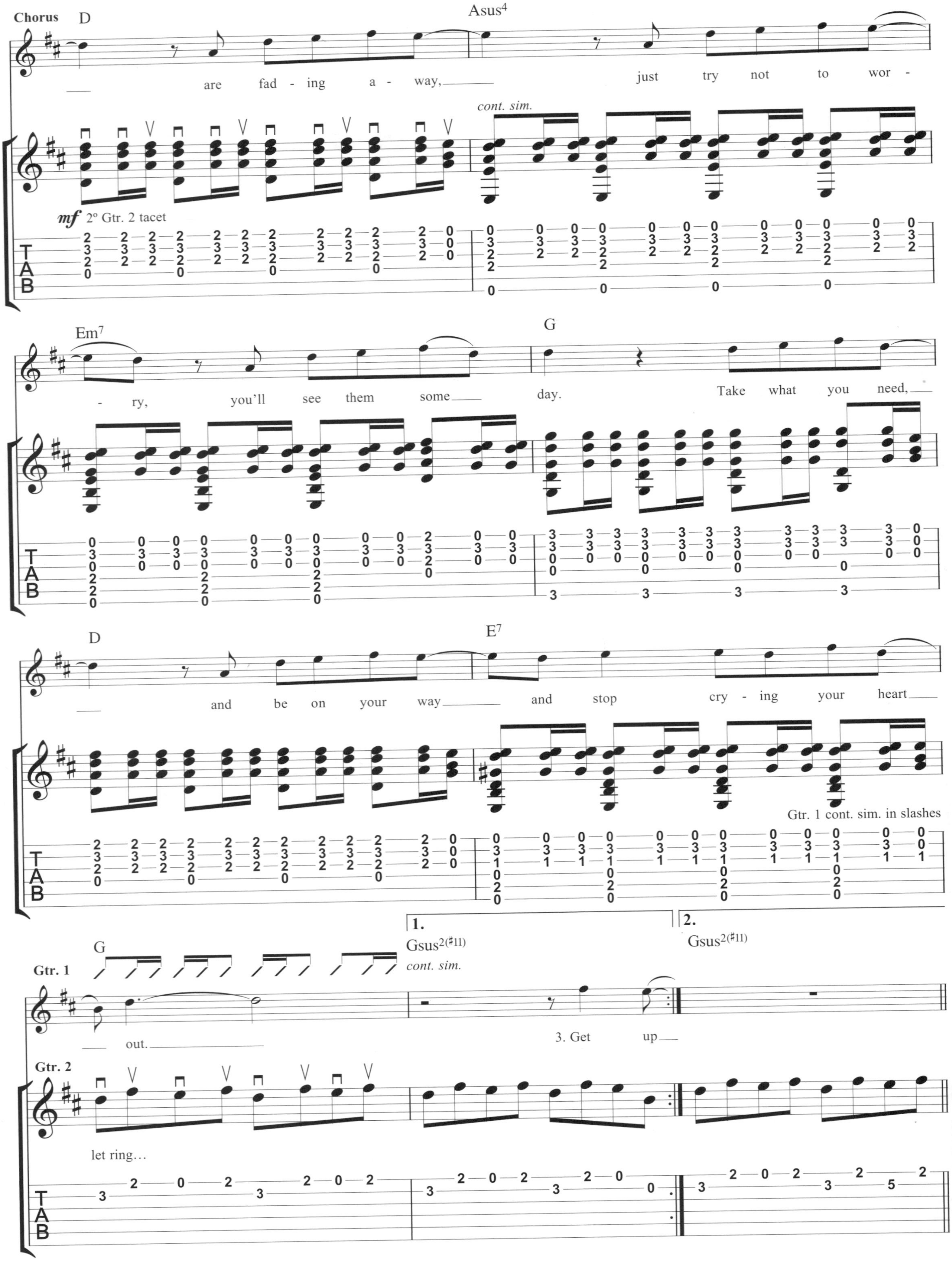
Chorus
D
Asus4
are fad - ing a - way, just try not to wor -
cont. sim.
mf 2º Gtr. 2 tacet
TAB
Em7
G
- ry, you'll see them some day. Take what you need,
D
E7
and be on your way and stop cry - ing your heart
Gtr. 1 cont. sim. in slashes
1.
2.
G
Gsus2(♯11)
Gsus2(♯11)
Gtr. 1
cont. sim.
out.
3. Get up
Gtr. 2
let ring…

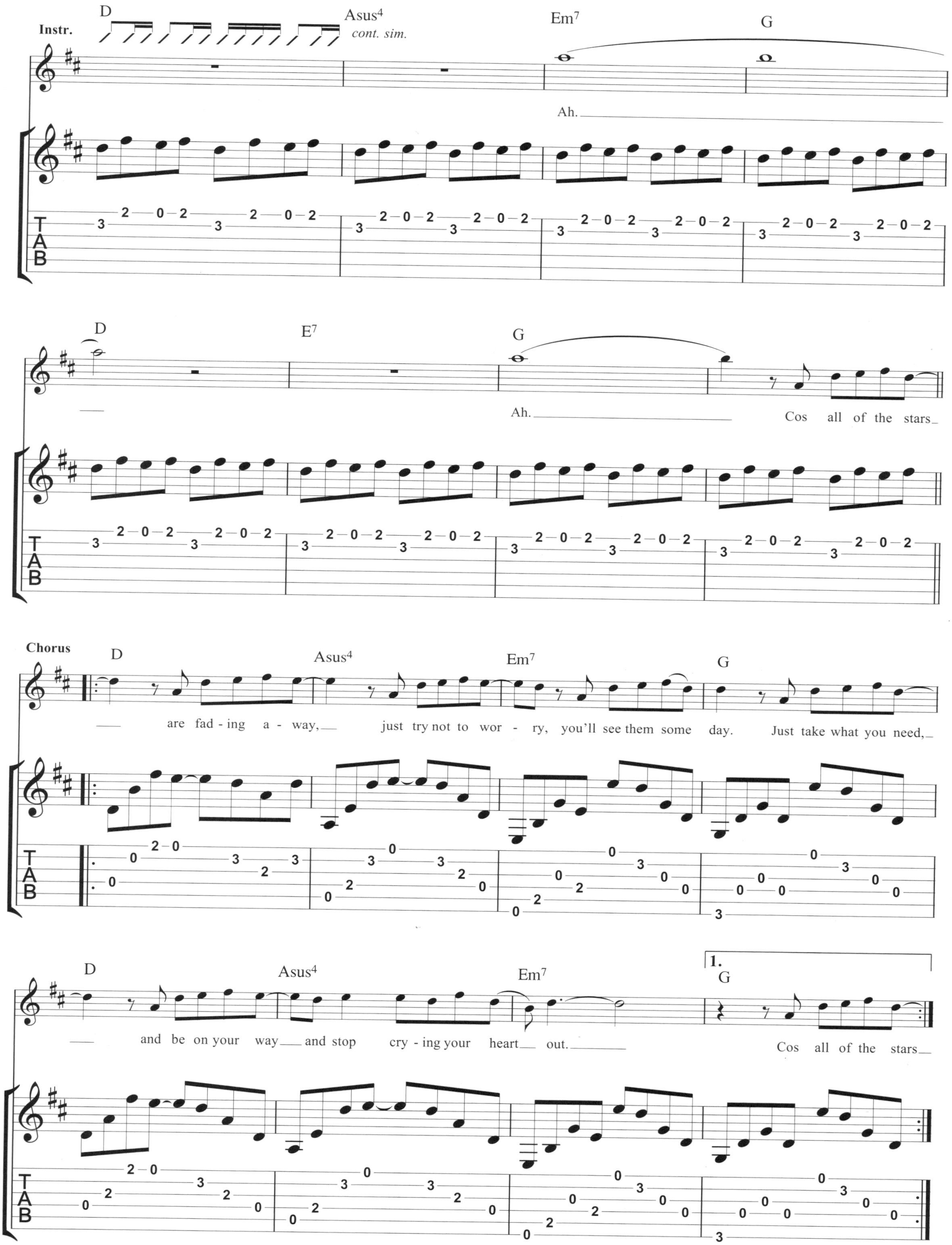
Instr.
D
Asus4
cont. sim.
Em7
G
Ah.
D
E7
G
Ah.
Cos all of the stars
Chorus
D
Asus4
Em7
G
are fad-ing a-way, just try not to wor-ry, you'll see them some day. Just take what you need,
D
Asus4
Em7
1.
G
and be on your way and stop cry-ing your heart out.
Cos all of the stars
TAB

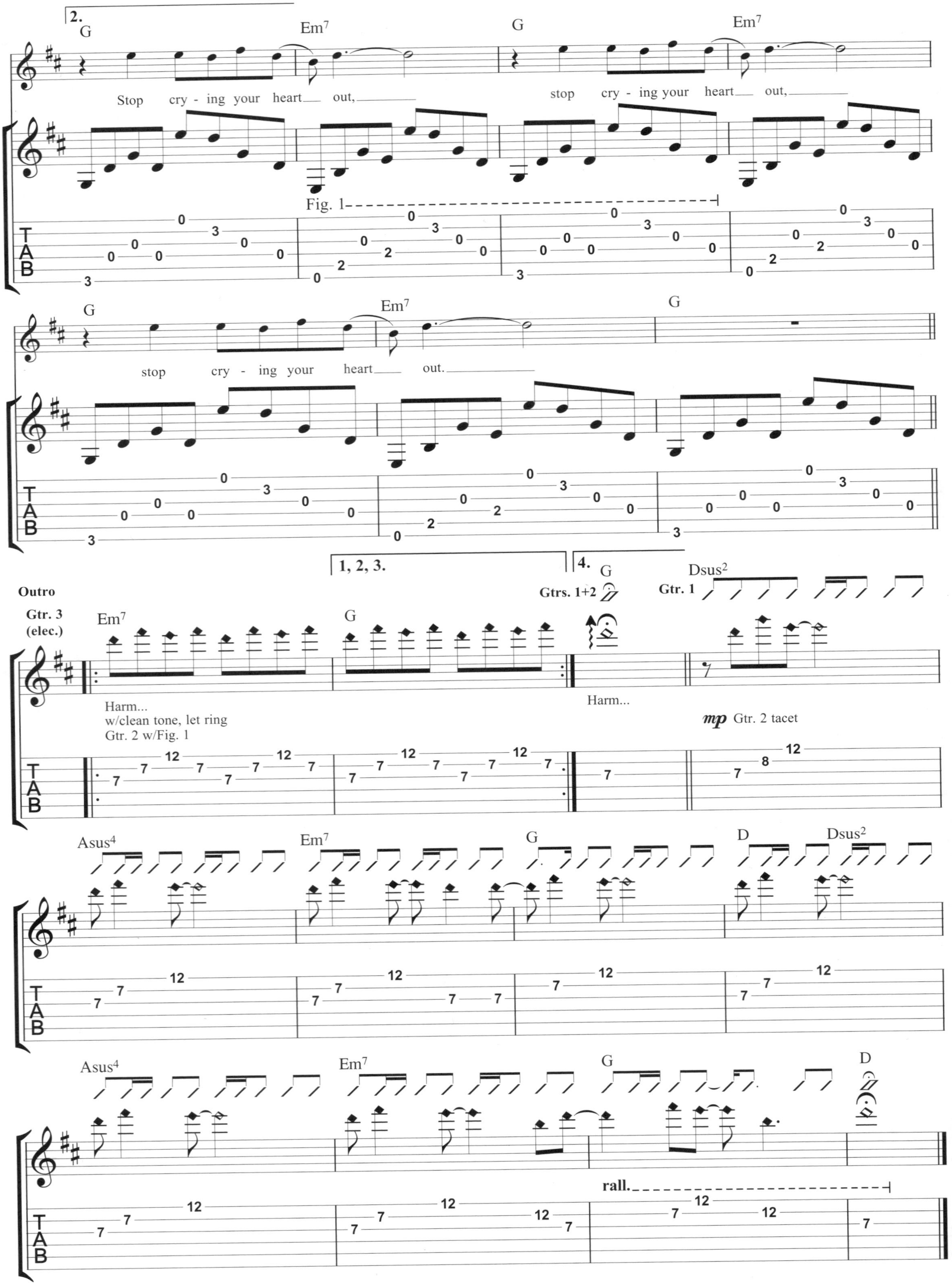
2.
G Em7 G Em7
Stop cry - ing your heart out, stop cry - ing your heart out,
Fig. 1
G Em7 G
stop cry - ing your heart out.
1, 2, 3.
4.
Outro
Gtr. 3 (elec.)
Em7 G
Harm...
w/clean tone, let ring
Gtr. 2 w/Fig. 1
Gtrs. 1+2
G
Harm...
Gtr. 1
Dsus2
mp Gtr. 2 tacet
Asus4 Em7 G D Dsus2
Asus4 Em7 G D
rall.

VEGAS TWO TIMES

WORDS & MUSIC BY KELLY JONES

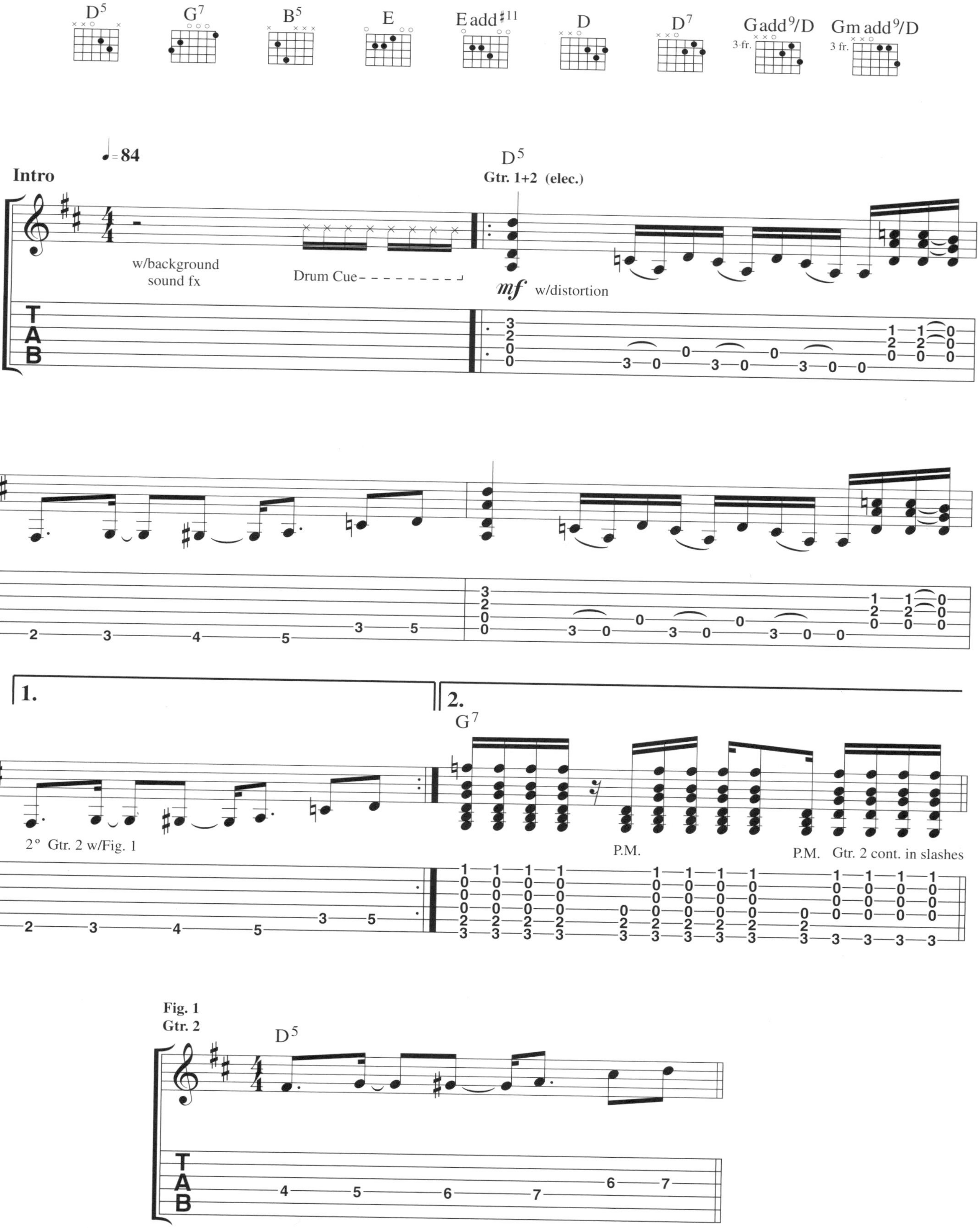

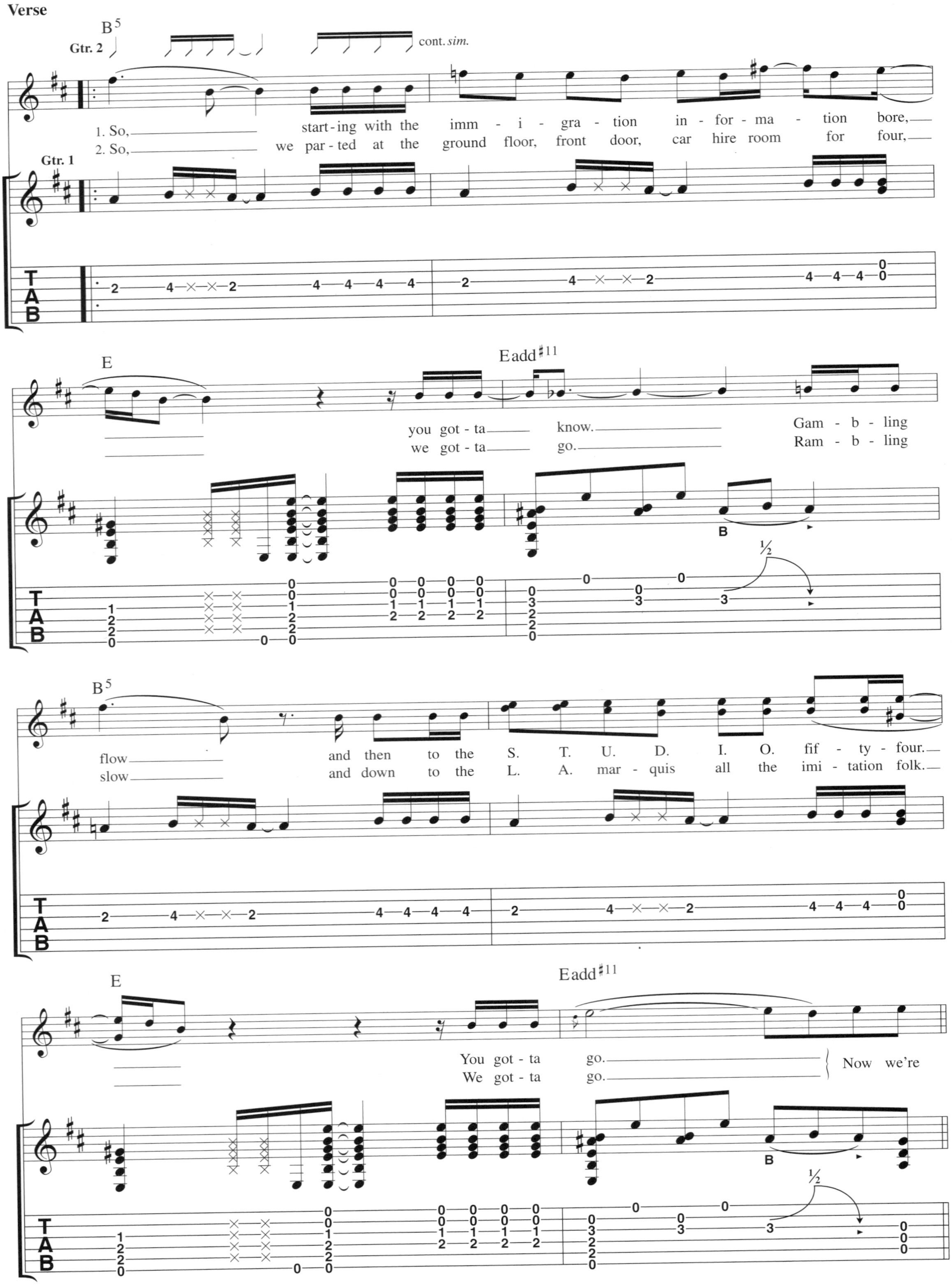
Verse
B5
Gtr. 2
cont. sim.
1. So, starting with the immigration information bore,
2. So, we parted at the ground floor, front door, car hire room for four,
Gtr. 1
E
Eadd♯11
you gotta know. Gambling
we gotta go. Rambling
B5
flow and then to the S. T. U. D. I. O. fifty-four.
slow and down to the L. A. marquis all the imitation folk.
E
Eadd♯11
You gotta go.
We gotta go.
Now we're

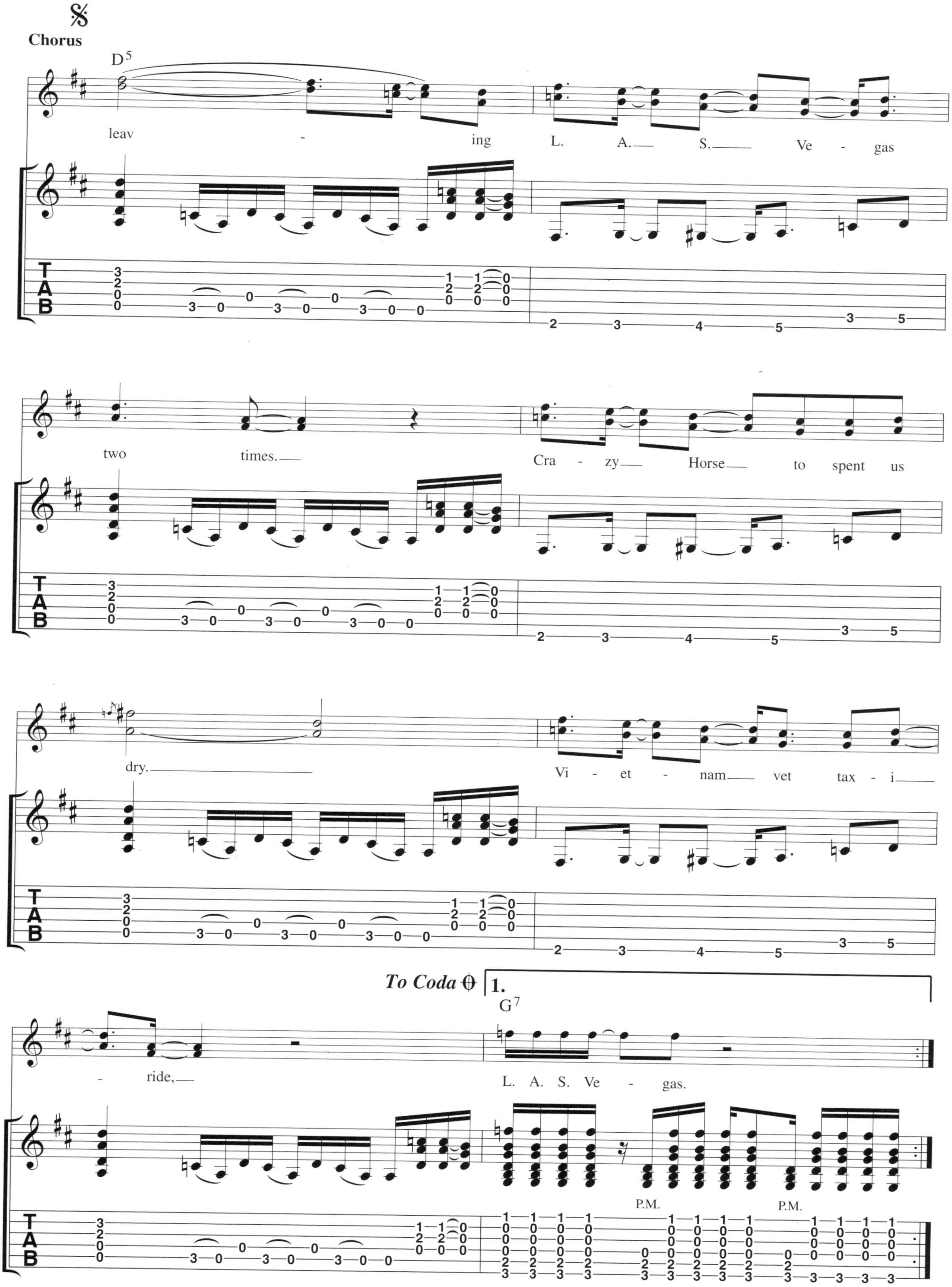
Chorus
D5
leav - ing L. A. S. Ve - gas
two times.
Cra - zy Horse to spent us
dry.
Vi - et - nam vet tax - i
- ride,
To Coda
1.
G7
L. A. S. Ve - gas.
P.M.
P.M.

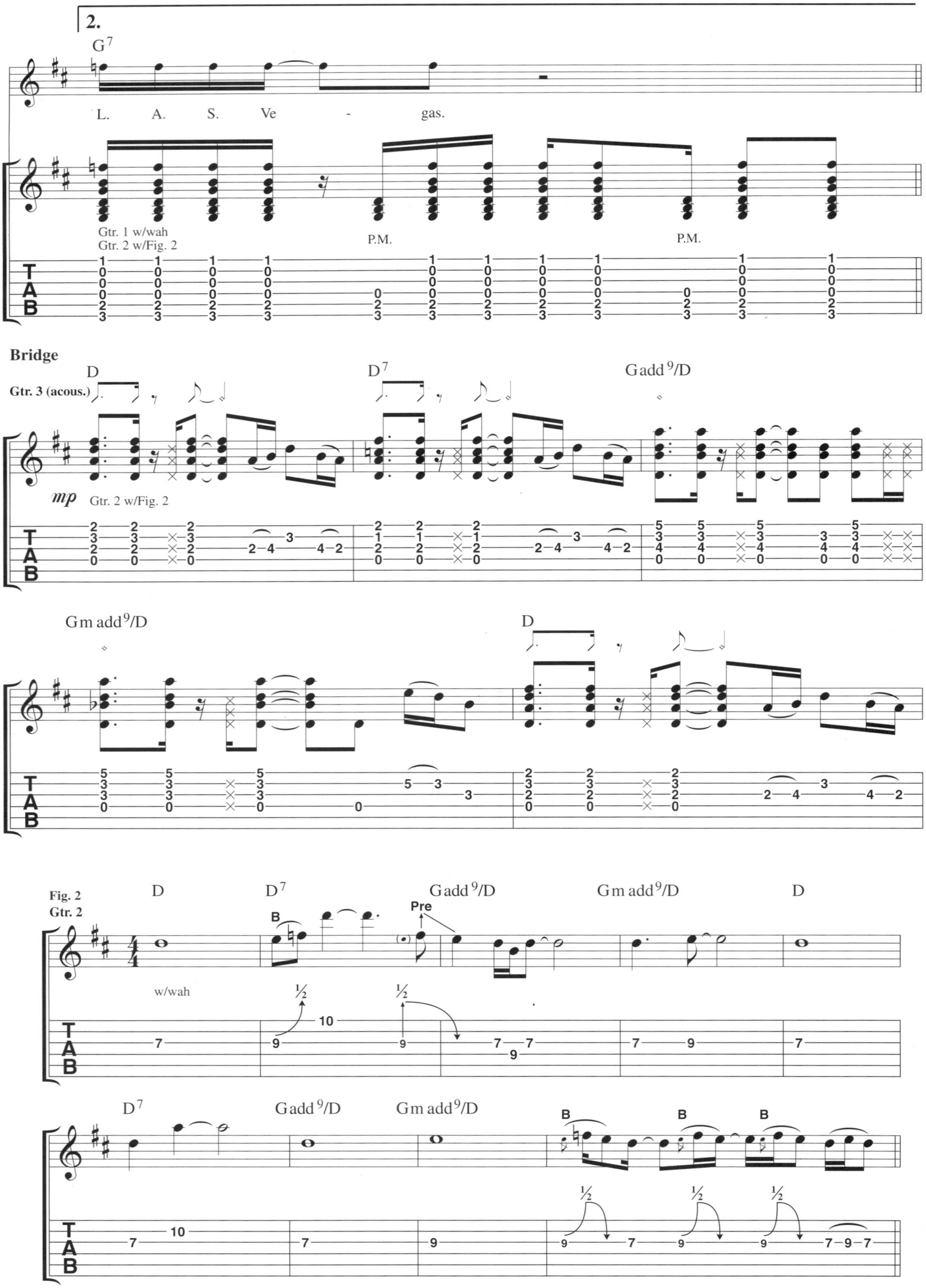
2.
G7
L. A. S. Ve - gas.
Gtr. 1 w/wah
Gtr. 2 w/Fig. 2
P.M.
P.M.
Bridge
D
D7
Gadd9/D
Gtr. 3 (acous.)
mp
Gtr. 2 w/Fig. 2
Gm add9/D
D
Fig. 2
Gtr. 2
D
D7
Gadd9/D
Gm add9/D
D
B
Pre
w/wah
½
½
D7
Gadd9/D
Gm add9/D
B
B
B
½
½
½

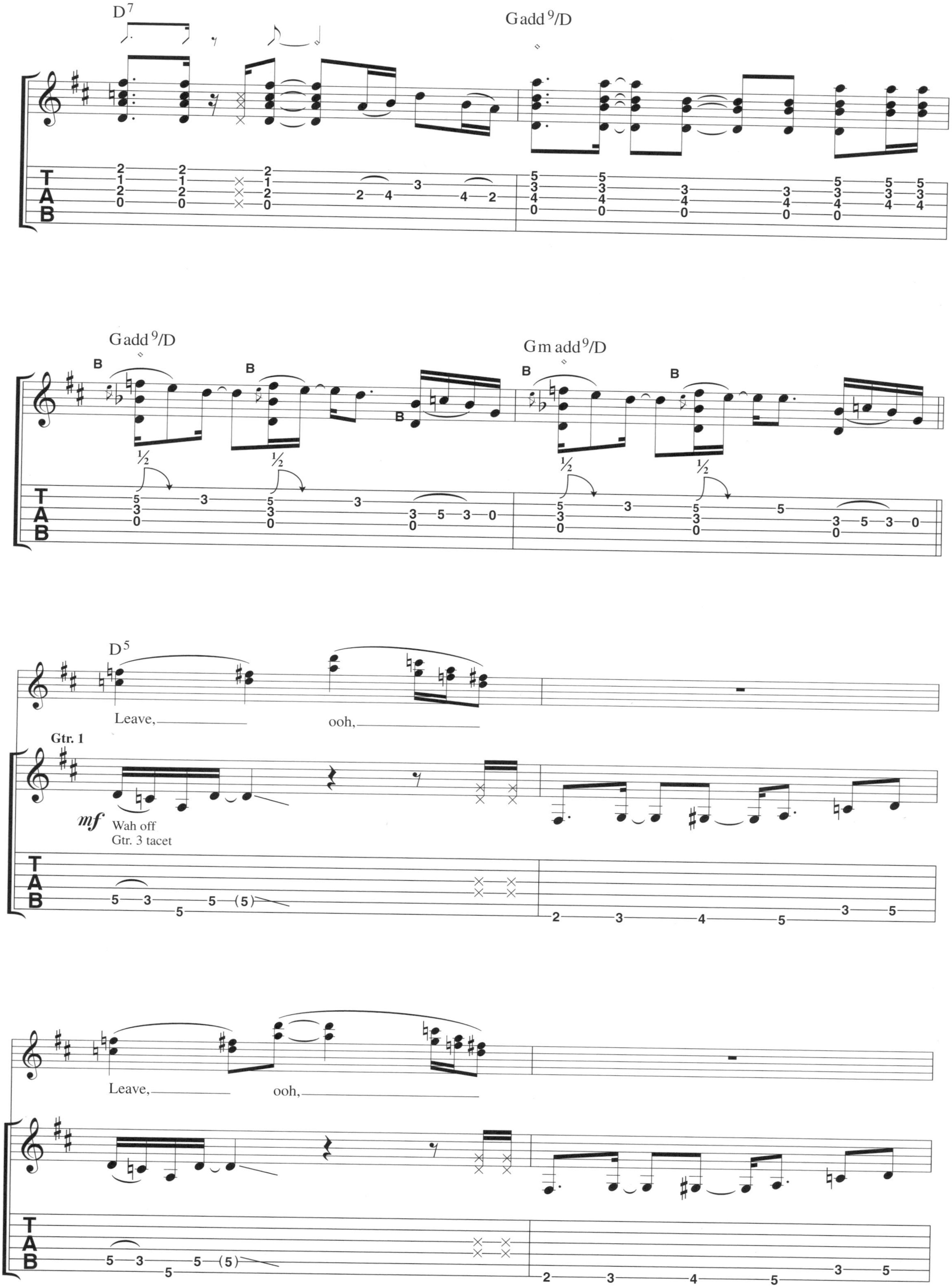
D7
Gadd9/D
Gadd9/D
B
1/2
Gm add9/D
D5
Leave,
ooh,
Gtr. 1
mf
Wah off
Gtr. 3 tacet
Leave,
ooh,

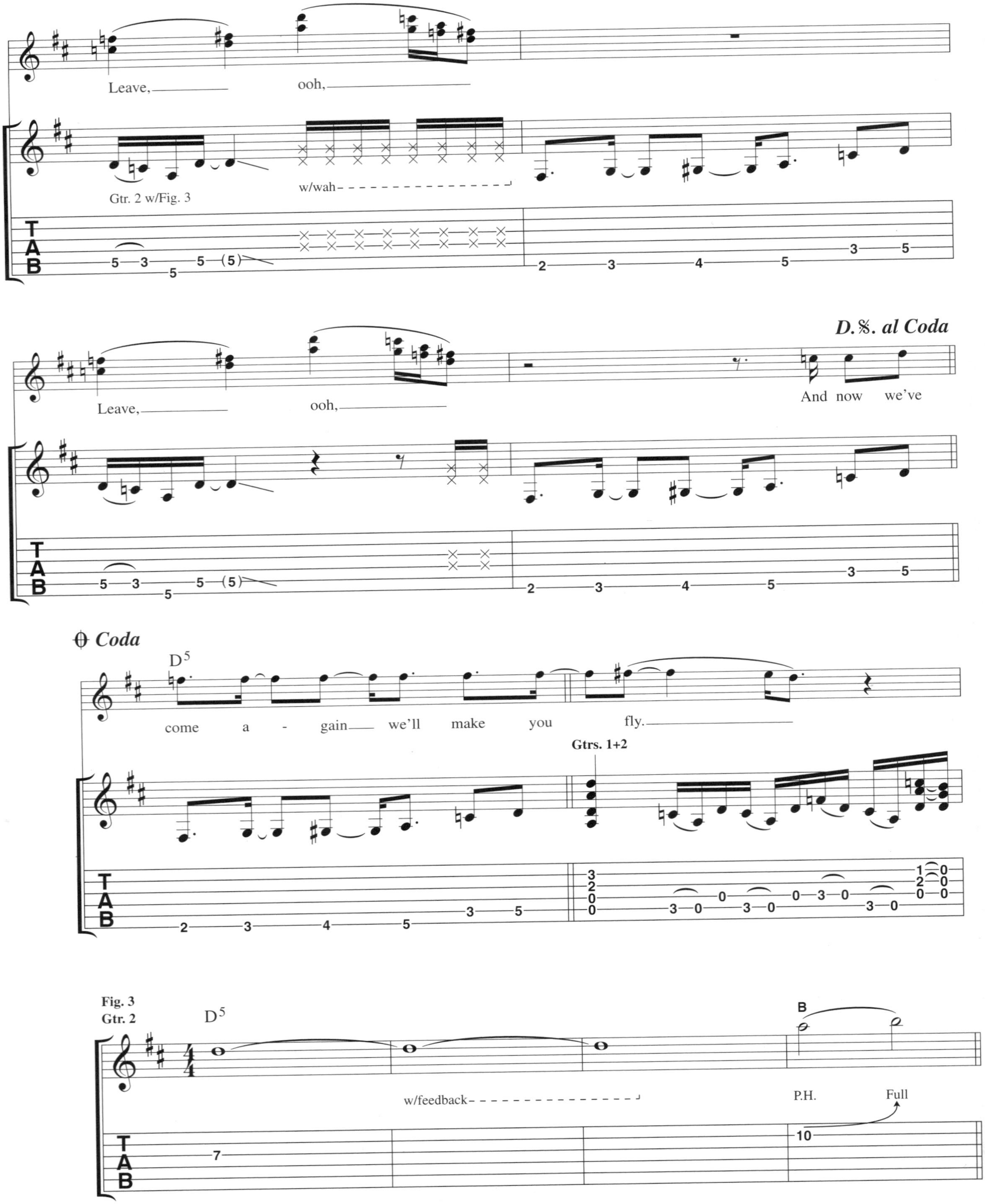
Leave, ooh,
Gtr. 2 w/Fig. 3
w/wah
D.%. al Coda
Leave, ooh, And now we've
Coda
D5
come a - gain we'll make you fly.
Gtrs. 1+2
Fig. 3
Gtr. 2
D5
B
w/feedback
P.H.
Full

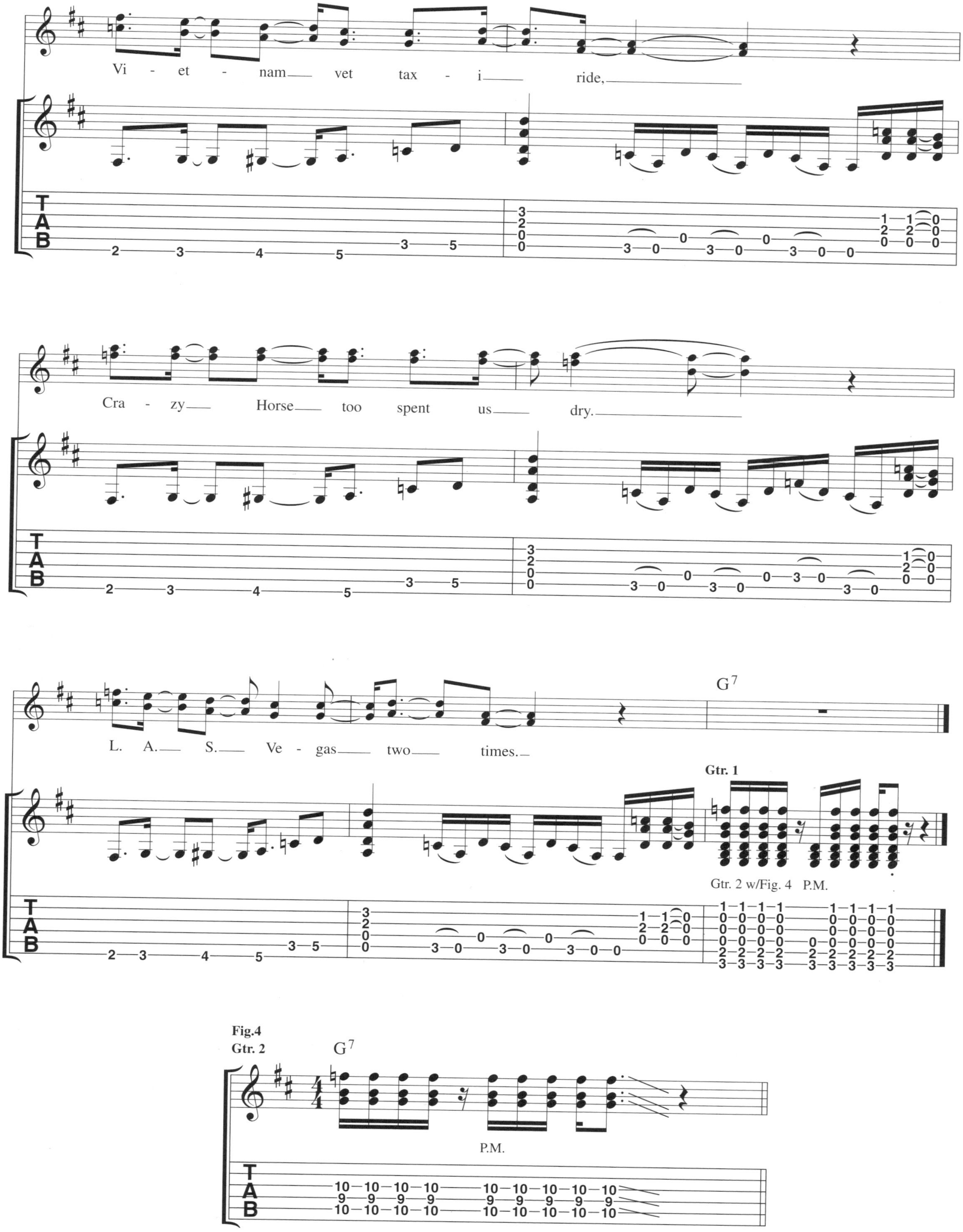
Vi - et - nam vet tax - i ride,
Cra - zy Horse too spent us dry.
L. A. S. Ve - gas two times.
G7
Gtr. 1
Gtr. 2 w/Fig. 4 P.M.
Fig.4
Gtr. 2
G7
P.M.

WHO NEEDS ENEMIES?

WORDS & MUSIC BY BEN GAUTREY, DANIEL FISHER, DAVID HAMMOND,
JONATHAN HARPER, KIERAN MAHON, TOM BELLAMY, HAL DAVID & BURT BACHARACH

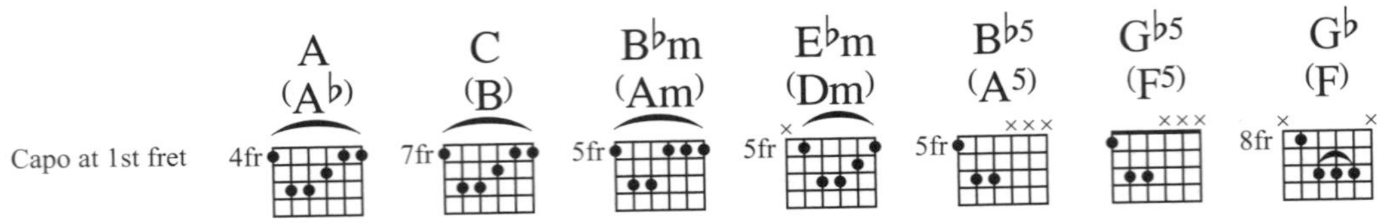

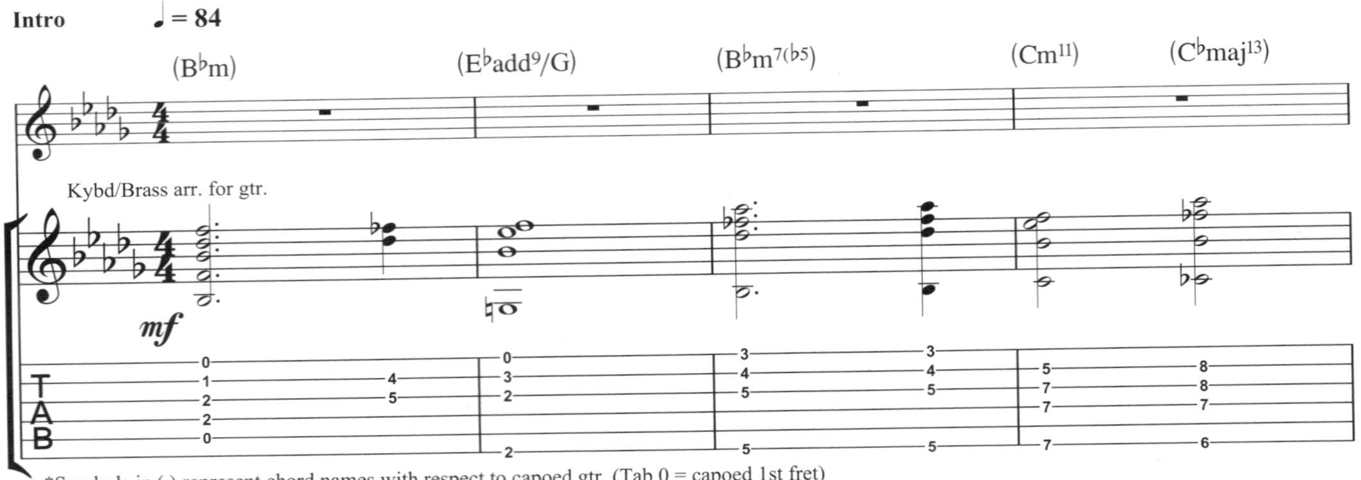

*Symbols in ( ) represent chord names with respect to capoed gtr. (Tab 0 = capoed 1st fret)
Symbols above represent actual sounding chords.

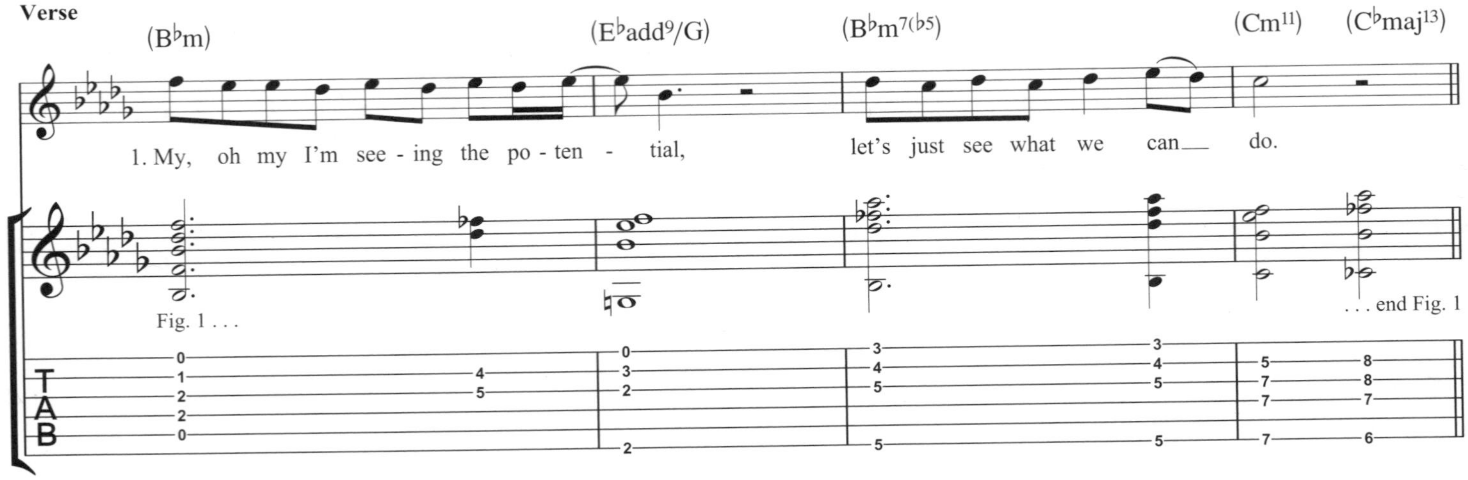

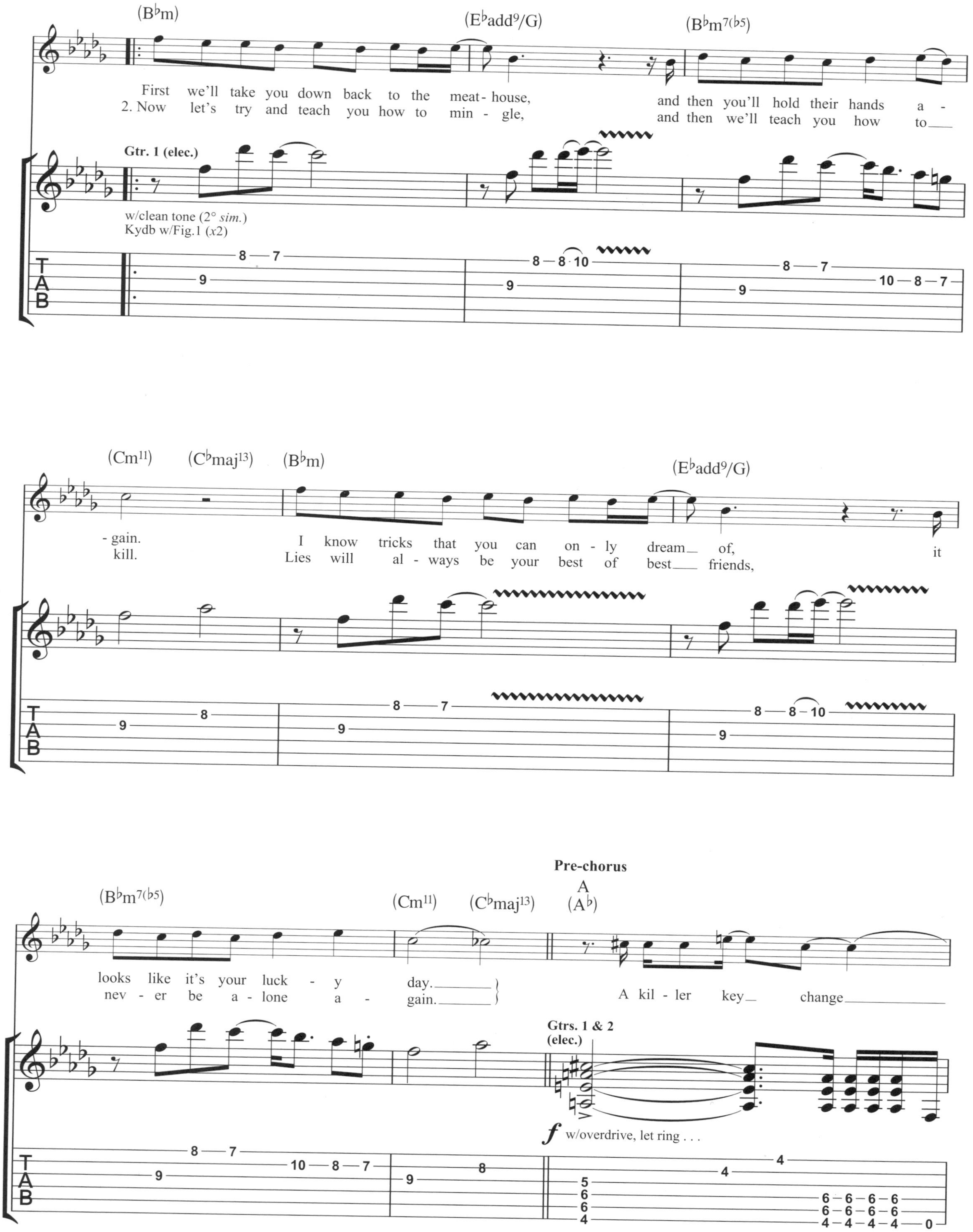
(B♭m)
(E♭add9/G)
(B♭m7(♭5))
First we'll take you down back to the meat-house, and then you'll hold their hands a-
2. Now let's try and teach you how to min-gle, and then we'll teach you how to
Gtr. 1 (elec.)
w/clean tone (2° sim.)
Kydb w/Fig.1 (x2)
TAB
(Cm11)
(C♭maj13)
(B♭m)
(E♭add9/G)
-gain. I know tricks that you can on-ly dream of, it
kill. Lies will al-ways be your best of best friends,
(B♭m7(♭5))
(Cm11)
(C♭maj13)
Pre-chorus
A
(A♭)
looks like it's your luck-y day.
nev-er be a-lone a-gain.
A kil-ler key change
Gtrs. 1 & 2 (elec.)
f w/overdrive, let ring . . .

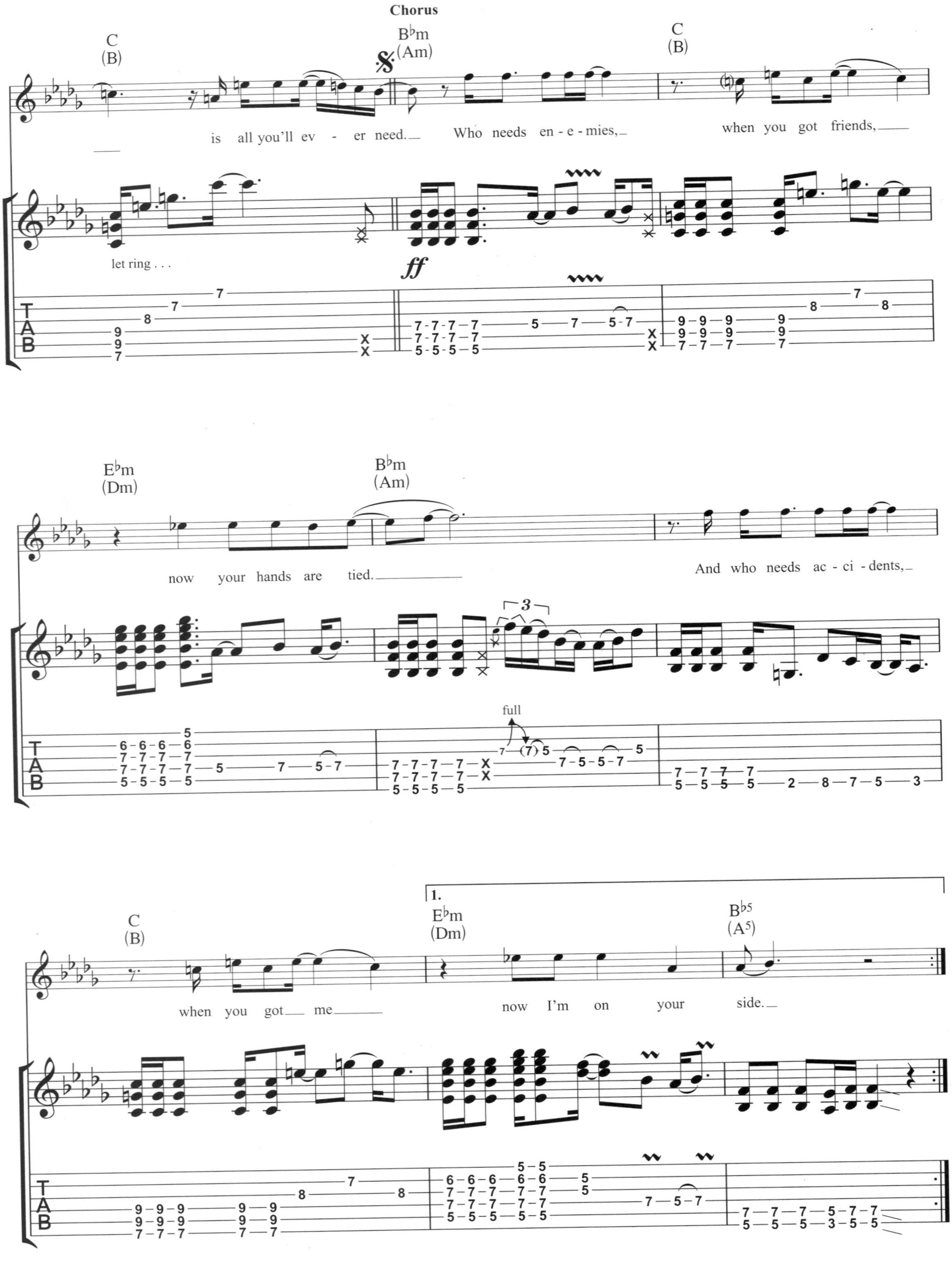
Chorus
C
(B)
B♭m
(Am)
C
(B)
is all you'll ev - er need.
Who needs en - e - mies,
when you got friends,
let ring . . .
ff
E♭m
(Dm)
B♭m
(Am)
now your hands are tied.
And who needs ac - ci - dents,
full
C
(B)
1.
E♭m
(Dm)
B♭5
(A5)
when you got me
now I'm on your side.

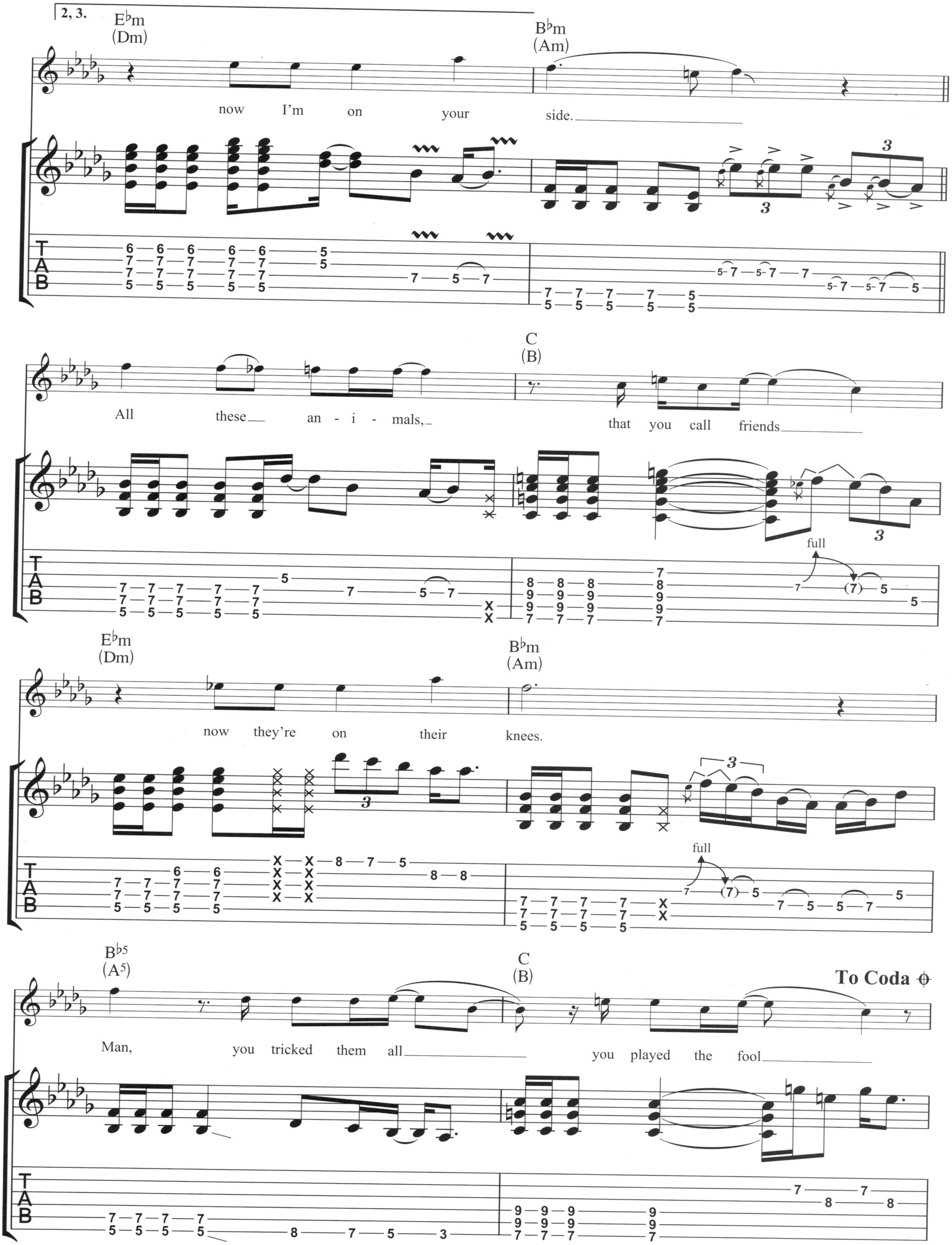
2, 3.
E♭m (Dm)
now I'm on your
B♭m (Am)
side.
TAB
All these an - i - mals,
C (B)
that you call friends
full
E♭m (Dm)
now they're on their
B♭m (Am)
knees.
full
B♭5 (A5)
Man, you tricked them all
C (B)
you played the fool
To Coda

E♭m
(Dm)
B♭5
(A5)
Middle
*(B♭m)
(E♭)
so damn ea - sy to bleed.
Gtr. 1
mf w/clean tone
Gtr. 2 tacet
1/2
*overall harmony (reference only)
(B♭m)
(E♭)
(G♭)
Made my name in func - tion - rooms by
(A♭)
(G♭)
(A♭)
(A)
drift - ing through the walls,
come on let me teach you boy,
a - teach you 'bout it all.
Instrumental
(B♭m)
(D♭)
(E♭)
(B♭m)
(D♭)
ff w/overdrive, let ring . . .

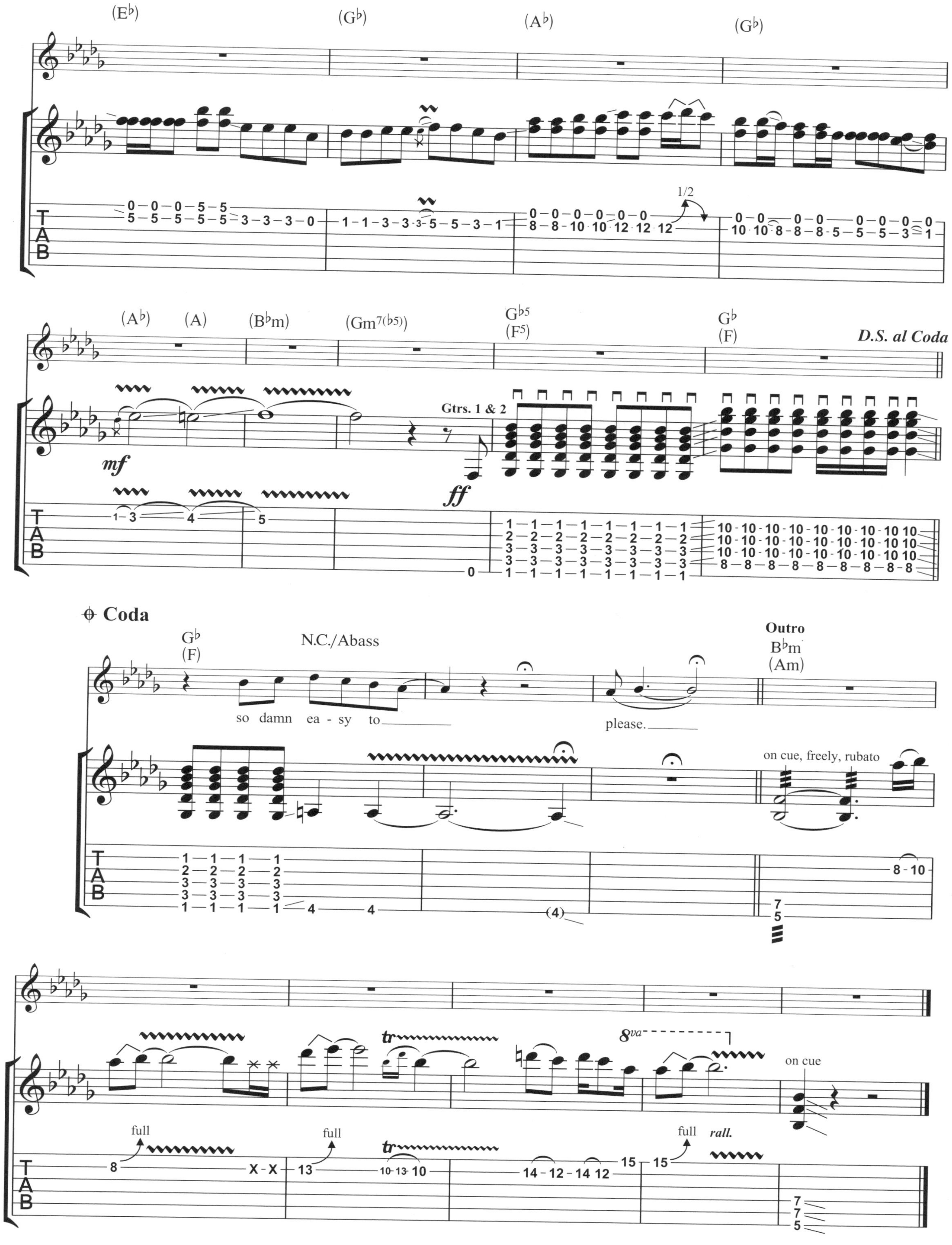
(E♭) (G♭) (A♭) (G♭)
1/2
(A♭) (A) (B♭m) (Gm7(♭5)) G♭5 (F5) G♭ (F)
D.S. al Coda
mf
Gtrs. 1 & 2
ff
Coda
G♭ (F)
N.C./Abass
so damn ea - sy to ___ please. ___
Outro
B♭m (Am)
on cue, freely, rubato
8va
on cue
full
full
full
rall.
tr

YELLOW

WORDS & MUSIC BY GUY BERRYMAN, JON BUCKLAND, WILL CHAMPION & CHRIS MARTIN

Gtrs. 1+2 Tuned:

① = D♯ ④ = B
② = B ⑤ = A
③ = G ⑥ = E

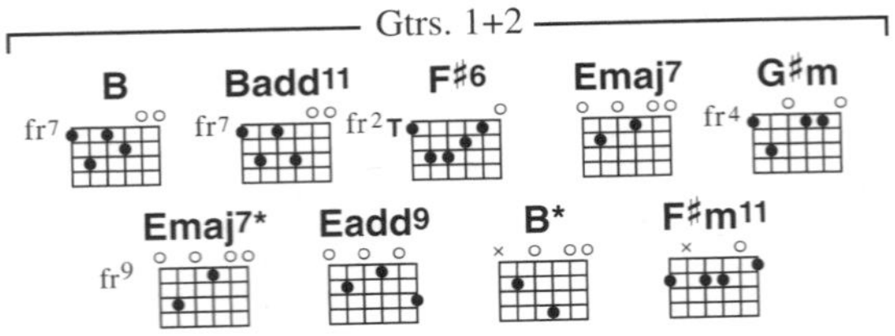

Gtr. 3: Standard Tuning

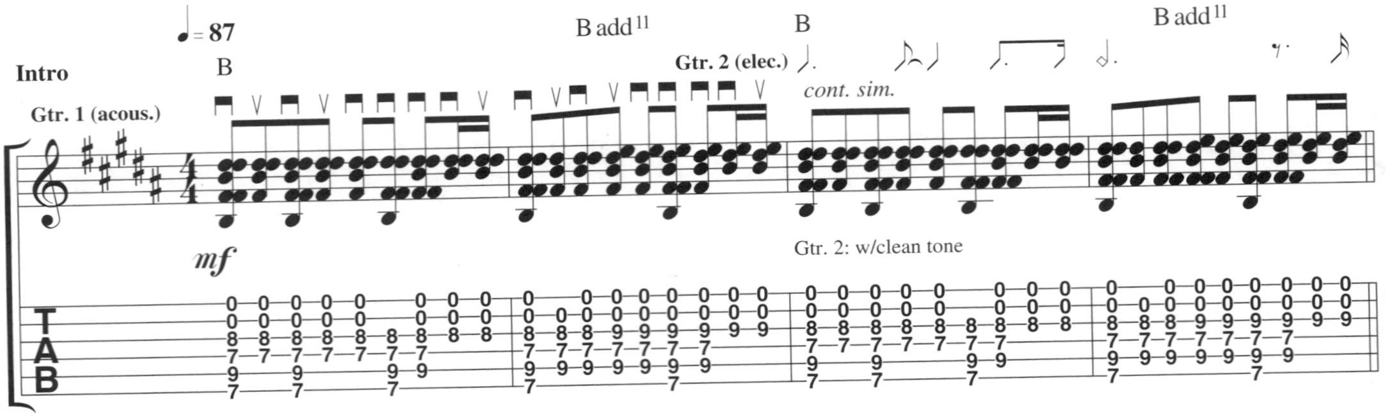

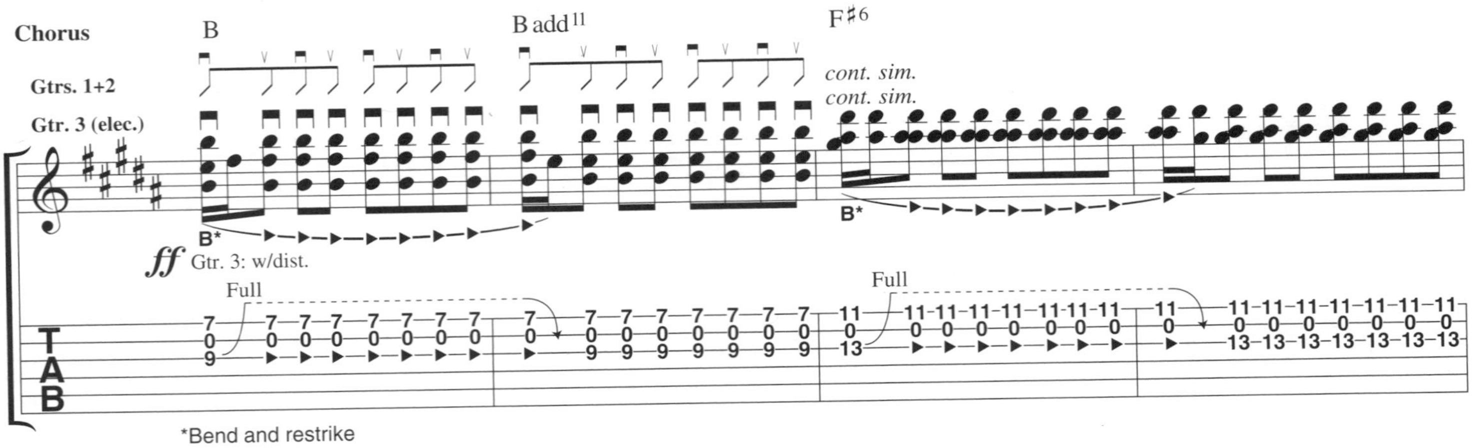

*Bend and restrike

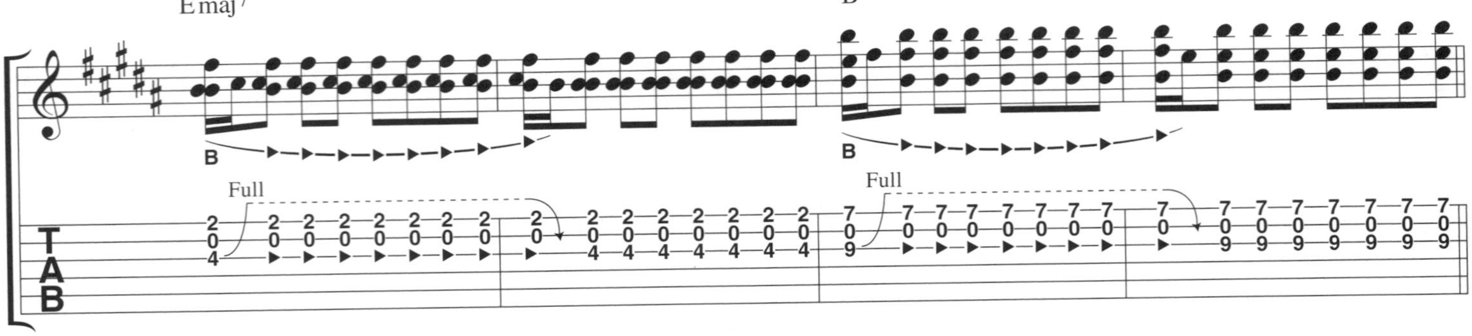

Verse
B
Gtr. 1
cont. sim.
F♯6
(1.) Look at the stars, look how they shine for you,
Gtr. 2
cont. sim.
(Gtr. 3)
mf
Emaj7
and ev-'ry-thing you do,
yeah, they were all yel-low.
Verse
B
F♯6
I came a-long, I wrote a song for you,
(2.) I swam a-cross, I jumped a-cross for you,
Gtr. 3: w/Fig. 1
Fig. 1
B
F♯6
Emaj7
Gtr. 3
w/clean tone

Emaj7
and all the things you do,
oh, what a thing to do,
TAB
B
and it was called yel - low.
'cause you were all yel - low.
I drew a line,
Gtr. 3: w/Fig. 1
TAB
Badd11
F♯6
So then I took my turn,
I drew a line for you,
TAB
Emaj7
oh, what a thing to've done,
oh, what a thing to do,
and it was all yel - low.
and it was all yel - low.
TAB

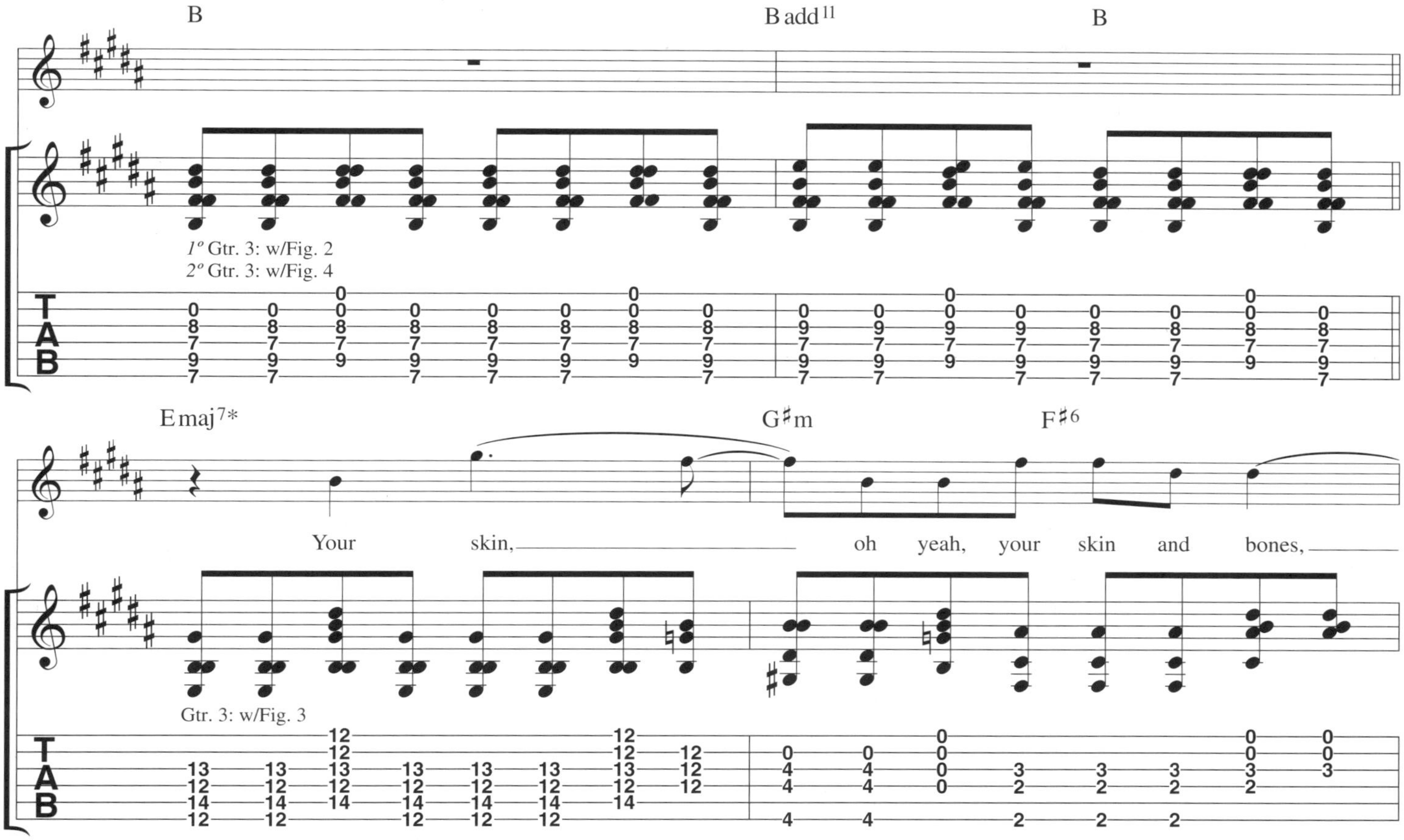
B
B add11
B
1º Gtr. 3: w/Fig. 2
2º Gtr. 3: w/Fig. 4
Emaj7*
G♯m
F♯6
Your skin, oh yeah, your skin and bones,
Gtr. 3: w/Fig. 3

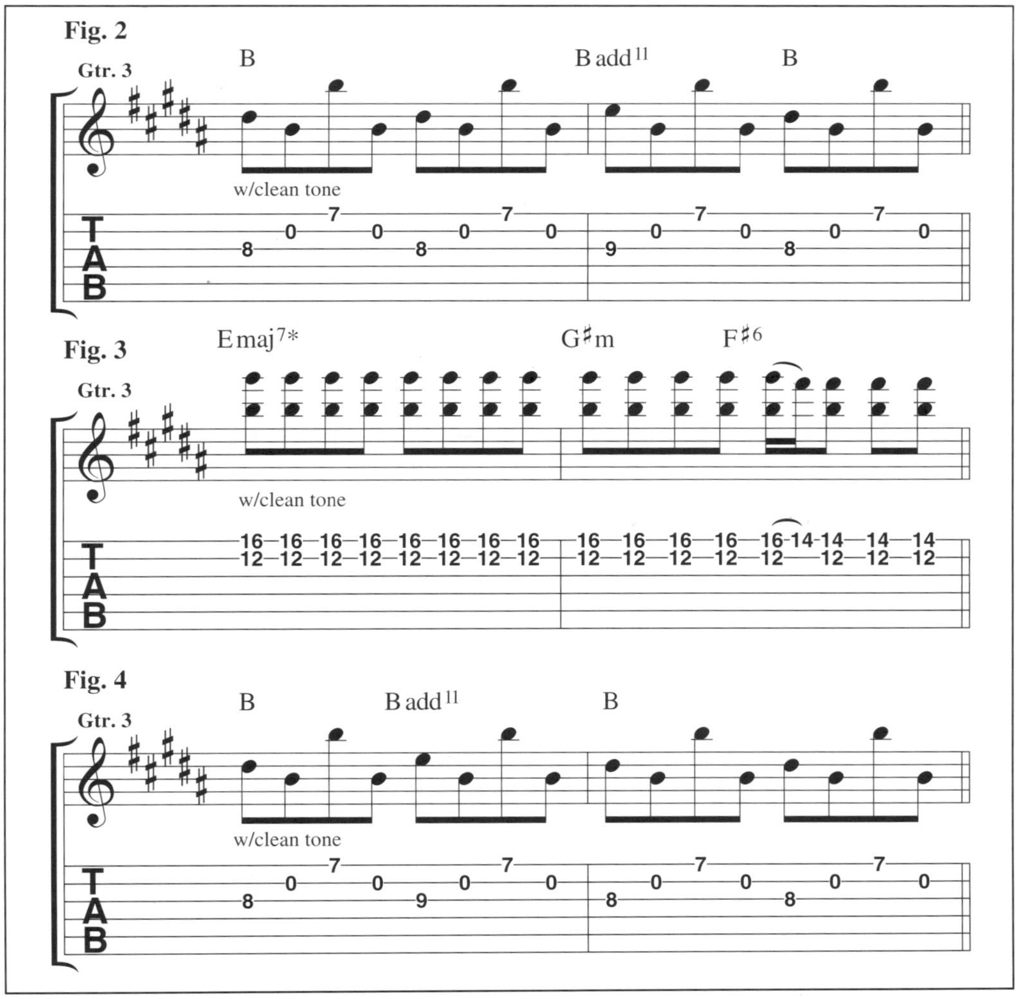
Fig. 2
Gtr. 3
B
B add11
B
w/clean tone
Fig. 3
Emaj7*
G♯m
F♯6
Gtr. 3
w/clean tone
Fig. 4
B
B add11
B
Gtr. 3
w/clean tone

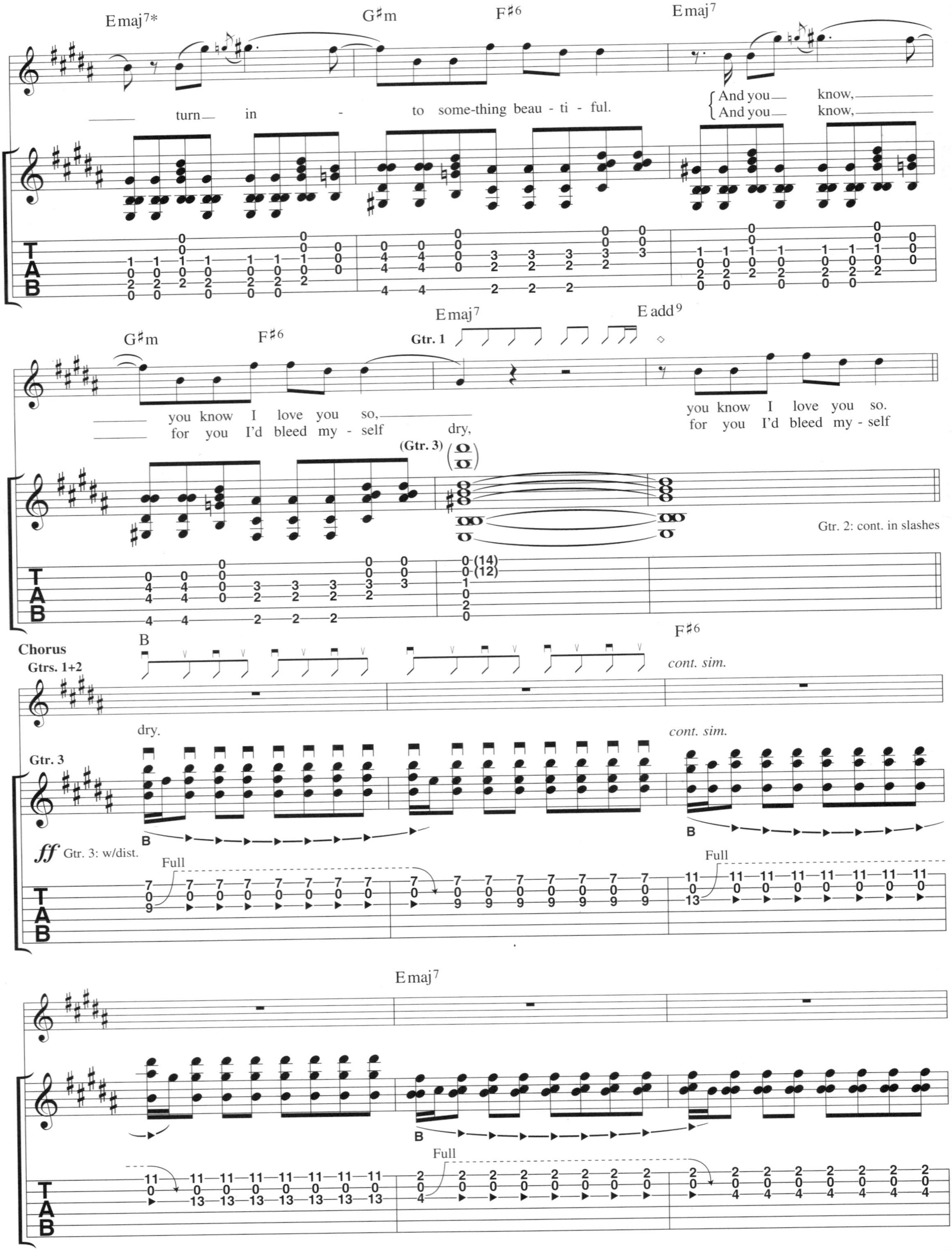
Emaj7*
G♯m
F♯6
Emaj7
turn in - to some-thing beau - ti - ful.
And you know,
And you know,
G♯m
F♯6
Emaj7
Eadd9
Gtr. 1
you know I love you so,
for you I'd bleed my - self dry,
you know I love you so.
for you I'd bleed my - self
(Gtr. 3)
Gtr. 2: cont. in slashes
Chorus
Gtrs. 1+2
B
F♯6
cont. sim.
dry.
Gtr. 3
cont. sim.
ff Gtr. 3: w/dist.
Full
Emaj7
Full

B
1.
2.
It's
Full
Chorus
B
true,
look how they shine for
Full
F♯6
you,
look how they shine for
Emaj7
you,
Full
look how they shine for,
B
Full

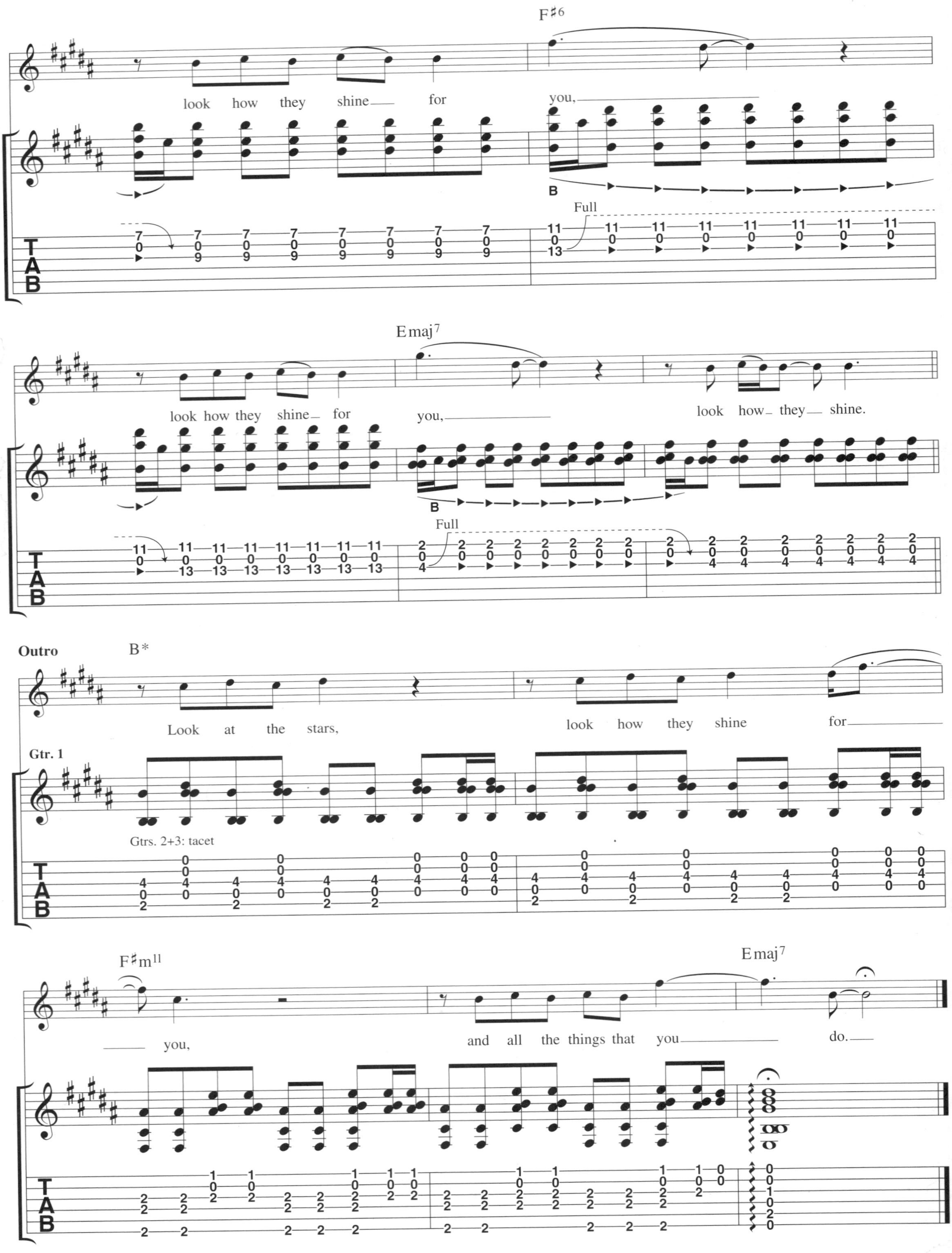
F♯6
look how they shine for you,
Full
Emaj7
look how they shine for you,
look how they shine.
Full
Outro
B*
Look at the stars,
look how they shine for
Gtr. 1
Gtrs. 2+3: tacet
F♯m11
you,
and all the things that you
Emaj7
do.

GUITAR TABLATURE EXPLAINED

Guitar music can be notated three different ways: on a musical stave, in tablature, and in rhythm slashes

RHYTHM SLASHES are written above the stave. Strum chords in the rhythm indicated. Round noteheads indicate single notes.

THE MUSICAL STAVE shows pitches and rhythms and is divided by lines into bars. Pitches are named after the first seven letters of the alphabet.

TABLATURE graphically represents the guitar fingerboard. Each horizontal line represents a string, and each number represents a fret.

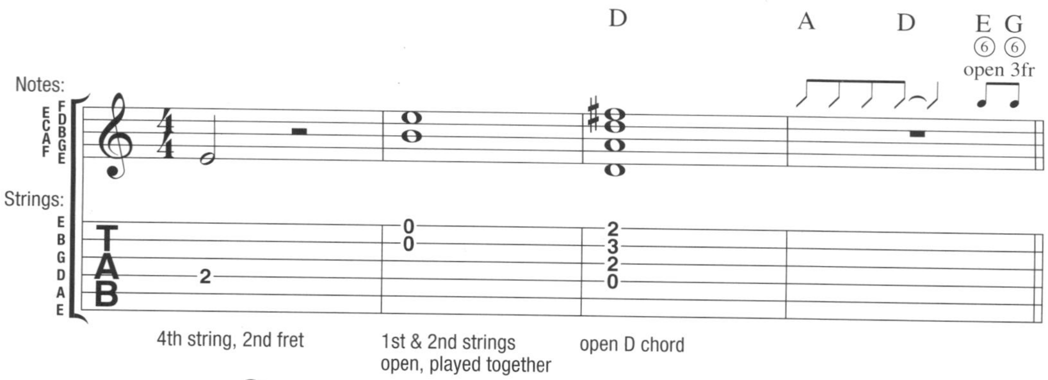

DEFINITIONS FOR SPECIAL GUITAR NOTATION

SEMI-TONE BEND: Strike the note and bend up a semi-tone (1/2 step).

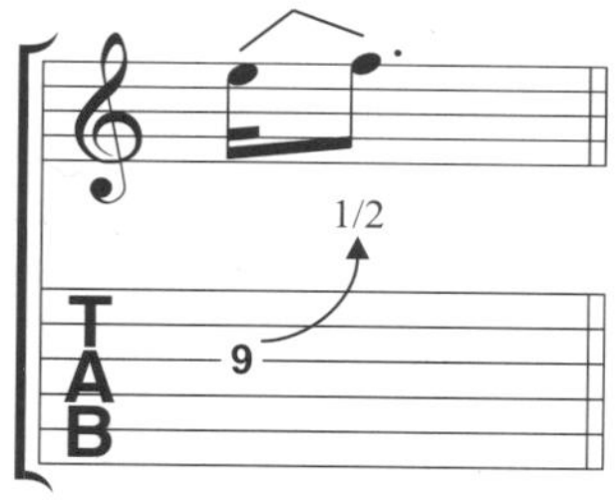

WHOLE-TONE BEND: Strike the note and bend up a whole-tone (whole step).

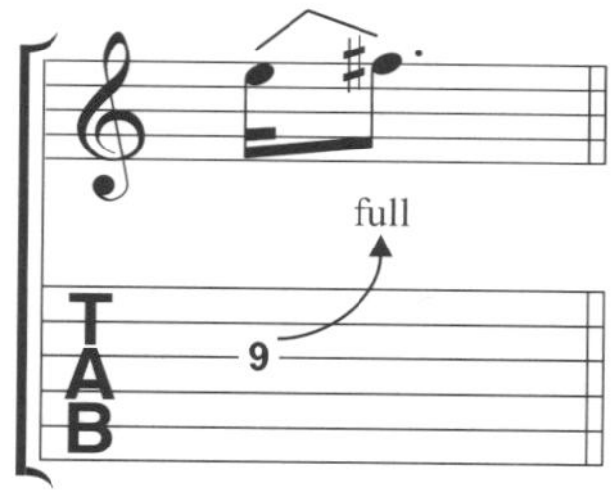

GRACE NOTE BEND: Strike the note and bend as indicated. Play the first note as quickly as possible.

QUARTER-TONE BEND: Strike the note and bend up a 1/4 step.

BEND & RELEASE: Strike the note and bend up as indicated, then release back to the original note.

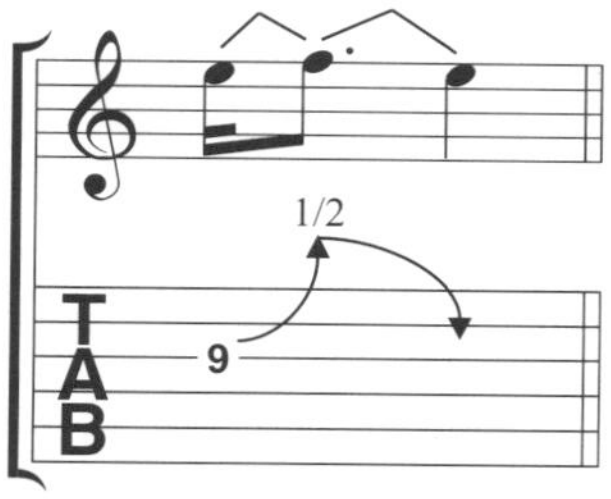

COMPOUND BEND & RELEASE: Strike the note and bend up and down in the rhythm indicated.

PRE-BEND: Bend the note as indicated, then strike it.

PRE-BEND & RELEASE: Bend the note as indicated. Strike it and release the note back to the original pitch.

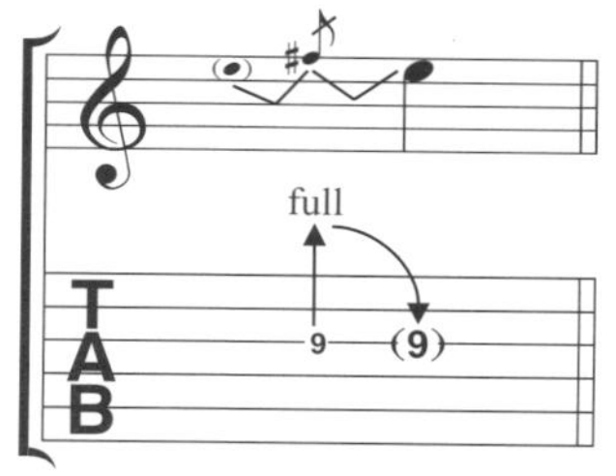

HAMMER-ON: Strike the first note with one finger, then sound the second note (on the same string) with another finger by fretting it without picking.

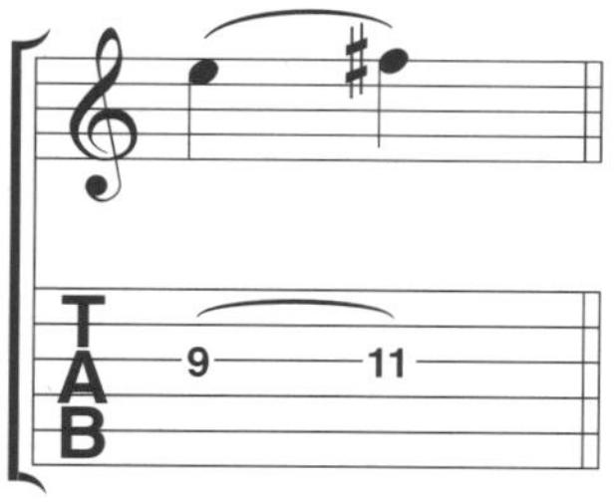

PULL-OFF: Place both fingers on the notes to be sounded, strike the first note and without picking, pull the finger off to sound the second note.

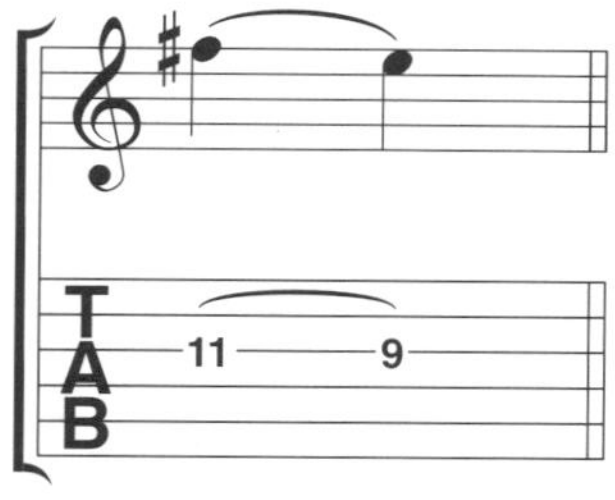

LEGATO SLIDE (GLISS): Strike the first note and then slide the same fret-hand finger up or down to the second note. The second note is not struck.

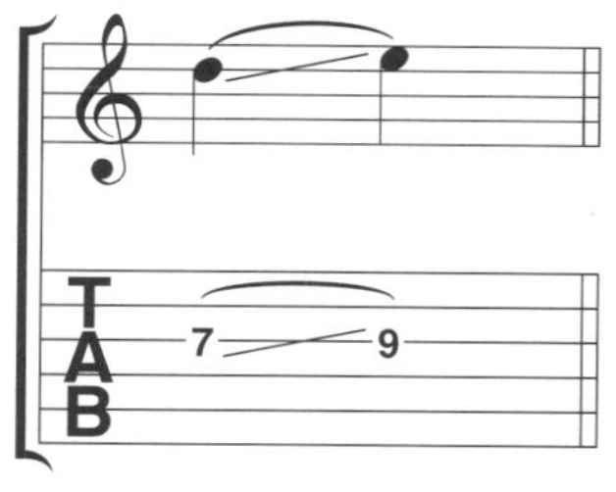

MUFFLED STRINGS: A percussive sound is produced by laying the fret hand across the string(s) without depressing, and striking them with the pick hand.

NATURAL HARMONIC: Strike the note while the fret-hand lightly touches the string directly over the fret indicated.

PICK SCRAPE: The edge of the pick is rubbed down (or up) the string, producing a scratchy sound.

PALM MUTING: The note is partially muted by the pick hand lightly touching the string(s) just before the bridge.

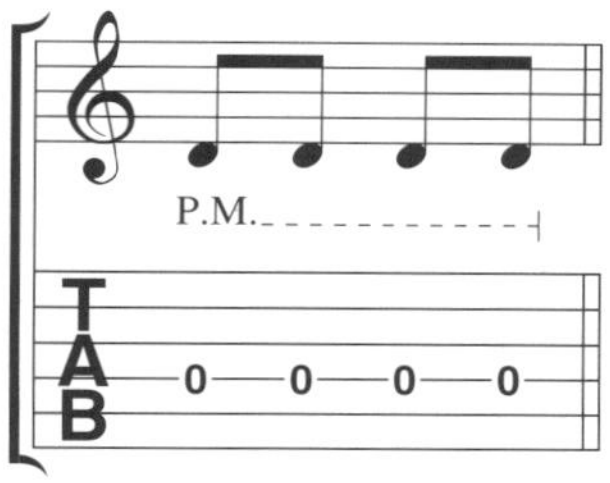

SHIFT SLIDE (GLISS & RESTRIKE): Same as legato slide, except the second note is struck.

NOTE: The speed of any bend is indicated by the music notation and tempo.